DATE DUE

DATE DUE			
MAY 1 3 2003			
MAY 1 5 2003			
GAYLORD			PRINTED IN U.S.A.

CARDIAC STIMULANT SUBSTANCES

MEDICINAL CHEMISTRY
A Series of Monographs

EDITED BY

GEORGE deSTEVENS

*CIBA Pharmaceutical Company
Division of CIBA Corporation
Summit, New Jersey*

Volume 1. GEORGE deSTEVENS. Diuretics: Chemistry and Pharmacology. 1963

Volume 2. RUDOLFO PAOLETTI (ED.). Lipid Pharmacology. 1964

Volume 3. E. J. ARIËNS (ED.). Molecular Pharmacology: The Mode of Action of Biologically Active Compounds. (In two volumes.) 1964

Volume 4. MAXWELL GORDON (ED.). Psychopharmacological Agents. Volume I. 1964. Volume II. 1967

Volume 5. GEORGE deSTEVENS (ED.). Analgetics. 1965

Volume 6. ROLAND H. THORP AND LEONARD B. COBBIN. Cardiac Stimulant Substances. 1967

In Preparation

U. S. VON EULER AND RUNE ELIASSON. Prostaglandin.

EMIL SCHLITTLER (ED.). Antihypertensive Agents.

CARDIAC STIMULANT SUBSTANCES

ROLAND H. THORP and LEONARD B. COBBIN

Department of Pharmacology
University of Sydney
Sydney, N.S.W., Australia

ACADEMIC PRESS
New York and London 1967

ACADEMIC PRESS INC.
111 Fifth Avenue, New York, New York 10003

United Kingdom Edition published by
ACADEMIC PRESS INC. (LONDON) LTD.
Berkeley Square House, London W.1

LIBRARY OF CONGRESS CATALOG CARD NUMBER: 66-30107

PRINTED IN THE UNITED STATES OF AMERICA

FOREWORD

The many advances made in medicinal chemistry within the past quarter-century have done much to further our knowledge of the relationship between chemical structure and biological activity. This relationship has led to a tremendous collaborative effort between chemists and biologists, and this has been evidenced further by the considerable number of reviews which have appeared on various aspects of medicinal chemistry. For the most part, these have been confined to single chapters on selected topics. Of necessity, in such a format, it has been difficult to cover a particular area very broadly.

The purpose of this series is to present a series of monographs, each dealing with a specific field in medicinal chemistry. Thus, these edited or authored volumes will make available to the medicinal chemist and biologist an opportunity to review critically a topic; consequently, a broader perspective of a subject can be realized.

GEORGE deSTEVENS

Drugs which can enhance the contractility of the failing heart play a very important role in therapeutics, but we are entirely dependent on two groups of substances—the cardiac glycosides and the catecholamines. Although these two groups, which are far from ideal as therapeutic agents, have been the subject of many hundreds of research papers, no synthetic substitutes for the cardiac glycosides have been manufactured as yet. There are many other cardiotonic substances which have been studied in far less detail, usually as isolated research projects.

Cardiac stimulant substances have been the major field of postgraduate study in our department, and the difficulties which students have experienced in obtaining an overall picture of the subject before being able to proceed to the detailed study of any particular aspect stimulated us to prepare this monograph. We believe that the presentation in one volume of current knowledge of cardiac stimulant substances will be of material help to research workers and may stimulate a more general approach to research in this field.

There is much to be learned about the comparative mode of action of cardiotonic drugs, and there are undoubtedly additional naturally occurring substances of both plant and animal origin which deserve study. It may prove that few if any of these could be put to therapeutic use, but when structural elucidation is complete new approaches to chemical synthesis may be revealed.

Since 1950, the Department of Pharmacology in Sydney has concentrated its research facilities in this field. The cultivation of *Digitalis* species in Australia, the metabolism and excretion of cardiac glycosides, and studies of the correlation between structure and activity in the cardiac glycosides have all been the subject of investigation during this period. In recent years the authors have become particularly interested in cardiac stimulant substances found in animal tissues, and are currently engaged in the isolation of such substances from spleen and blood. This work has been greatly expanded by the cooperation of Smith Kline and French Laboratories and their Australian associated company who have made possible the establishment of a Research Institute in this department with studies of cardiotonic substances as a primary objective. This has resulted in the development of isolation procedures and has led to collaborative studies between chemists and pharmacologists on a scale hitherto impossible in a university department.

We have drawn freely from the work of our students, and we wish to express our thanks to all those whose studies have added to our knowledge and have helped to provide some of the information collected in this book. We would particularly like to express our thanks to Dr. Diana M. Temple of the Smith Kline and French Research Institute, who has contributed to the more chemical sections of this book and whose criticism and comments have been most helpful. For some of the illustrations we are indebted to Mr. F. Michal whose skill in photography, as well as his knowledge of pharmacology, has made him one of our busiest and also one of our most helpful colleagues. Our thanks are also due to the authors and publishers who have so willingly granted us permission to reproduce various illustrations in the text. To Mrs. Wilma Bailey and her assistant, Miss Sue, McCaughey, we are indebted for the painstaking work of typing the manuscript and collating the references.

February, 1967   ROLAND H. THORP
                                                    LEONARD B. COBBIN

CONTENTS

CARDIAC STIMULANT SUBSTANCES

CHAPTER 1

FIELDS OF RESEARCH IN THE STUDY
OF CARDIAC STIMULANT SUBSTANCES

The purpose of this chapter is to explore the general problems and interesting facets of the study of cardioactive substances. It is therefore introductory throughout, and to maintain continuity and readability the authors have deliberately eschewed the documentation of statements by references. The various facets mentioned are dealt with in further detail throughout this book and they are documented at that stage. We could list here a very considerable bibliography of review articles but again these are referred to in the general text, and the reader will find them mentioned and listed in the sections to which they principally refer.

I. The Status of Cardiotonic Drugs in Therapeutics and Research

There is a wide range of drugs which exhibit an action on the heart and they may be stimulant or depressant. This represents a very important area of therapeutics since cardiac failure and the occurrence of abnormal rhythm in the heart have become some of the most common accompaniments of aging in our present civilization. The conquest of infectious diseases highlights the need for increased knowledge of the degenerative disorders and for improved therapeutic agents to relieve them.

The cardiac stimulant drugs generally play a more impressive role and are far more remarkable in their actions than those drugs which depress the myocardium and the conducting mechanism of the heart. The latter group which includes drugs such as quinidine and procaine amide could be expanded readily by the synthetic chemist, since antiarrhythmic properties are among the side effects of a great many drugs such as the antihistamines, antimalarials, and local anesthetics, which are used for quite different purposes. Depressant effects are

1

observed as toxic symptoms with a very wide range of organic compounds and are often nonspecific and can be seen on a wide range of tissues. However, some drugs such as adenosine and acetylcholine show a remarkably specific action in depressing or arresting the heart and show little depressant action on visceral smooth muscle in the former case or even a powerful stimulant action in the latter.

The cardiac stimulant drugs are a much more restricted group, which so far have defied the efforts of the synthetic chemist to produce stimulant activity in new groups of compounds. Although the range of cardiac stimulant drugs is large, those used in therapeutics are confined to two very uniform groups. Digitalis and allied plant glycosides comprise one group, which is characterized by a slow and cumulative onset of action but a prolonged effect in increasing the contractile force of the heart. These drugs exhibit an action so remarkable that the chronic invalid whose life would otherwise be short is returned to a relatively normal and active way of life and may survive for many years. The effect is so impressive that the similarity between the action of the cardiac glycosides and hormone replacement therapy immediately springs to mind. The second important group of cardiotonic drugs is the catecholamines of which noradrenaline and adrenaline provide the cardiac stimulants we depend upon for emergency use. Their action is immediate and short-lived and appears to be very different from that of the cardiac glycosides so that their value lies in such fields as resuscitation rather than in the treatment of chronic conditions.

Both these groups of drugs produce a very dramatic increase in force of contraction in isolated cardiac muscle whether the muscle is beating spontaneously or whether it is electrically stimulated. There are a number of other substances not made use of in therapeutics, which can also produce a similar effect. The alkaloids from *Erythrophleum* are notable examples. A small amount of the alkaloid cassaine produces a rapid increase in the contractile force of cardiac muscle, which persists until the drug is removed. The xanthines, caffeine, theophylline, and theobromine, are also stimulant to the myocardium, and this action is seen again with alkaloids from *Veratrum* sp. No therapeutic use can be made of these substances because the concentration of the drug which stimulates isolated myocardial tissue is high enough for the drug to prove grossly toxic to many other systems of the body, which occurs when attempts are made to repeat these results *in vivo*. For this reason the cardiac glycosides and to a lesser extent the catecholamines have been the subject of extensive studies of their cardiac stimulant or positive inotropic action, whereas the same action has been reported for the cardiotonic alkaloids in early papers but very few studies have been made since. There are pharmacologists, particularly in industry, who believe that *in vitro* tests as screening methods for new drugs are just so much waste of time and that unless a result is obtained *in vivo* the report should be marked negative. This may be true if a search for substances of possible therapeutic use is the sole aim of the investigator but it must be emphasized that mass screening tests have not proved a very successful means of achieving this object, and the majority of the major advances in pharmacology have a more rational background than this.

For the pharmacologist whose interest centers around the mechanism of drug action the cardiotonic drugs offer a major challenge, and one which should be approached on a broad front by investigation of the whole range of substances which produce this effect and by comparison of their properties one with another. In the field of long-acting cardiac stimulant drugs we see the last example of complete dependence on drugs from natural sources. Not a single synthetic drug has yet reproduced the properties of the cardiac glycosides, and every one of the several million cardiac failure patients must depend on the commercial cultivation of *Digitalis purpurea, Digitalis lanata,* or *Strophanthus* sp. and the extraction and purification of glycosides from these sources.

From the standpoint of therapeutics it may be argued that the cardiotonic glycosides work well enough and provide an excellent therapy for congestive cardiac failure. The cardiac glycosides certainly restore the failing heart but they do so in doses very close to those which produce major toxic symptoms of cardiac arrhythmia, nausea and vomiting, visual abnormalities, and central nervous disturbances. One even wonders if these drugs were to be evaluated today whether they would pass the requirements for freedom from toxicity demanded by the regulatory agencies of the various countries and whether their use would be generally permitted!

A very large number of cardiac glycosides have been isolated and they are abundant in the flora of many countries. There is no doubt that many more exist and await purification. The toxicities of a great many of them have been determined on cats, rabbits, guinea pigs, pigeons, and other laboratory animals, and these results have been compiled and published. Unfortunately, for many we do not have accurate knowledge of the ratio of these figures to the doses which produce a clear cardiotonic effect. In other words the therapeutic ratio is often unknown. Where, however, we do have this information it is unfortunately not very encouraging since it is relatively similar from one glycoside to another and no one glycoside so far has been shown to have an outstandingly better therapeutic ratio than any other. There are some workers who believe, largely from these observations, that the "toxic effects" are inseparable from the "therapeutic effects" of the cardiac glycosides and that the former are simply an extension of, and result directly from the latter. In the cardiac glycosides alone there has been little evidence against this view until recently. Although hydrogenation of the unsaturated lactone ring in ouabain has been known to reduce the potency to a very large extent it apparently reduces the toxicity to an even greater degree so that there is an improvement in the therapeutic ratio. Although much larger doses would be required to produce the same toxic effect as that of the unsaturated analog the margin of safety appears to be somewhat greater.

The general picture of the cardiac glycosides is one of a group of drugs substantially similar in their qualitative effects, although varying quantitatively in potency and duration of action. If we had only any one of these we could put it to therapeutic use; and their interchangeability is reflected by the preferential use of digitoxin by some clinicians, digoxin by others, and the frequent use of strophanthin in continental Europe. In research publications we also notice the use of a wide variety of glycosides and the interpretation of results from one to another with general acceptance of their similarity.

II. The Relationship between Structure and Activity in the Cardiotonic Drugs

Since so few comparisons have been made of cardiotonic drugs generally, very few comparisons have been made between structure and pharmacological activity. It is quite possible and very probable that several different chemical structures may each produce cardio-tonic effects either by occupying different receptors in a chain of bio-chemical reactions, or that they may achieve the same end result by very different mechanisms involving different biochemical systems.

There have been extensive studies of the relationship between struc-ture and activity within the several major groups of cardioactive drugs, the cardiac glycosides, the catecholamines, and the cardiotonic alka-loids, but there has been little cross reference. It would appear, and this is discussed later, that a case can be made for similarities between the cardiac glycosides and the *Erythrophleum* alkaloids but it would seem that the other substances act in different ways or by virtue of quite different chemical conformation.

Although a very considerable amount of work has been done on structure-activity relationships in the cardiac glycosides, the very difficulty of their chemistry has precluded investigators from examining structural features which would appear to be of vital importance. Either conclusions have to be drawn from the relative potency ratios of dif-ferent naturally occurring glycosides, or relatively minor semisynthetic modifications have to be made in the well-known glycosides and then the effects of the changes assessed. Alterations in chemical structure cause alterations in absorption, metabolism, and access to cardiac tissue when these substances are assessed *in vivo*. It is essential that structure-activity relationships should be studied by testing the various compounds on isolated cardiac preparations such as the guinea pig auricle or cat papillary muscle preparation as well as by intravenous toxicity tests on whole animals, and, furthermore, the *in vivo* and *in vitro* tests should preferably be performed in the same species. There is no doubt that the positive inotropic activity of cardiac glycosides is easily reduced. There have been no instances comparable with the acetylation of morphine of any chemical modifications causing in-creased activity to levels greater than that of the parent substance. In general, a fine gradation of pharmacological effects correlated with structural changes has not yet been described. There is room for far more research on this topic but the problem is an enormous one since the chemistry of the cardiac glycosides is so difficult. It is no exag-geration to say that the work of fifty chemists might be insufficient to occupy the full time of one pharmacologist.

III. New Cardiotonic Substances from Plants

There is no difficulty in isolating new cardiac glycosides from plants, and there are undoubtedly more which can be isolated, but of particular interest is the isolation of *other* substances which have cardiotonic activity. There are many reports of such substances occurring in the tropical flora but often these are not substantiated by later tests or the substances have not been available in sufficient quantities for full and careful pharmacological study. Around the early 1950's interest centered upon alkaloids such as ibogaine isolated from *Iboga* sp., but despite initial claims these did not appear to have cardiotonic properties. More recently the alkaloids of *Voacanga* sp. have been studied, but, again, with the exception of the initial work in France and Belgium, it has not been possible to show a clear cardiotonic effect with these alkaloids upon the isolated papillary muscle or guinea pig auricle preparations. The alkaloids of *Erythrophleum* sp., on the other hand, do have an unquestionable cardiotonic effect and it has been reported that ivorine, an alkaloid from *Erythrophleum ivorense,* is exceedingly potent. The screening of plant extracts for cardiotonic activity is a worthwhile undertaking and a very simple one. It is also one which should precede the isolation of any chemical substances as it is easy for chemists to spend considerable effort on the isolation of alkaloidal materials which, although interesting chemically, may be entirely inactive. For this type of study there are many simple techniques using isolated myocardial tissue, which, when carefully performed, give a rapid and clear indication of stimulant or depressant properties.

IV. Cardiotonic Substances in Animal Tissues

In addition to the fact that the slime glands of the toad secrete cardiotonic substances akin to the cardiac glycosides of the digitalis type, there is no doubt that there are substances present in animal tissues which have powerful cardiotonic actions.

If isolated cardiac preparations are arranged to beat in physiological saline solutions (e.g., the isolated Langendorff heart preparation), they always show a progressive decline in contractile force and yet when tissue extracts or serum are added to the perfusion fluid, a clear increase in force of contraction has frequently been reported. It is very easy for pharmacologists to criticize results of this kind and attribute them to known pharmacologically active substances, but the known substances can be eliminated and still the effects are observed. The tissue extracts can be analyzed by pharmacological methods for known tissue autocoids and evidence produced that these do not fully account for the cardiotonic effect. Artificial mixtures of known substances in the proportions found in tissue extracts can be prepared and yet again they may not account for the full cardiac stimulant action of the extracts themselves. There is, surely, no reason to assume that in 1966 we have been able to discover all the chemicals which exist in the body concerned with physiological regulatory processes. Elegant chromatographic methods, electrophoresis, and molecular sieving, all developments of the last decade, are tools for the unraveling of problems of this kind. It is certainly true that the discovery of new information is limited by the methodology of the time, and in retrospect the isolation of insulin, oxytocin, or adrenaline from tissues presented great difficulties to the pioneers of autopharmacology, most of which would have been swept away if modern techniques had been available.

The pharmacologist whose interests lie in the elucidation of chemical regulation of bodily function can liken himself to a gold prospector. When first an area is opened up, new facts, like gold, are turned up comparatively easily; but as time goes on finer sieving and careful reexamination of previously explored areas become essential. There are, however, two main errors in our analogy. First there comes a point where the economics of gold prospecting prohibit its pursuit. The return is too small for the expense involved. The second is that our prospector only expects to find more gold but in ever-diminishing quantities. In the field of autopharmacology the cost of discovering new substances becomes ever greater but it can never be considered an uneconomic pursuit because a successful discovery will be something quite new which may open the door to the synthesis of a new range of drugs or draw attention to properties hitherto unsuspected in compounds already in the archives of the organic chemist.

Great success has followed the search for drugs in plants and even today large sums of money are spent in isolating and examining new alkaloids from the flora of every country, but worthwhile discoveries are few and far between. The study of pharmacologically active substances in the animal kingdom is comparatively unexplored and could

well be very rewarding. The recent discovery of a cardiac stimulant, eptatretin, in the hagfish and the occurrence of a powerful smooth muscle stimulant in the cockroach gut are pointers that the Invertebrata and Agnathans, as well as the Vertebrata, may have much to interest the pharmacologist. It is time that we paid more attention to the animal kingdom and made a few more preliminary sorties into this almost unexplored territory.

V. Problems of Pharmacological Testing and Assay

It has been customary to screen new cardiac glycosides by determining their toxic dose in the cat or the guinea pig. As long as we can be sure that this dose bears a constant relationship to the positive inotropic effect this method is acceptable, but if we are searching for new drugs which we hope will be specifically cardiotonic it is most certainly not. We must now choose only methods in which increased contractile force is the criterion of activity. Unfortunately all methods which measure this property are either extremely variable or laborious and cumbersome or both. We are, regretably, unable to offer any method which will determine cardiotonic activity with any real accuracy. We have methods for the estimation of the known hormones with a high degree of accuracy, and frequently they make use of the properties for which the hormone is used therapeutically but this is not necessarily so. Sometimes, as with insulin, the property made use of is a proven toxic extension of the therapeutic action. In this case the incidence of hypoglycemic convulsions in mice is the criterion of a common assay method and no one would dispute that this is directly related to the blood sugar-lowering effect of insulin in diabetes. In some cases, as in the assay of vitamin B_{12}, the assay method is quite unrelated to the clinical use of the drug, but evidence has shown that it is the same substance, vitamin B_{12}, which prevents pernicious anemia and also acts as a growth substance for microorganisms. In the search for new cardiotonic substances, we cannot yet relinquish the desired therapeutic effect as our assay criterion, although it may later be shown that a particular cardiotonic substance exhibits other properties which are more readily and precisely adaptable for assay purposes.

At present we must confine our tests to those methods involving isolated cardiac muscle and contend with the problems of an inaccurate assay. If we purify a new substance by chromatography we will not be able to produce an accurate balance sheet for the activity of all the fractions. We would hope to be able to show which fractions are devoid of activity, those in which it is low, and those in which it exceeds by a considerable margin the starting material which we must regard as our "standard" in such experiments. To the chemist this is unsatisfactory and frustrating, to the biologist more understandable, but to both it is an unpleasant difficulty we cannot at present avoid.

VI. Cardiotonic Substances as a Challenge to the Pharmaceutical Industry

If a new cardiotonic substance were found which acted to reverse cardiac failure without producing toxic effects at higher dose levels, the treatment of congestive heart failure would be as simple as the treatment of a vitamin deficiency. This may never be possible. It may eventuate that overdosage of such a substance always produces disorders of conduction in the heart, but it is certainly not impossible that drugs with a wider therapeutic ratio than digitalis may be found.

If this area of pharmacology is tackled with the vigor it deserves, and if new substances are found, whether they be of plant, animal, or synthetic origin, provided that they have a more favorable therapeutic ratio than the drugs presently available for treatment of cardiac failure, then a major breakthrough in a fundamental field of therapeutics will have been made. The synthetic chemist will then be able to explore the effects of modification of structure with possible increase in therapeutic advantage.

To the authors, the autopharmacological approach is attractive, and an examination of substances as yet unidentified which occur in the tissues appears to be an important means of accumulating more knowledge of the fundamental regulatory processes which exist in the organism. By analogy, with the tactics adopted in the therapeutic restoration of patients suffering from vitamin or hormone deficiencies, it is possible that congestive cardiac failure may result from deficiency of a naturally occurring substance in the mammalian organism, and that if the hypothetical substance could be identified, a better means of treating this pathological condition could be introduced into medicine. Although concrete physiological evidence for such a substance has not been provided, many scientists are now supporting this approach as an experimental hypothesis, and at the 23rd International Physiological Meeting in Tokyo in 1965, it was interesting to discuss this concept with many physiologists and pharmacologists who believe that a sufficient case exists for further investigation.

CHAPTER 2

METHODS FOR THE ASSESSMENT
OF CARDIAC STIMULANT SUBSTANCES

I. Introduction and General Considerations

A. Specificity and Sensitivity of Methods

When attempting to assay cardiotonic activity one cardinal principle must be adhered to. This is the obvious requirement that the assay must measure cardiotonic activity, that is to say an increase in contractility or in the force of contraction of cardiac muscle. Obvious as this is it has not always been realized largely because the classic cardiac stimulants, the cardenolides of digitalis and its congeners, exhibit a number of other properties which may be, and often are, utilized for assay purposes.

A different situation is presented when the aim of the assay is the estimation of a known cardiac glycoside, whether this is for drug standardization purposes or for research. In this case any method may be adopted as long as it can be shown that the chosen method gives results which parallel the efficacy of the preparation when used clinically or when compared with weighed amounts of the pure drug. Many methods used to assay cardiac glycosides are unsuitable for the study of other cardiotonic substances because their use involves the assumption that since the cardiac glycosides give valid results in such an assay other cardiac stimulants will also. Methods such as the guinea pig assay of the British Pharmacopoeia or the pigeon intravenous assay are therefore invalid for this purpose until it can be shown that the dose-response curve for cardiac arrest in the guinea pig or pigeon emesis parallels the dose-response curve for increased cardiac contractility.

In this chapter methods of both kinds are discussed: those suitable for the estimation of cardiac glycosides and those valuable when the existence of a cardiac stimulant effect is all that is known about the

substance. Much of the confusion on this matter stems from the outstanding cardiotonic property of the cardiac glycosides as well as the
acceptance of methods conferred by long usage as assays for these
drugs.

Assay methods for cardiotonic substances vary very greatly in their
sensitivity and hence in their suitability for the determination of small
amounts of active substances. On the one hand, such methods as the
heart-lung preparation of the dog may require large amounts of a material amounting to many milligrams whereas the isolated embryonic
chick heart preparation will give a complete and precise assay of a
cardiac glycoside when less than 1 μg of the material is available. In
Table 2.1, therefore, an indication of the sensitivity has been given
by tabulating the amount of a cardiac glycoside, usually ouabain, which
is sufficient for an assay with reasonable limits of error ($\pm$20%). These
figures are indicative only since technical variations from one worker
to another can result in more or less of the substance being required.
The figures, however, are adequate amounts if the methods are used
as detailed later in this chapter.

B. Historical Background and General Survey of Methods

A century ago the varying composition of different samples of
digitalis leaves rendered necessary a method for a biological check of
tinctures and other galenical preparations prepared from plant material.
Fagge and Stevenson (1865) made experiments with frogs and various
warm-blooded animals, but considered that frogs were the most suitable test animals. These early methods were simply toxicity tests in
which either the time taken for a subcutaneous dose of digitalis extract to cause cessation of the heart beat, or the amount required to
cause cessation after a fixed time, was measured (Houghton, 1898,
1909). The most widely accepted method (Hatcher and Brody, 1910),
however, was that in which the glycoside solution was administered
to anesthetized cats by intravenous injection over a lengthy period of
time and the dose required to cause cardiac arrest was determined.
This formed the basis of the method adopted in the U.S. Pharmacopoeia, and an essentially similar method using the guinea pig (Knaffl-
Lenz, 1926) was adopted in the British Pharmacopoeia. Since these
methods involve considerable errors due to variable absorption and

Table 2.1

The Sensitivity of Various Assay Methods for Cardiotonic Substances
and the Amounts of Drug Required for an Assay with
Reasonable Limits (± 20%) of Accuracy

Method	Dose for one experiment (ouabain unless otherwise shown)	Amount for complete assay
Isolated cat papillary muscle (Cobbin, 1959)	0.1–1.0 μg in 1 ml bath	10 μg
Isolated guinea pig auricles (Loeb, 1965)	0.5–5 μg in 5 ml bath	50 μg
Isolated hen atria (Lock, 1963)	24 μg in 30 ml bath	250 μg
Staircase phenomenon of frog ventricle (Hajdu, 1957)	1–2 μg in 3 ml bath (strophanthidin)	20 μg
Cat aortic strip	50 μg in 5 ml bath[a]	
Isolated guinea pig heart (Langendorff preparation)	Concentrations of 10^{-7}–10^{-6}[a]	
Heart lung preparation of dog (Walker *et al.*, 1950)	0.1–0.2 mg per dog	1–2 mg
Strain-gauge arch on dog heart (Boniface *et al.*, 1953)	0.5–1 μg/kg adrenaline[a]	
Experimental cardiac failure in dogs (Davis *et al.*, 1955b)	1.0–1.2 mg digoxin per dog[a]	
Intravenous cardiac arrest in cats	0.12 mg/kg	2–3 mg
Intravenous cardiac arrest in guinea pigs	0.1–0.3 mg/kg	2–5 mg
Isolated embryonic chick heart (Wright, 1960)	0.015 μg digoxin in 0.05 ml bath	0.3 μg digoxin

[a] Method unsuitable for assay purposes but of value for the comparison of the effect of cardiotonic substances one with another.

unrelated toxicity due to impurities, attempts were made to use isolated hearts from various species (Langendorff, 1895; Straub, 1931).

These methods were dependent upon the toxicity of cardiac glycosides and it was not until Starling devised the heart-lung preparation

that the stimulant effects of these drugs were demonstrated quantitatively. From whole heart preparations attempts were next made to
use segments of cardiac muscle from various areas of the heart, and,
as a result of such a study, Cattell and Gold (1938) developed a preparation of the isolated cat papillary muscle which has since been widely
used for the assessment of cardiotonic activity (Cattell and Gold,
1941). As a screening test for this property the method is valuable but
it lacks precision and reproducibility because of the variation from one
papillary muscle to another both in size and in the degree of "failure"
present in the muscle. It must be noted too that the papillary muscle
preparation is a hypodynamic one since it undergoes a rapid decline
from the initial systolic tension and there is no means by which the
power of the isolated muscle can be related to its previous performance in the living cat. Cattell and Gold concluded that it was not possible to correlate the magnitude of the increased tension developed in
response to a drug with the concentration of it.

Strips from the left ventricle have been used by several workers,
and Masuoka and Saunders (1950) used rat ventricle to demonstrate
the cardiotonic effect of ouabain. With this preparation, however,
recovery is incomplete on washing out the drug (Bhatt and Macdonald, 1960), and it is unsuitable for the repeated series of doses
which an effective assay method involves.

Closely related to ventricle strip preparations is the use by Hajdu
(1957) of the whole frog ventricle and the observation that the changing force of contraction upon varying the stimulation rate, the "staircase phenomenon," undergoes a reversal in the presence of cardiac
glycosides. It is not clear to what extent this phenomenon is related
to cardiotonic activity but it has been shown by several workers that
some substances which are not shown to be cardiotonic in other tests
can effect staircase reversal.

In 1928 a comparison was made of two samples of digitalis leaf
with an International Standard Powder (Trevan and Boock, 1928),
and it was considered that the isolated auricles of the rabbit heart
also could be the basis of a suitable assay method. There was a reversible increase in amplitude of beat which was proportional to the
dose of digitalis added. Bhatt and Macdonald (1960) reaffirmed the
possible value of this method and it was later suggested (Lock, 1963,
1965) that chicken auricles might provide an even better preparation

in which the effect is more easily reversed by washing away the drug and with which a long series of different doses might be studied, one after another.

Many other investigators have suggested methods of this kind using cardiac tissue but special mention needs to be made of the embryonic avian heart. The isolated heart of the chick embryo at 46 hours was shown (Lehman and Paff, 1942) to exhibit abnormal rhythm and later cessation of beat when bathed in dilute solutions of cardiac glycosides. The time which elapses between the application of the drug and cessation of beat was shown to correlate well with the concentration of the glycoside. This method does not appear to depend primarily upon cardiotonic activity as it is the result of the action of the cardiac glycosides in blocking conduction in the heart but it has proved to be a most valuable method for the estimation of minute amounts of cardiac glycosides obtained by elution from paper chromatograms in the study of the metabolism of these drugs (Wright, 1960). The embryonic duck heart has also been used and is claimed to be more sensitive than that from the chick (Friedman and Bine, 1947).

Certain cardiac glycosides are capable of inducing prolonged contracture in frog skeletal muscle (Freund, 1936), and this has been used (Shigel *et al.*, 1963) to assess the cardiotonic activity of a series of steroidal substances. It was shown that the induction of contracture paralleled the known cardiotonic activity in these compounds. Strips of aorta have also been shown to exhibit a state of contracture (Leonard, 1957) which could be utilized for assay purposes. Methods using isolated preparations of heart muscle, or other tissues which can be shown to respond to cardiotonic substances, have the advantage that they require comparatively small amounts of test material and they do not involve other physiological systems or gross metabolic effects in the testing of new drugs. They can never be more than a preliminary step to the use of preparations which are more nearly physiological and approach more closely the living animal. Progressively, methods may be chosen with this end in view. The heart-lung preparation has been very widely used for this purpose notably by Krayer and Mendez (1942), Farah (1946), Maling and Krayer (1946), and Farah and Maresh (1948). These workers have examined not only cardiac glycosides but also various cardiotonic alkaloids and synthetic substances by this method. It was also used by Walker *et al.* (1950) to establish

the similarity of action of digoxin and ouabain. The results are reproducible and correlate reasonably well with clinical findings. The disadvantage still remains that the preparation does not indicate the
side-effects or associated pharmacology which the substance may
show in intact animals and the next series of methods involves measurements on the heart in situ. This has been done by using the Cushny
myocardiograph either writing mechanically on a smoked drum or by
using a strain-gauge transducer to convert the developed tension to an
electrical output which can be recorded on a chart recorder in the
usual way. The reliability of this technique and the significance of
factors which might influence the recording have been carefully
assessed by Walton *et al.* (1950a) and Cotten (1953), and a comparison
has been made between the use of Cushny myocardiograph using
strain-gauge and the application of strain-gauge arches directly to
the heart (Cotten and Bay, 1956). Both techniques appear to be valuable, the latter having the advantage that it can be fitted in a previous
operation and used later in a conscious dog. Very elegant methods
have been developed by Rushmer and West (1957) using measurements of ventricular circumference and pressure and applying electrical correlates of these directly to computers.

With the development of *in vivo* techniques the degree of failure due
to the experimental method lessens and the heart becomes nearer to
the normal state and as a consequence an ideal drug for the treatment
of the heart in failure might show up very poorly by such tests. Such
a hypothetical substance should be capable of restoring the failing
heart to normal but be without any toxic effect on the myocardium in
larger doses. Positive inotropic effects in the normal heart are much
less obvious than in a heart in failure since the former can handle a
large increase in venous return whereas the insufficient heart is unable
to do so and venous accumulation results. When this situation is reversed by drugs the effects are therefore far more apparent. Efforts
have therefore been made to induce chronic failure in dogs by production of myocardial infarcts or by loading the heart by restricting
the diameter of the pulmonary artery. These methods have been shown
to produce failure which responds to treatment with cardiac glycosides in a manner similar to the human condition (Davis *et al.*, 1955a,b).

Ultimately of course, the assessment of cardiotonic drugs must be
made in the human subject and this has been attempted by electro-

cardiographic studies in normal humans by Gold *et al.* (1942) and Gold (1946) and in patients by Gold *et al.* (1944) and Gold (1945). Studies have been made by suturing a strain-gauge to the right ventricle (Braunwald *et al.*, 1961) in man and by an ingenious technique of recording the movements of the left ventricular border under fluorocardiography (Luisada *et al.*, 1948; Haring and Luisada, 1953). These and further techniques are needed to provide objective measurements of the clinical value of new drugs and will become more widely adopted with the stimulus of the development of new cardiotonic drugs.

II. Methods for the Assay of Cardiotonic Activity in New Compounds

The methods described in this section are applicable to the assay of any cardiotonic substances and depend upon the production of increased contractility in cardiac muscle. Common to all these methods is the measurement of contractility, and frequently the alternatives of isotonic or isometric measurements may be chosen. In practice no method is purely isotonic or purely isometric. In the former case the tissue will contract against a set tension which will increase somewhat as shortening takes place and in the latter a small change in length is inevitable in order that a transducer may produce a measurable output. A number of investigators have studied the relative merits of either system. Blinks and Koch-Weser (1963) regard neither of them as inherently preferable for the study of the effects of drugs on myocardial contractility. The thermodynamic study of muscle has shown that isotonic recordings can be a poor and misleading guide to the functional state of the muscle, and Hajdu and Szent-Györgyi (1952) regard isometric recording as more informative although no clear experimental evidence has been put forward in support of this. Two comparative investigations of the two methods have been made. Nayler (1961), using the toad ventricle, observed a greater responsiveness to changes in contractility resulting from modifications in the ionic composition of the perfusion fluid when the isotonic system was employed, and it may be that this is due to better fluid exchange afforded by the pumping action of a freely contracting muscle. This may be a significant factor for dense muscular tissue such as the mammalian ventricle but is less likely to be so with contracting auricles or other thin structures. In studies of Ca^{++} exchange in contracting auricles, in fact, Grossman and Furchgott (1964) found no significant difference between auricles allowed to shorten under isotonic conditions and those restricted to the isometric state.

Loeb (1965) examined the two systems in some detail using isolated guinea pig auricles and came to the conclusion that for the assay of cardiotonic substances either system could be used. Auricles arranged for isotonic recording exhibited greater sensitivity to drugs on more occasions than did auricles arranged in the isometric mode but the latter were more stable and showed less irregularities during the course of long experiments.

Myocardial contractility is usually expressed in terms of some index associated with the conditions of the experiment rather than in any fundamental units which relate to the muscle itself. It is sometimes measured as isometric tension, isotonic shortening, velocity of shortening, cardiac output, and stroke volume. Whichever index is taken, changes in performance of the heart resulting from changes in the properties of the contractile mechanism are considered to represent changes in myocardial contractility, whereas changes in performance arising from changes in the physical conditions outside the contractile system are not. Alterations in developed tension or contraction length alone do not necessarily indicate a change in contractility. A change in the duration of the active state of the muscle could also be the result of increased contractility although the peak tension developed might not have changed. More relevant information can be obtained from high speed isometric recording in which both the duration and the intensity of the active state may be studied. Siegel and Sonnenblick (1963) have suggested a method for the quantitative evaluation of myocardial contraction, and they regard the ratio of the maximum rate of tension development to the integrated isometric tension as being a quantitative index of myocardial contractility.

When studies center solely upon chemical stimulants of myocardial contractility the need for such exactness may be more apparent than real and the choice of the method of recording may be made according to which produces the steepest dose-response relationship or the greatest sensitivity depending upon the requirements of the assay.

A. Standards of Reference

In the assay of a new cardiotonic substance no reference standard is, of course, strictly applicable but comparison with known substances which do increase cardiac contractile force is desirable. The two main groups of cardiotonic substances, the catecholamines and the cardiac glycosides, producing this effect exhibit different degrees of latency and duration of action. In the following assays adrenaline causes a rapid cardiotonic response usually of quite brief duration whereas the onset of action of the cardiac glycosides is very much slower and persists for long periods of time. The fundamental mode of action of these two groups of drugs upon cardiac muscle is almost certainly different.

It is desirable therefore that representative substances from both classes be used for comparison in any assay for cardiotonic activity for which a standard preparation of the substance under examination does not exist. Comparison with adrenaline tartrate on the one hand and ouabain on the other provides criteria by which the stimulant property of the unknown substance can be assessed. Of the many cardiac glycosides which may be used in this way much of the published work describes the use of ouabain since it is readily water soluble and is one of the most potent of the cardiac glycosides. Strophanthin K has also been used, particularly in European laboratories; it also has the advantage of ready solubility. Digitoxin and digoxin, however, often prove unsatisfactory owing to their limited solubility in water. Alcoholic solutions should be avoided even when diluted to a concentration of 5% or less since interfering effects may be produced upon several of the preparations of isolated heart muscle.

B. Methods for Use with Microquantities on Isolated Organs

1. The Isolated Cat Papillary Muscle

The use of the isolated papillary muscle as a test preparation for cardiotonic substances stems from the work of Cattell and Gold (1938) who investigated the response of strips of muscle from various parts of the hearts of several animal species to cardiac glycosides. These included strips of auricular and ventricular muscle, moderator bands, trabeculae carnae, and papillary muscles from the cow, dog, cat, rabbit, and guinea pig. These workers concluded that the best survival and the most consistent results were obtained by using the papillary muscle of the cat. The method has also been studied by

Weeks and Holck (1943), White and Salter (1946), and White *et al.* (1948). The papillary muscles may be dissected out with little damage to the muscle fibers, and the fibers are more nearly parallel than is usually the case in other areas of the heart. These muscles, especially in young animals, are thin and small so that it is easier to maintain a responsive state in physiological solutions than is the case with thicker preparations from other parts of the heart which are difficult to oxygenate.

This preparation has been widely used over the past ten years for research in this field and has been found to provide a useful assay method although by no means an ideal one. The procedure described below is essentially that used by White and Salter (1946). The method has the advantage that it may be performed in small volumes of solution and as little as 1 ml of bathing fluid is adequate to surround the muscle. Concentrations of ouabain of one part in 10^7 or adrenaline tartrate of one part in 10^6 give a definite increase in force of contraction. The drugs may be applied repetitively to the same muscle although there is a decline in sensitivity over the course of several hours. The method has the disadvantage of poor reproducibility from one preparation to another owing to the variation in size and degree of failure from one muscle to another. Also, it is difficult to abolish the effects of a dose of an active drug and restore the muscle to the pre-drug condition. On a good preparation eight or ten doses of a drug may be compared but they need to be arranged so that important comparisons are not made between doses given at the beginning and end of the series. In our experience the method gives a comparative assessment of cardiotonic activity only when the results of four to six experiments on separate muscles are surveyed and even then the results are not accurately quantitative and can in no way be regarded as giving a precise assay figure. A clearly positive result may be followed by serial dilution of the drug to give the relative order of activity but little more than this can be expected.

The main advantage of the method is that it does depend upon cardiotonic action and a positive result is almost always supported by similar findings on other preparations. The muscle is quite sensitive to environmental changes, both ionic and thermal, and, consequently, may sometimes fail to give a positive response with active substances because of toxic impurities, the presence of traces of solvents, or pH deviation.

Apparatus. The papillary muscle is suspended in a small bath surrounded by an outer jacket through which water at 37°C is circulated. The lower end of the muscle is attached to the bottom of the bath and the upper end is tied to a silver chain hanging from an isometric transducer. Figure 2.1 shows a suitable form of bath having a capacity of 2 ml. It is desirable to use a light silver chain rather than a thread to link the muscle to the transducer since the thread may introduce baseline shift due to stretching or shrinking under the in-

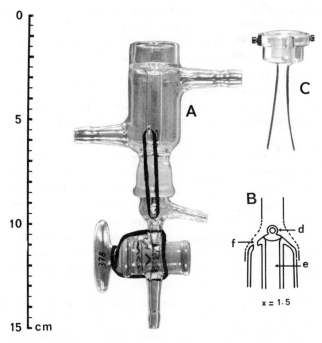

Fig. 2.1. Isolated organ bath for papillary muscle preparation. The chamber in which the muscle is suspended has a capacity of approximately 1.5–2 ml but 1.0 ml of solution is adequate to cover the muscle. From photograph A it cannot be seen that the cone joint on the top of the stopcock fits closely into the base of the bath tube with a minimum dead space. The cone, drawn in detail in B, is sealed across and terminates in a small glass eyelet (d) to which the muscle is tied. The lumen of the stopcock connects to a tube passing right through the cone and opening (e) beneath the eyelet so that the bath may be emptied. Oxygenation is arranged through the side tube above the stopcock which admits the gas into the cone of the joint from which it enters the bath fluid through a sintered glass plug (f). C shows the Lucite cap carrying two silver strip electrodes which lie on either side of the muscle.

fluence of air currents and moisture. The lower end of the muscle is tied to a glass loop on the upper end of the stopcock unit by means of cotton thread. The muscle does not contract spontaneously and is stimulated through electrodes of silver strips attached to the rim of the bath and placed on opposite sides of the muscle. The muscle is stimulated with rectangular pulses at a rate of 70–90 per minute, pulse duration 0.5–2 msec, and usually 5–20 volts is required for maximal contraction.

Measurement of tension can be achieved by using any suitable isometric transducer such as those manufactured by Statham Instruments, Offner, or Sanborn. In view of the expense and unnecessary versatility of these instruments when use is restricted to a single assay process, a simple and inexpensive isometric transducer has been designed for this purpose (Thorp and Wilson, 1965). Another excellent device is the DC displacement transducer.* The sensitivity of the transducer is adjusted so that a deflection of 1 μ is produced by a mass of 1 gm applied at A (Fig. 2.2), and corresponding displacement of the recorder pen is 1 cm. Any suitable recorder may be used, the essential requirements being a paper speed of 1 mm per second, maximum pen amplitude of 4–8 cm, a linear response to 50–100 cycles per second, and adequate sensitivity. For convenience a time switch may be included in the recorder circuit so that the paper drive and pen are disconnected for 45 seconds in every minute. This compresses the length of the record to one quarter and makes it easier to see the change in force of contraction under the influence of drugs added to the bath.

Setting Up the Preparation.   Papillary muscles from large kittens or young adult cats are most suitable. The heart is removed under ether anesthesia and dropped into physiological saline at room temperature. Blood is removed by gentle squeezing and then the right ventricle is opened and the papillary muscles are dissected out. It is usually possible to find two or possibly three suitable muscles in one heart. The ventricular end of the muscle is tied to a small silver ring for attachment to the base of the organ bath and a light silver chain is tied to the attachment to the tricuspid valve. The muscle is then

---

*Sanborn displacement transducer Model DCDT-50 requires 6 volts of DC supply and gives an output of ± 1–1.5 volts of DC for the maximum displacement of the core of ± 0.05 inches.

Fig. 2.2. The papillary muscle bath assembled below a displacement transducer. The application of a mass of 1 gm at A deflects the core approximately 1 μ and produces a displacement of the recorder pen of 1 cm.

mounted in the organ bath filled with Krebs-Henseleit solution A and aerated with 5% CO_2 in O_2 and maintained at 37°C. The bathing solutions used are two modifications of Krebs-Henseleit solution described by Creese (1949) and having composition shown in Table 2.2.

The tension recorder is calibrated after attaching the muscle by slackening the tension to zero and then applying a weight at A, usually 3 gm, corresponding to the desired resting tension and noting the position of the recorder pen. The weight is then removed and the tension

adjusted by racking up the transducer until the pen comes to rest at
the same position as before. The sensitivity of the recorder is next adjusted by replacing the weight and altering the gain until 1 gm produces
a deflection of 1 cm.

Table 2.2
Krebs-Henseleit Solution[a]

Stock solutions	Solution A	Solution C
NaCl, 0.9%	198 ml	243 ml
NaHCO$_3$, 1.3%	42 ml	–
KCl, 1.15%	10 ml	10 ml
CaCl$_2$, 1.22%	6 ml	3 ml
MgSO$_4$·7H$_2$O, 3.82%	2 ml	2 ml
Na$_2$H PO$_4$ · 12 H$_2$O	0.11 gm	0.11 gm
Glucose	0.26 gm	0.26 gm
Distilled water	2 ml	2 ml
Aeration gas	5% CO$_2$ in O$_2$	O$_2$
pH	7.5	7.5

[a] As modified by Creese (1949).

Next stimulation is commenced, and the muscle should contract
with a force corresponding to 1 gm or rather less. In 15–30 minutes
the force of contraction will increase and may reach a stable value of
3 gm or more. This level of contractile force may be maintained for an
hour or even for several hours when the technique of dissection is
mastered and the setting-up procedure is rapid.

The preparation is most suitable for the assay of stimulant substances when a degree of failure is present but with good preparations
the force of contraction may be nearly at the optimal level for the
muscle under the conditions of the experiment and may remain so for
many hours. Failure can often be induced simply by lapse of time or
better, we have found, by exchanging the solution in the bath for
Krebs-Henseleit solution C and using oxygen for aeration. In fact when
the technique has been mastered it is usually quite satisfactory to use
this solution throughout. In solution C the force of contraction will
decline, at first quite rapidly and then more slowly. When the force of
contraction has fallen to between 10 and 30% of its original value the
muscle is regarded as hypodynamic and is suitable for cardiotonic

assays. This period of decline may take 30 minutes to 2 hours, and is promptly reversed by replacing solution A in the bath.

Various other methods, such as the addition of a barbiturate, may be used to produce a hypodynamic state but although such preparations usually respond by increased force of contraction to known cardiotonic substances, such methods appear to us to be less physiological and to introduce an unknown chemical factor into the experiment. We prefer therefore the use of a modified solution C which appears to be nontoxic to the muscle and produces a readily reversible fall in contractility. It is essential that drugs be prepared in the same solution (Krebs-Henseleit solution C) and added to the bath at the same temperature since the preparation is quite sensitive to temperature variations and ionic changes.

Figure 2.3 shows the effect of concentrations of ouabain, digoxin, and noradrenaline and gives the increase in force of contraction as a percentage of that in the hypodynamic state prior to the addition of the drugs. Figure 2.4 shows the results obtained by Sciarini and co-workers (1948) for progressive additions of ouabain to such a preparation.

Factors Influencing the Papillary Muscle Assay.   The rate of stimulation is important in establishing the maximum force of contraction, and Fig. 2.5 shows the effect of increasing the rate of stimulation from 3 to 75 per minute. A well-defined staircase phenomenon is exhibited and in several thousand such preparations it has been shown (Cobbin, 1959) that the optimum rate of stimulation lies between 70 and 90 per minute.

The effects of varying the ionic constituents of the bathing solution have been reported by several workers (Greiner and Garb, 1950; Garb, 1951a,b; Green *et al.*, 1952; Brooks *et al.*, 1955) and their general conclusions are in agreement. It is found that increased Ca^{++} concentration increases the force of contraction and a lowered concentration diminishes it. Varying the K^+ concentration causes opposite effects, an increase in concentration decreasing the force of contraction and vice-versa. It has been reported by Green *et al.* (1952) that the contractility of the myocardium is closely dependent upon the Ca^{++} concentration and that its excitability is influenced primarily by the K^+ concentration.

The pH of the bathing solution is important and should be checked routinely as also should solutions to which drugs are added. The pH should be 7.5 ± 0.05 and drug solutions adjusted to this value.

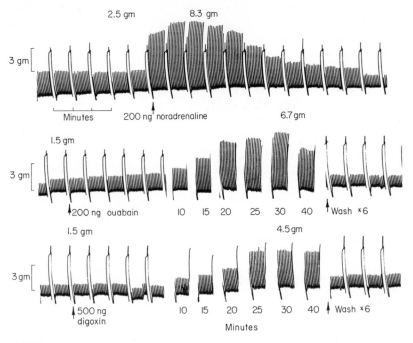

Fig. 2.3. A record showing the response of the isolated cat papillary muscle to noradrenaline, ouabain, and digoxin. The height of the closely spaced lines is proportional to the force of contraction which is also indicated above the tracing at the time of injection of the drug and at the peak of the inotropic effect. The long vertical lines correspond to periods when the chart recorder is arrested (recording for 10 seconds per minute to condense the otherwise lengthy record). Since the action of the cardiac glycosides takes a long time to reach the peak effect only sample strips of those two records are given at the stated intervals.

The inclusion of glucose in the bathing solution is not considered to be essential provided that the solution is adequately oxygenated. Large muscles exceeding 1 mm in diameter have been shown histologically to be oxygen deficient due to inadequacy of diffusion as a means of oxygenation for all but the thinnest of tissues (Garb and Chenoweth, 1949).

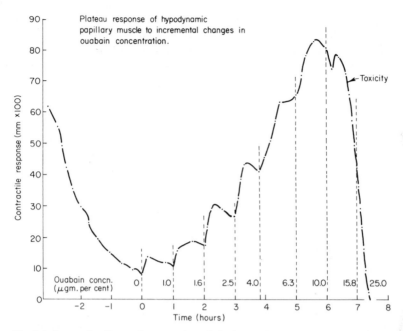

Fig. 2.4. Increasing force of contraction of the isolated papillary muscle with incremental increases in ouabain concentration after which the force of contraction settles to a new level after 20 to 90 minutes (Sciarini *et al.*, 1948).

Advantages of the Isolated Papillary Muscle Preparation as an Assay Method for Cardiotonic Substances. In summary this preparation presents the following advantages:

(*a*) Since it is an isolated preparation of cardiac muscle it is independent of nervous or humoral influences and represents a test object directly related to the site of action of myocardial stimulant drugs *in vivo*.

(*b*) Since it does not beat spontaneously variations in amplitude with variations in rate can be avoided.

(*c*) In the absence of a functional circulation increases in amplitude secondary to an improved supply of nutrient substrates are not encountered.

(*d*) By appropriate choice of bath volume considerable economy can be exercised regarding the amounts of drugs and substances under examination, which are added to the bath.

(e) Reliable and reproducible results are obtained with this preparation provided variation in the environmental conditions (with the exception of the addition of the test material) is avoided.

Unfortunately the method cannot be readily used as a precise quantitative assay but it gives responses which may be roughly quantified on
one preparation and become more precise with repetition on several
muscles.

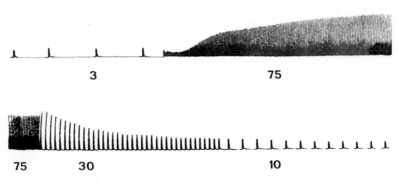

Fig. 2.5. The staircase effect in papillary muscle from the cat as a result of altered
rate of stimulation. The figures below the tracing represent the rate of stimulation as
stimuli per minute. The height of the contraction is linearly proportional to the developed tension (Cobbin, 1959).

2. Isolated Auricles of the Guinea Pig

A preparation of mammalian cardiac muscle which presents a number of advantages over the papillary muscle is the isolated auricle
preparation. Bhatt and Macdonald (1960) studied preparations of
rabbit atria and, more recently, Lock (1963, 1965) has studied hen
atria which he found to be more sensitive and to give more reproducible results than those of the rabbit. The guinea pig auricle has
also been investigated by Giotti and Buffoni (1949).

In an extensive study of methods for estimating cardiotonic activity,
Loeb (1965) considered that guinea pig atria were to be preferred
since they are of small size and are very sensitive to cardiac glycosides. It was not considered that rat atria would provide a very suitable test object since the rat heart is known to be very resistant to
cardiac glycosides and may therefore be less responsive to cardiotonic

drugs generally. The preparation now to be described is that recommended by Loeb and which she found to respond well to known cardiotonic drugs. She found this preparation preferable to the hen auricles used by Lock (1963, 1965). The method is very similar to the isolated papillary muscle with the difference that this preparation is spontaneously beating and both force of contraction and increase in rate are used in the assay.

Setting Up the Preparation.   Guinea pigs weighing 400–700 gm are suitable and are killed by a blow on the head. The left side of the thorax is then opened and the heart is rapidly removed and placed in a beaker of oxygenated Krebs-Henseleit solution at 35°C. The dissection requires some care and the following routine is useful.

The aorta is located and, handling the ventricles only, an incision is made at the atrioventricular (AV) junction and extended circularly to separate the atria from the ventricles. All the ventricular tissue is then cut away, and upon inversion of the auricular pair the superior and inferior venae cavae can be seen. All fat and vessels are removed, care being taken to avoid damage to the sinoatrial node at the opening of the superior vena cava. When completed the dissection should present the twin atria joined in the center. Figure 2.6 shows the dis-

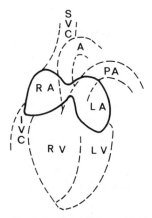

Fig. 2.6. Diagram showing the dissection of the auricular pair from the guinea pig heart. The solid line shows the auricular pair ready for mounting. Key: A, aorta; LA, left auricle; RA, right auricle; LV, left ventricle; RV, right ventricle; PA, pulmonary artery; IVC, inferior vena cava; SVC, superior vena cava.

section in diagrammatic form. The dissected auricles are next mounted in an organ bath as illustrated in Fig. 2.7 by attaching stainless steel hooks at either end. The hooks at the lower end are welded to an insulated support and a thread is tied to the upper hook for attachment to the myograph.

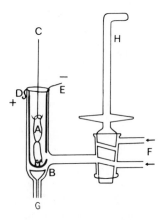

Fig. 2.7. The isolated organ bath used for the guinea pig auricle preparation. The volume of the bath is approximately 5–7.5 ml and the inside diameter is 12–14 mm. The bath and stopcock are immersed in a thermostat containing water. KEY: A, auricular pair supported by stainless steel hooks; B, organ bath with sintered glass base; C, thread to recording device; D, insulated support also serving as one electrode (anode); E, second electrode (cathode); F, physiological solution; G, gaseous mixture; H, two-way tap.

The bath is filled with Krebs-Henseleit solution made up according to the formula in Table 2.3.

The force of contraction may be recorded by any suitable transducer arranged either for isometric or isotonic recording although the former is preferable since there is less baseline fluctuation over long periods of time. Figure 2.8 shows the arrangement adopted by Loeb (1965) using a Statham Pressure Transducer with a rounded Lucite button resting on the pressure diaphragm. The button is depressed by a lever system to which the auricles are tied. The transducer comprises a Wheatstone bridge and is supplied by 10 volts of DC and the output from the bridge is amplified by a transistor amplifier. The recording is made by means of an Offner Dynograph (Type 542) direct writing recorder.

In order to monitor the maintained resting tension of the muscle a high resistance voltmeter is connected to the output of the amplifier and is adjusted so that 100 mV corresponds to a force of 1 gm. The tension developed with each beat does not show appreciably since the meter movement is insufficiently rapid in response. A suitable resting tension for most muscles is 1–4 gm although the apparatus described is linear to 20 gm. The systems described for the isolated papillary muscle will prove equally suitable.

Table 2.3
Formula for Physiological Saline[a]

NaCl	6.92 gm
KCl	0.35 gm
$CaCl_2 \cdot 2H_2O$	0.37 gm
$KH_2P\ O_4$	0.16 gm
$MgSO_4 \cdot 7H_2O$	0.29 gm
$NaHCO_3$	2.10 gm
Glucose	1.80 gm
Distilled water	1.0 liter
pH	7.4
Aeration	5% CO_2 in O_2

[a] Krebs and Henseleit (1932).

When the atria are first set up an interval of about an hour is allowed to elapse before drugs are added to the bath, and during this time the bathing solution is changed every 2 minutes by overflow washing arranged automatically by a process timer. At the end of this time the atrial activity will have attained a stable value and the tissue will beat steadily and produce a constant force of contraction. A convenient size of bath is 7.5 ml and the drugs under test, diluted in Krebs-Henseleit solution, are added in volumes of 0.2 ml or less. After the drug has produced its full effect washing is resumed at intervals of 1 minute. The number of washes and the time which must be allowed for the drug action depend upon the substance under examination. Some typical results are given below.

Adrenaline: The sensitivity to adrenaline usually lies between 4×10^{-9} and 2×10^{-7} gm per milliliter. The response reaches a maximum in 1–1.5 minutes and is abolished by 5 washes at 1 minute intervals.

Ouabain: Suitable concentrations of this drug range from 1–10 ×
10^{-7} gm per milliliter. Usually 10–15 minutes must be allowed for the
maximum response and 15 washes at 1 minute intervals are necessary to restore the muscle to the basal state. If larger doses of cardiac
glycosides are given and the muscle beats arrhythmically then a longer
period of washing will be necessary before a subsequent dose may be
given.

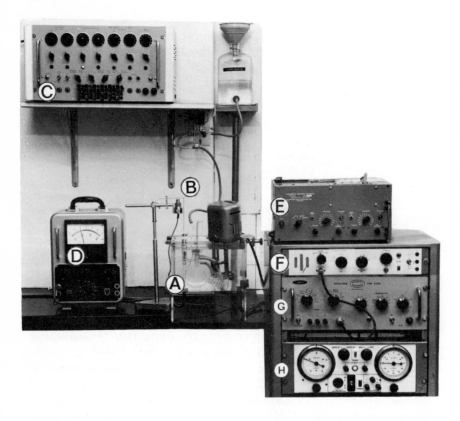

Fig. 2.8. The general arrangement of apparatus used by Loeb (1965) to record the
contractions of the guinea pig auricle. KEY: A, muscle bath in a thermostatically controlled water bath; B, measuring device, in this case the Statham pressure transducer;
C, Cassella automatic assay apparatus; D, Philips electrometer; E, Offner Dynograph
recorder; F, square wave stimulator; G, low frequency sine wave generator; H, clock
relay device.

Stimulant drugs cause an increase in the developed tension with each beat and a proportionately smaller increase in the rate of beating. Loeb has used the product of these two values as the "work index" which is plotted against the doses of the drugs administered as a percentage of the work index value in the basal pre-drug period. Figures 2.9 and 2.10 show the curves obtained for different doses of ouabain and adrenaline plotted against change in force of contraction, change in rate, and work index. This method was used by Loeb (1965) for the routine assay of a cardiotonic factor from spleen during purification of this material by chromatographic methods. Figure 2.11 shows a dose-response curve for an active eluate compared with a series of inactive eluates using adrenaline as a standard of comparison.

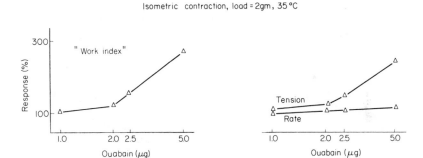

Fig. 2.9. Results obtained with different concentrations of ouabain on the isolated guinea pig auricles when the results are expressed as changes in rate, tension, and the product "work index" of the pre-drug values (Loeb, 1965).

The isolated guinea pig auricle preparation appears to give more reproducible results from one preparation to another than does the cat papillary muscle and also permits of a longer series of doses being given to the same preparation without the development of tachyphylaxis. It is difficult, however, to reduce the size of the organ bath to very much less than 5 ml due to the larger size of the auricles than the papillary muscle.

3. Amphibian Heart Preparations

In 1913, Clark observed that, "Excised frog hearts after perfusion (with saline) for a few hours pass into a hypodynamic state in which both the force of contraction and rate of conduction is markedly impaired." The isolated amphibian heart is still being used as an assay method for cardiotonic substances. Hajdu and Szent-Györgyi (1952) suggested that the staircase phenomenon in the frog heart might be used to assay cardiac glycosides, and Hajdu (1953) has studied the effect of these and other drugs on this phenomenon, and Hajdu *et al.* (1957) used this method for the detection of a cardiotonic substance in mammalian tissues. Extensive use of measurements of the force of contraction of the isolated ventricle of the toad heart has also been made by Curtain and Nayler (1963) for the assay of cardiotonic substances in human plasma.

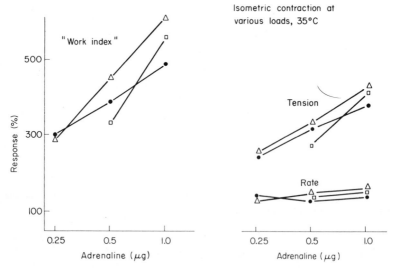

Fig. 2.10. Results obtained with different concentrations of adrenaline and different loads upon the isolated guinea pig auricles. The results are expressed as percentage changes in rate, tension, and the product "work index" of the pre-drug value (Loeb, 1965). Load: □, 1 gm; △, 2 gm; ●, 4 gm.

Despite its widespread usage the physiology of amphibian hearts differs very materially in several respects from that of mammalian species. Frequency-dependent changes in the duration of the active state appear, for example, to be of great importance to the strength of contraction of the amphibian ventricle (Niedergerke, 1956), whereas it is the intensity of the active state which plays the major role in changes in the force of contraction of mammalian atrial muscle (Kruta, 1937). Mammalian ventricular muscle appears to behave in an intermediate manner (Abbott and Mommaerts, 1959; Sonnenblick, 1962; Trautwein

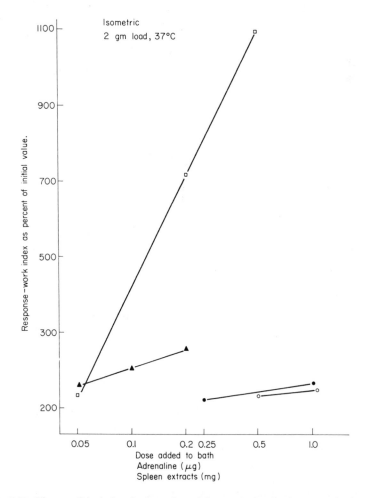

Fig. 2.11. The use of the isolated guinea pig auricle preparation for the assay of column eluates of the cardiotonic factor from spleen (see Chapter 7) in comparison with adrenaline as a standard. Each point is the average of 4–6 responses given in random sequence. Δ, adrenaline; □, an active spleen extract; ● and ○, inactive column eluates.

and Dudel, 1954). Great differences in the response of heart muscle fibers from warm-blooded and cold-blooded animals have also been reported by Penefsky and Hoffman (1963).

Assays based on changes in the staircase phenomenon in the frog heart were described by Hajdu (1957) who devised the following technique using the leopard frog *(Rana pipiens)*. Frogs stored at 10–12°C for at least 6 weeks were used, and in order to abolish the natural beat of the heart all auricular tissue was destroyed by cauterization after the ventricle had been cannulated. The ventricle was tied to a cannula of 16 gauge stainless steel hypodermic tubing, and a thinner tube of 21 gauge terminating in a small glass bead was passed down the cannula so that it rested inside the apex of the ventricle. The upper part of this rod was attached to a transducer connected to an ink-recording oscillograph through a pad of soft rubber to reduce random vibrations due to oxygenation and minor movements of the ventricle. The ventricle was stimulated by making one connection to the tube which passed through the cannula and through the glass bead. The other electrode dipped into the fluid surrounding the heart.

The stimulus frequency which produced maximal tension was determined using rectangular pulses of 5 msec duration and then reduced stepwise until the tension showed a decrease to about 95% of this value. To check that the decreased tension was due to the change in stimulation rate a higher frequency was then applied once more so that the tension returned once more to the original figure. The frequency which produced a 95% contraction tension was termed CFI 95 (critical frequency interval for 95% of maximum tension). The CFI 95 value was variable from less than 1 second to several minutes, and experimental conditions were chosen so that the CFI 95 frequency was usually between 2 and 120 seconds. For the bioassay the concentration of the cardiotonic substance in the bath was plotted against the CFI 95 value, and an approximately linear relationship was observed. The critical frequency interval for any tension shows a seasonal variation in the frog and is much shorter in summer frogs than in winter frogs. Keeping the frogs at 12°C during the summer or at room temperature in winter decreased this variation. The relationship between concentrations of strophanthidin and the CFI 95 value is shown in Fig. 2.12 from which the variation in the CFI 95 in the absence of the drug due to different experimental conditions may be

seen. The CFI 95 of summer frogs used without pretreatment by cooling was usually too low to be measured by the methods these workers
employed.

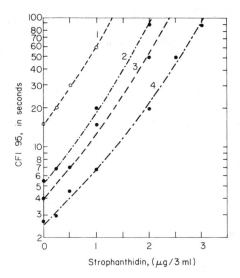

Fig. 2.12. The effect of strophanthidin on the CFI 95 of frog hearts under different
experimental conditions. *Curve 1:* Winter frog refrigerated at 12°C. *Curve 2:* Winter
frog kept at 21°C for 2 weeks. *Curve 3:* Summer frog, 12°C for 6 weeks. *Curve 4:*
Summer frog, 21°C for 2 weeks (Hajdu, 1957).

Using this method Hajdu was able to obtain potency ratios for
strophanthidin, digitoxin, and periplogenin. He showed that glycosides such as strophanthin which readily become bound to heart muscle
lengthen the CFI 95 value according to the total amount of the drug
added although the concentration may remain constant.

When the toad heart (from *Bufo marinus*) was substituted for that
of the frog it was shown to exhibit the same type of staircase phenomenon but it was practically unresponsive to cardiac glycosides as was
previously shown by Issekutz (1923). Hajdu therefore proposed that
the use of the two hearts might form a differential assay since he
suggested that steroids without a lactone ring such as deoxycorticosterone, progesterone, or corticosterone or unrelated substances such
as adrenaline alter the CFI 95 value in both hearts, whereas the glycosides with a lactone ring, the cardiotonic glycosides, have no action

on the toad. One of the cardiotonic alkaloids, coumingine, was shown to have a strong action on the hearts of both species.

The fact that a range of steroids not cardiotonic on the isolated papillary muscle (Cobbin, 1959) gives a positive result in this test and the inability of the frog and toad heart together to differentiate the cardiotonic alkaloid cast serious doubts on the specificity of the frog heart, either alone or in conjunction with the toad heart as an assay method for cardiotonic substances.

De Salva and co-workers (1955) considered that the frog heart assay cannot be directly used for clinical purposes and bears no direct quantitative relation to cardiotonic activity in man. They found, for example, that digoxin and digilanid were of almost identical toxicity in the pigeon emesis test but digoxin was nearly 30 times stronger on the frog heart staircase assay.

Brousseau *et al.* (1957) have also studied this problem and devised an assay depending upon the abolition of the staircase phenomenon in the frog using substantially the same methods as Hajdu. They found the staircase effect to be abolished with doses of 1 μg of digitoxin when the stimulus interval was changed incrementally from 2 to 4 seconds and then to 10 seconds. They also observed abolition of the staircase with estradiol, progesterone, anhydrohydroxyprogesterone, testosterone, and methyltestosterone, but not with corticosterone, prednisone, or hydrocortisone. The most active steroid of this type was ethynylestradiol which abolished the staircase with 2.5 μg and reversed it with higher doses. Since this substance is not stimulant to the isolated hypodynamic papillary muscle (Cobbin, 1959), again it appears that this phenomenon does not show adequate specificity for cardiotonic substances for it to be used for the detection and estimation of new substances.

Cobbin (1959) investigated the staircase phenomenon in the isolated cat papillary muscle and showed that it was clearly to be seen in fresh preparations when the stimulus interval was decreased from approximately 6 to 0.8 second. When, however, some of his preparations become hypodynamic the staircase was either lost or, after longer periods, became reversed so that the force of contraction at 0.5 second stimulus interval was less than that at 6 seconds. He showed that the existence of the hypodynamic state did not run parallel with the intensity of the positive staircase and that cardiac glycosides restored the staircase pattern toward the initial state by increasing the force of contraction at slower rates of stimulation.

Curtain and Nayler (1963) have used the isolated ventricle of the toad *(Bufo marinus)* heart in substantially the same arrangement as that described by Hajdu, and discussed above, with the exception that they used isotonic recording by arranging a shutter at the upper end of the rod passing down the cannula to interrupt a light beam falling upon a photocell. This preparation showed increased force of contraction with cardiotonic plasma extracts and with adrenaline. No comparisons were given with cardiac glycosides and the assay of the cardiotonic substance is expressed in terms of the dose of adrenaline giving a comparable response. Experiments by Michal (1966) have shown this preparation to be somewhat insensitive to adrenaline since a dose of 1–2 μg per milliliter is required to elicit a well-defined increase in contractile force compared with 5–10 ng per milliliter for the isolated guinea pig auricle. An active preparation of the cardiotonic factor from ox spleen (Temple *et al.*, 1966) gave an immediate and maintained increase in force of contraction, whereas the same preparation tested on the guinea pig auricle produced a much more slowly developing response.

In view of the variable results reported for preparations from the amphibian heart it is the opinion of the authors that these methods alone are unreliable. Taken in conjunction with supporting evidence from mammalian cardiac tissue they may have some small value as an assay method since the amphibian heart muscle remains functional for a very long time after removal from the animal although it is not as sensitive to cardiotonic substances as mammalian preparations.

4. Aortic and Arterial Strips

In 1905 Meyer investigated the responses of segments from arteries to various drugs and physiological solutions. Isolated arterial strips have been investigated by a number of workers since that time, and Furchgott and Bhadrakom (1953) reported that a very satisfactory preparation consisted of spirally cut strips of the rabbit thoracic aorta. These authors have described the responses of this preparation to adrenaline, noradrenaline, isoprenaline, and nitrite. Furchgott (1960) gave a detailed description of this preparation and discussed its value for the study of drugs which act on arterial smooth muscle.

Leonard (1957) has shown that such strips also respond to cardiac glycosides by contracture as compared with a prompt contraction in response to the usual vasoconstrictor substances. His technique was as follows: New Zealand white rabbits were anesthetized with pentobarbitone, and a section of carotid artery 1–2 cm long was removed and placed in Krebs-bicarbonate solution. The artery was next cut spirally by slipping it over a steel rod covered with polythene catheter tube. The rod was attached to the end of a large brass bolt which passed through a fixed nut so that the combination formed virtually the lead screw of a lathe. A cutting wheel mounted in a dental hand piece was lowered so as to cut into the vessel as the bolt was turned. By this means a helix 2 mm wide was prepared and a strip approximately 10 mm long was used for each experiment. Histological examination showed that the smooth muscle cells were oriented for the most part in the long axis of the strip.

The artery strip was next mounted vertically between two clamps, and the upper one was attached to a Statham strain gauge. The bath of Krebs-bicarbonate solution (see Table 2.3) was next moved into place and the initial tension set between 0.2–0.3 gm. The bath was aerated with 95% oxygen, 5% carbon dioxide, and the strip tension was continuously recorded on an ink-writing oscillograph. Electrical stimulation was made by connections to the clamps at each end of the muscle and 60 cycle AC was used, the voltage of which could be varied by a Variac transformer. A timer was included in the circuit to apply the stimulus for periods of 0.5 second, or longer, with a repeatability of 0.1%.

When first set up the preparation showed a gradual fall in tension, probably due to relaxation of smooth muscle elements which had been stimulated by the trauma of setting up. After half an hour this relaxation was complete and the tension was then adjusted to 0.1–0.2 gm and the baseline then remained essentially stable. Such a preparation contracts under the influence of vasoconstrictor drugs such as adrenaline, noradrenaline, 5-hydroxytryptamine, and hypertensin.

The strip could not be stimulated by rectangular pulses of short duration and when both voltage and duration were increased sufficiently to cause contraction the muscle appeared to suffer damage. Alternating current of the order of 10 volts applied for 0.5–15 seconds caused a contraction, after a latent period of 1–3 seconds, which continued long after the stimulus had ceased. Complete relaxation took 10–12 minutes. The tension developed was nearly maximal but when responses of 5–15% of the maximal were elicited the whole cycle was shortened to less than 5 minutes. In K^+-free Krebs solution the contractions were still observed in response to electrical stimulation but relaxation was incomplete and the baseline did not fall to the previous level. Contracture sometimes also occurred in the absence of stimulation.

The cardiac glycoside strophanthin and the genins strophanthidin and digitoxigenin were found to behave in a qualitatively similar manner. Strophanthidin in a concentration of 30 μg per milliliter enhanced the response to electrical stimulation, and the picture generally seen resembled that resulting from electrical stimulation in K^+-free solution. Leonard was able to detect concentrations of 0.5–2 μg per milliliter of strophanthidin in sensitive preparations since there was an increased contractile response in each case. With higher concentrations of strophanthidin relaxation was incomplete after the contraction, and repeated washing was necessary to abolish the contracture.

The authors investigated smooth muscle strips prepared in the same way from cat or guinea pig aortae and found that the cat aorta provided the best preparation for comparative studies they were making between adrenaline, cardiac glycosides, and the cardiotonic substance from spleen. Without electrical stimulation the cat aorta responded with a rapid contraction to adrenaline as shown in Fig. 2.13 and with a much slower contracture to ouabain. Upon washing out the drugs the baseline was rapidly restored with adrenaline, but only slowly after ouabain. An active preparation from ox spleen behaved more like ouabain. The onset of contracture was slow and return on wash out was also slow. This method gave a good dose-response relationship; a fourfold change in the dose of spleen extract causing a change from a minimal response to an almost maximal response. This technique is a valuable one to distinguish between cardiotonic effects of an adrenaline-like nature and those resembling the cardiac glycosides, and it is undoubtedly a promising technique for assay purposes.

5. The Langendorff Preparation

The classic isolated perfused heart originally described by Langendorff has been very widely used to assess the activity of cardiotonic drugs although it suffers from a number of disadvantages. The heart

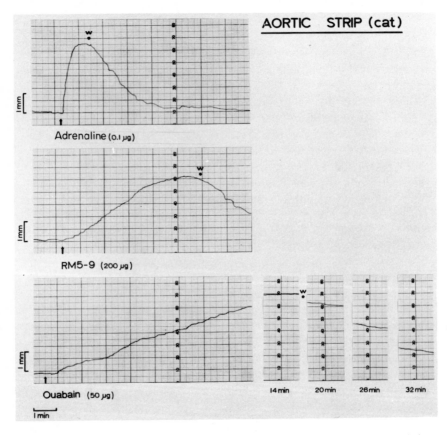

Fig. 2.13. The effect of adrenaline, an active cardiotonic extract of spleen, and ouabain on the isolated aortic strip of the cat. The time base is 2 minutes for each major division and 30 seconds for the minor ones.

always exhibits some degree of failure and the myocardium is almost certainly inadequately supplied with oxygen. Using any simple system of perfusion presents difficulties in establishing exact concentrations of drug in the heart since injections are usually made into the inflow cannula just before it enters the heart. Varying rates of flow will therefore result in varying degrees of dilution of the drugs. Many preparations are very short lived, and the essential requisites for a useful Langendorff preparation were established by Chenoweth and Koelle (1946). An all-glass apparatus permitting recycling of the perfusion fluid has been described by Anderson and Craver (1948), but in this system drugs are administered under circumstances by which precise concentrations cannot readily be established. Thorp (1949) overcame this difficulty by using a series of calibrated reservoirs, one for each test solution, and connecting them in turn to the preparation by a series of stopcocks. In this case the perfusion pressure was maintained by the pressure of the aerating gases, and provided great care was taken to ensure that the pH, oxygenation, and pressure remained the same when changing from one reservoir to another reproducible cardiotonic effects were obtained. For research in which only small amounts of cardiotonic substances are available it is essential to conserve the perfusion fluid; Rand (1956) used an apparatus in which the perfusion fluid was recirculated by using a small Lucite centrifugal pump to return it to the reservoir after it had left the heart. In this way it was possible to keep the total volume of the perfusion fluid to 70 ml when using small hearts from kittens or guinea pigs.

Drugs which improve coronary flow can also produce increased amplitude of contraction due to better oxygenation of the tissue and often due to temperature changes consequent on the more rapid flow of perfusion fluid. An increase in amplitude unsupported by other evidence cannot therefore be taken as proof of a cardiotonic action. This method is a useful qualitative one for the confirmation of cardiotonic effects in new substances, but it is one which is extremely difficult to quantify and from which to obtain more than very approximate ratios of activity is almost impossible.

C. Methods Applicable to Larger Quantities of Drug and Employing the Failing Heart Under Conditions Approximating Those in the Whole Animal

These methods require larger amounts of the substance under test than do any of the isolated myocardial methods but they involve the use of blood as the perfusion fluid and therefore provide logical follow-up methods for these substances prior to clinical trials. They may be discussed in three categories progressively approaching the intact animal. First, the heart-lung preparation of Starling has been used and modified by many workers and is capable of giving results which are acceptable to those who regard isolated tissue preparations as of dubious value. More advanced than this are preparations in which the force of contraction of the ventricles is recorded in the open-thorax animal by the use of strain gauges. Probably the methods most nearly resembling conditions under which cardiotonic drugs are used in therapeutics are those involving artificially induced cardiac failure in dogs.

1. The Heart-Lung Preparation

The heart-lung preparation has been described in the dog by Starling and his colleagues (Knowlton and Starling, 1912; Patterson and Starling, 1913; Fuhner and Starling, 1913; Evans and Matsuoka, 1914). Since then it has been used extensively for the assessment of cardiotonic drugs and was developed to a routine technique by Krayer and Mendez (1942). It was used by Farah and Maresh (1948) to study the ratio of the doses of various cardiac glycosides which produce a therapeutic effect, cardiac irregularity, and finally ventricular fibrillation.

In order to see a marked therapeutic effect with cardiac glycosides, or other cardiotonic substances, it is necessary that the heart be in a state of failure. This may be allowed to take place spontaneously or it may be induced by a barbiturate or other toxic agent. Farah and Maresh allowed a certain degree of spontaneous failure to develop by waiting 30–60 minutes after setting up the preparation. They were able always to show cardiac improvement when cardiac glycosides were administered to these preparations, but in some experiments sodium pentobarbitone was added to the venous supply reservoir to enhance the degree of failure.

In their study they showed that the left and right atrial pressures gradually rose throughout the experiment together with a gradual fall in cardiac output and a decrease in heart rate. After the administration of a cardiac glycoside the left atrial pressure started to fall and this was followed by a corresponding fall in the right atrial pressure and an increase in systemic output. These three criteria were used to assess the therapeutic effect of the cardiac glycosides administered by continuous infusion. After infusion had continued for some 60 minutes cardiac irregularities became manifest and the atrial pressures commenced to rise again and the systemic output fell. The dose which had been given up to the time when the atrial pressures fell was termed the "therapeutic dose," that which had been given up to the point at which irregularities developed was termed the "irregularity dose," and that which was necessary to cause ventricular fibrillation was termed the "lethal dose." They showed that for ouabain, digoxin, digitoxin, oleandrin, and lanatoside B the ratios of these three doses to each other were constant. The therapeutic dose was usually about 15% of the lethal dose and the irregularity dose about 60% of it.

Walker *et al.* (1950) also used the heart-lung method in dogs to study the effects of digoxin and ouabain. It had been suggested that, whereas ouabain exerted a direct stimulant action on the failing heart, digoxin had a venous pressure-reducing effect which was the more predominant. Right auricular pressure and cardiac output were recorded, and failure was induced by the addition of thiopentone or pentobarbitone to the blood in the venous reservoir in some experiments. Spontaneous failure was used in other preparations and this was accelerated by providing a high peripheral resistance or by raising the venous reservoir. Since thiopentone was added continously the deterioration of the heart was progressive; the results obtained showed an improvement in cardiac output and a fall in right auricular pressure which was in reality much more pronounced since they were superimposed on a gradual decline in contractility. Both digoxin and ouabain acted in a qualitatively similar manner although the potency of the digoxin was weaker than that of ouabain by some 50%. The doses given were usually 0.1 mg of ouabain and 0.2 mg of digoxin.

Rothlin and colleagues (1955) studied the effects of lanatoside C in the heart-lung preparation of the dog in which failure was induced by dinitrophenol. They showed that lanatoside C reversed the failure but the effect of dinotrophenol in increasing the oxygen consumption of the heart muscle was unaltered in the presence or absence of the glycoside. When, however, these workers used anoxic blood in the heart-lung preparation they were unable to reverse the failure with lanatoside C; they suggested that an ample supply of oxygen is essential for the cardiotonic action of lanatoside C when failure is induced by dinitrophenol. When the metabolic blockade produced by dinitrophenol, in high dosage, was severe lanatoside C again failed to reverse the effect. They considered that as long as a minimal but adequate energy supply exists for the myocardium the cardiac glycosides are capable of improving the performance of the heart.

The heart-lung preparation gives clear responses to cardiotonic drugs when failure is induced provided that the degree of failure is not carried to extremes. The method has the main disadvantage that the doses of cardiotonic drugs need to be large but it has a high degree of reliability and does not give false positive results.

2. *The Direct Measurement of Cardiac Contractile Force with the Myocardiograph and Strain Gauges*

The mechanical myocardiograph was described by Cushny (1897, 1899, 1910, 1918), and a commercial form (C. F. Palmer Ltd., London) is illustrated in Fig. 2.14. Essentially it comprises two arms the tips of which are sutured to the exposed heart. The apparatus is suspended from a stand and is free to move in a circular orbit. Contractions of the myocardium are recorded by movements of the two arms with respect to each other and are transmitted by a thread passing to a lever on a kymograph. When correctly set up gross movements of the heart are not recorded since the thread passes in the axis of movement. This apparatus has been used by Loubatières (1948, 1950, 1951a,b). The diagram of Fig. 2.15 is taken from Loubatières's very useful review on this topic (Loubatières, 1951c). The apparatus which Loubatières used has in addition to the system in the photograph (Fig. 2.14) a calibrated spring which can be adjusted by a collar and thumbscrew to exert tension pulling the two arms of the apparatus apart and imposing a load on the muscle. Usually 250–300 gm abolishes the contractions seen on the record. By this means the myocardium may be studied under either isotonic or isometric conditions. Loubatières showed that not only did the amplitude of contraction increase after the injection of a cardiotonic drug but also the tension required to abolish contractions increased by nearly 50%. The apparatus is used in open-thorax animals under artificial respiration and is attached to the surface of the right auricle in such a position that the movement of the two arms is in the direction of maximum contraction.

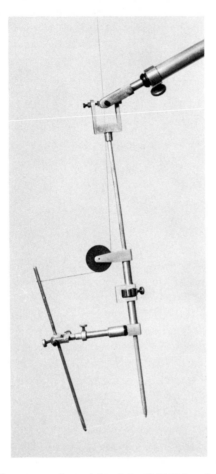

Fig. 2.14. A Cushny myocardiograph (made by C. F. Palmer Ltd., London). The tips of the two arms are sutured to the surface of the heart and the magnification is adjustable by sliding the two arms to different positions through the transverse pivots. Gross movements of the instrument do not affect the recording appreciably since the thread (black) transmitting the relative movement of the arms passes through the center of the universal joint from which the apparatus is suspended. In the photograph the tips of the arms are held together by a white thread which takes the place of the heart for the purposes of illustration.

A similar technique has been described by Walton and Brodie (1947), and the effect of secondary circulatory changes on the validity of the records obtained with the myocardiograph have been investigated by Brill *et al.* (1949) and Walton *et al.* (1950a) who studied

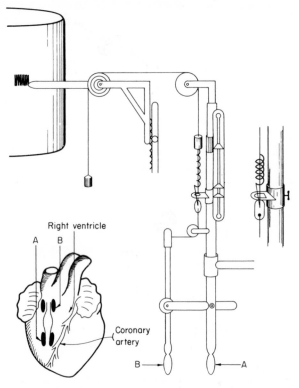

Right ventricle

Coronary artery

Fig. 2.15. Cushny myocardiograph modified by Loubatières to provide adjustable tension upon the myocardial segment by means of a spring and calibrated scale (Loubatières, 1951c). The tips of the arms (A,B) are sutured to the corresponding areas A and B on the heart.

changes in diastolic length, systemic arterial pressure, total flow volume, venous pressure, and coronary flow. They showed that with some drug groups these circulatory changes were small and had little effect on the measurements of myocardial contraction changes. Walton *et al.* (1950b) compared the increase in contractile force of the ventricle of dogs produced by a series of eight glycoside preparations and con-

cluded that there were no statistically significant differences in contractile force changes when the drugs were given in comparable
"Cat-Unit" dosage. They used the Cushny myocardiograph modified
by cementing a resistance wire strain gauge to the movable arm and
fixing the upper end of it by sliding a wedge behind it so that the two
arms were held apart and a slight tension was maintained on the muscle
segment between their tips. They also used a strain-gauge arch directly
sutured to the muscle of the ventricle. A similar apparatus was used
by Cotten and Maling (1957) to study contractile force in relation to
stroke work and fiber length during changes in ventricular function.
They showed that there is a linear relationship between ventricular
contractile force and ventricular stroke work during changes in atrial
or aortic pressure or produced by noradrenaline. No consistent relationship was found between contractile force and systemic output or
stroke volume. This method has tended to give place more recently
to the directly sited strain gauge but still presents the advantage that
the tension on the muscle segment is adjustable with ease.

Resistance strain gauges sutured to the surface of the ventricles
have been used to study the effect of cardiac glycosides (Walton and
Gazes, 1951) and sympathomimetic amines (Gazes *et al.*, 1953), and
it has been shown that the method smoothly follows the force of contraction both in anesthetized animals and in those in which the gauges
have been chronically implanted previously and from which recordings
are made in the fully conscious animal. Boniface and co-workers
(1953) have described the preparation and use of resistance wire strain
gauges for this purpose using small industrial gauges cemented to
thin metal strips and either lacquered or enclosed in a hermetically
sealed tube of brass. These authors found that none of a variety of
insulating resins then available was adequate to withstand corrosion
and breakdown from body fluids within the animal and hence preferred
the latter arrangement. They described the following operative
technique.

Dogs were anesthetized with pentobarbitone, and positive pressure
respiration was used. The chest was opened through the fourth left
intercostal space and the heart rotated to expose the anterior aspect
of the right ventricle and the pericardium was resected over this area.
The strain-gauge arch was attached by cotton thread sutures to the
anterior surface of the right ventricle with one end near the AV
sulcus and the other near the septum. Two or three sutures in each

position were threaded through holes in the metal feet of the strain-
gauge arch and tied. Lead wires were brought out and the wound
closed. They encountered some complications from adhesions, tearing
of the sutures, and breaking of the lead wires. The dogs were treated
with antibiotics and allowed to recover. Adrenaline in doses of 0.5–1.0
μg per kilogram given intravenously was used to check the integrity
of the preparation. The gauges were connected to an amplifier and
direct ink-writing oscillograph, and the force of contraction was read
as a percentage change since the coupling of the gauge to the myocardium in chronic animals sometimes loosened and failed to transmit
the full force of the contraction although relative changes were adequately recorded.

3. Experimentally Induced Cardiac Failure

Numerous attempts have been made to induce chronic heart failure
in experimental animals but early methods produced only a low incidence of the condition and were unsatisfactory for the assessment
of cardiotonic drugs. Myers (1954) produced acute and chronic myocardial failure in dogs by injecting necrosing solutions into the myocardium through the chest wall. He used a 3% suspension of zinc
hydroxide, and to produce chronic failure made four injections at
separate sites on three occasions at intervals of 10–14 days followed
by further dosage if necessary. In 178 dogs ten showed chronic congestive failure and the characteristic symptoms observed in dogs suffering naturally from this condition. Ascites, peripheral edema upon
local inflammation, cough, and labored respiration together with distension of the external jugular veins were seen. When cardiac glycosides were given, diuresis and increased activity followed but it was
noted that the dose required was large and approximated the human
dose.

Davis *et al.* (1955b) described a procedure for progressive constriction of the pulmonary artery in dogs by means of which right-sided
congestive heart failure developed in all animals so treated. They were
able to use such animals to study the effects of digoxin administration,
and they observed a direct myocardial action similar to that seen in
patients with congestive heart failure. Their method was essentially
the following.

A ligature of nylon-sheathed steel wire, or woven nylon string, was placed around the pulmonary artery in anesthetized dogs. The ends of the ligature were brought through a silver tube to a subcutaneous position to enable the constriction of the artery to be increased from time to time under local anesthesia. The ligature around the pulmonary artery passed through four 3/16 inch diameter nylon beads and was wrapped in surgical sponge to give more even constriction and to minimize local damage to the vessel wall. The blood pressure was measured in the right ventricle, right atrium, and femoral artery before and after each tightening of the ligature. The ligature was tightened until either the mean atrial pressure rose to 150 mm Hg or the femoral arterial pressure fell to a dangerous level. If the constriction was adequate ascites would appear a day or two after but if not then the ligature was further tightened at 3 to 7 day intervals until fluid retention occurred.

In 13 dogs, of which three died within 24 hours of the operation, 10 exhibited a syndrome very similar to that seen in human congestive heart failure. Cardiac enlargement, venous engorgement, tachycardia, hepatomegaly, and ascites were consistently seen. A stable state of circulatory function was rare, the cardiovascular function either improved or became progressively more severe.

In a second paper, Davis *et al.* (1955a) give an account of 7 dogs, treated in the manner previously described, that were given digoxin in a dose of 1.0–1.2 mg intravenously after a control study period of 40–60 minutes. The right atrial pressure decreased within 15 minutes in all cases, cardiac output increased in 5 of the 7 dogs by an increase in stroke volume. The femoral arterial pressure remained generally unchanged. There was increased renal excretion of sodium accompanied by diuresis.

The authors likened their observations to those seen in human patients and pointed out that an improvement in cardiovascular function occurs only in the presence of myocardial depression. In normal dogs digoxin decreases cardiac output, and similarly in human patients suffering from cor pulmonale the drug is only effective when cardiac decompensation is present. On a body weight basis the acute dose of digoxin in the dog was 3–5 times as great as that used in man and the maintenance dose in the dog of either digoxin or digitoxin was also proportionately greater.

This technique presents a definite test of the value of a cardiotonic substance. It is, of course, unsuited for assay purposes but may be used to compare the dosages and efficacy of one preparation with another under experimental conditions in the animal which are closely comparable with congestive heart failure in man.

A method of inducing acute cardiac collapse by the injection of a barbiturate intravenously in acute preparations of cats has been developed by La Barre and Garrett (1955). The cat is anesthetized with chloralose, the thorax is opened, and artificial respiration is established. The amplitude of contraction of the heart is recorded by means of the Cushny myocardiograph, and blood pressure is also recorded. An intravenous injection of pentobarbitone sodium is then given slowly until the blood pressure has fallen to about 20 mm Hg. This requires a large dose and from 80–200 mg may be needed totally. There is severe depression of the myocardium and the amplitude of beat is markedly decreased; unless some other treatment is given the animals frequently die.

The cardiac stimulant drug is next given by intravenous injection and the amplitude of beat is greatly enhanced together with a prompt rise in blood pressure. La Barre *et al.* (1962) report that such preparations can be rapidly restored by digitalis extract or by erythrophleum alkaloids. This method could be useful as a quick indication of cardiotonic effects in the heart perfused with blood. Central vasomotor effects probably play no significant part in view of the large dose of barbiturate given, although a very powerful central nervous stimulant such as picrotoxin or triazole would probably produce a similar result. It is therefore necessary to perform preliminary tests to establish that the primary action of the drug is on the myocardium and that this is the site of origin of the analeptic action.

III. Biological Methods Suitable Primarily for the Assay of Cardiac Glycosides and Aglycones

When the problem is one of assaying cardiac glycosides either as the pure substances or in plant extracts a further range of methods is available, which depend upon properties other than the cardiotonic action of these drugs. Such methods are of value when the activity of impure mixtures of cardiac glycosides needs to be determined, where the activity of one glycoside is to be compared with that of another, and where minute amounts of these drugs are to be measured. These methods comprise those for which there is no limitation on the amount of drug available as exemplified by the guinea pig or cat toxicity methods, and the pigeon emesis test. Others, such as the embryonic avian heart preparation, can be used for microgram quantities of these drugs.

Typical of the uses of these methods have been the adoption of the guinea pig assay for the examination of cardiac glycoside activity in the Australian flora by Thorp and Watson (1953) prior to the isolation and characterization of new glycosides by Watson, the very many comparisons made by Chen and his colleagues (Chen *et al.*, 1936, 1942, 1943, 1951; Chen, 1945; Chen and Anderson, 1947; Chen and Henderson, 1954) of the potency of different cardiac glycosides by the cat method, which was for many years the standard method of the U.S. Pharmacopoeia, and the extensive use of the embryonic chick heart method by Shepheard *et al.* (1954) for the study of the metabolism of digoxin, digitoxin, and lanatoside C where small amounts of chromatographic eluates were to be assayed.

For pure preparations chemical and spectrophotometric assay methods are available, but these will not be discussed in any detail in this chapter as they are applicable only to pure preparations and are described in the appropriate chemical reviews.

A. Standards of Reference

Since different samples of crude digitalis preparations vary considerably in potency an International Standard was established in 1936 and then contained by definition 10 "International Units" per gram. The International Unit is equivalent to about 1.3 Cat Units as originally established by Hatcher and Brody (1910) before it was appreciated that the assay of drugs in terms of a biological response gave fallacious results due to animal variation. This powder is a preparation of *Digitalis purpurea* leaf and the Third International Standard dating from 1949 contains 13.16 Units per gram.

For use in a biological assay the powder is extracted with alcohol following precisely the method laid down in the British Pharmacopoeia (1963). The alcoholic extract is deemed to retain its potency for not more than one month. The United States Pharmacopoeia, Sixteenth Revision (1960), describes a substantially similar method.

The purpose of this standard preparation is for the assay of pharmaceutical preparations of *Digitalis purpurea,* and it is assumed that the ratios of the component glycosides in the standard will be reasonably similar to those of the test sample or at least that the ratios of the therapeutic activity to the biologically assayed activity will be the same for both materials.

It follows that the use of this standard for other purposes is invalid. If, for example, amounts of ouabain are to be assayed a chemically pure specimen of the same drug should be used as the standard and the same applied for other pure glycosides. When comparing different glycosides one with another, variation of results from one biological assay to another is inevitable due to different ratios of absorption, utilization, and metabolism, and the results must be regarded as approximate. Comparisons of the same glycoside, a standard preparation of it and an unknown sample, should give identical results by any assay method provided that any contaminants present in the unknown sample are pharmacologically inactive and neither facilitate nor inhibit the actions of the test glycoside.

B. Pharmaceutical Assay Methods

The methods now to be described are those used for the control of pharmaceutical preparations of digitalis leaf, where plenty of material is available. They also provide suitable techniques for the screening of plant extracts for cardiac glycosides. With the widespread adoption of pure glycosides in therapy these methods are becoming very rarely used in pharmaceutical manufacture.

1. The Intravenous Cat Assay

The cat assay, originally described by Hatcher and Brody (1910), has been variously modified by many workers but was included in the United States Pharmacopoeia until the Fourteenth Revision when an assay using pigeons was submitted largely because of the difficulty in obtaining sufficient cats in many laboratories.

Cats are lightly anesthetized with ether and injected intravenously with small doses of the standard or test sample, extracted under closely specified conditions and suitably diluted, at intervals of 5 minutes until cardiac arrest occurs. The degree of anesthesia and the rate of administration of the extracts are very important factors and must be uniform throughout any assay. It is desirable that the doses of each preparation should be such that between 13 and 19 injections are required to produce cardiac arrest. If barbiturate anesthesia is substituted for ether or urethan the fatal dose of digitalis may be considerably higher although the variance between animals may be less.

The rate of injection must be such that time is allowed for the drug to act upon the heart but not so long that metabolism of the drug reduces its effects. The total time for each cat to receive the drug before cardiac arrest should be about 1 hour, but difficulties arise because there is great variability from one animal to another and when testing extracts of unknown strength 6 cats may well be needed in order to establish a suitable rate of injection for the assay proper. For a valid assay both standard and unknown samples need to be compared on the same occasion and 10–12 cats are required for each extract preferably being used alternately for the standard and the unknown. The fiducial limits for an assay of this kind are rarely better than $\pm 15\%$. For the screening of new glycosides the method is of some use if the electrocardiogram is recorded as the drug is administered since the characteristic chronotropic effect of the cardiac glycosides can then be observed and evidence obtained that the pharmacologically active material exhibits properties typical of cardiac glycosides.

2. *The Guinea Pig Assay*

The guinea pig assay is the method reported as official in the British Pharmacopoeia (1963) and is based on the suggested method of Knaffl-Lenz (1926). Guinea pigs are much easier to obtain than cats, they do not require as long a period of infusion to cause cardiac arrest, and the variance within a group is somewhat smaller than it is with cats.

Tinctures of the standard preparation and of the unknown sample are diluted and injected by continuous intravenous infusion into guinea pigs anesthetized with urethan and given artificial respiration. The rate of administration should be such that cardiac arrest occurs after 20–40 minutes, and when the comparison is completed the mean infusion time should not differ from one group to the other by more than 10%. Care must be taken that materials for injection do not contain more than 10% of alcohol, and preferably less than 5%, since this increases the toxicity of the cardiac glycosides and will apparently lessen any differences between the standard and unknown samples.

The weight of the guinea pigs should lie in the range 200–600 gm and there should be less than 100 gm difference between the lightest and heaviest animals. They should also be distributed between the standard and unknown groups in such a way that the difference in the mean weights for each group is less than 10%. Using 6 guinea pigs in each group the fiducial limits of the estimated potency can be expected to be approximately ± 20% of that value. The experimental conditions in these assays need to be very carefully controlled. The choice of animals, sex, and anesthesia, the mode of preparation of the solutions for injection, and the speed of injection all are capable of major effects upon the lethal dose so determined; and these factors have been the subject of much investigation aimed at devising a uniform and reliable technique (Rothlin, 1947; Miles and Perry, 1950).

Like the cat assay method this assay suffers from a number of disadvantages. The preliminary determination of an approximate rate of administration for an unknown sample may require up to 6 animals since the variation from one to another is great. The end point of cardiac arrest is rather indefinite. Some workers open the thorax as soon as the heart becomes irregular and complete the determination of the end point by observing the heart. As arrest approaches, the heart may show periods of ventricular fibrillation interspersed with a few normal beats; some criterion for "cardiac arrest" needs to be decided by the operator. The use of the electrocardiogram is advantageous as the dose given when the ventricle commences to fibrillate makes a suitable end point, which is more clearly defined than the cessation of electrical activity. When plant extracts are examined by continuous infusion in this way an electrocardiographic picture similar to that seen with a known cardiac glycoside can be taken as good evidence that such a material is present in the extract.

The guinea pig method presents so many advantages over the use of cats that the latter are now no longer used for assay purposes.

3. The Pigeon Intravenous Assay

It was shown by Hanzlik and Stockton (1929) that the doses of digitalis preparations required to cause vomiting in pigeons correlated well with the therapeutic doses, and Burn (1930) showed that the results are comparable with those obtained in the cat assay. The ratio of emetic dose to cardiotonic potency is not, however, uniform from one cardenolide to another since Chen *et al.* (1948) showed that the aglycone of ouabain is equally as emetic as ouabain but only half as potent as a cardiotonic substance.

The United States Pharmacopoeia, Sixteenth Revision (1960), describes an assay using pigeons in which cardiac arrest in lightly anesthetized birds is taken as the end point. A wing vein is cannulated and doses of the standard and unknown preparations are injected in a volume of 1 ml per kilogram of body weight. Between 13 and 19 such doses at 5 minute intervals should be required to cause cardiac arrest. Usually 6 pigeons for the standard preparation and 6 for the unknown are necessary to give fiducial limits of the order of ± 20%. This method is very similar to the guinea pig assay although the latter is probably to be preferred for the screening of plant materials for cardiac glycosides, the pigeon method being adequate for pharmaceutical control applications.

C. Sensitive Assay Methods for the Estimation of Minute Amounts of Cardiac Glycosides

The isolated embryonic avian heart has provided the most sensitive test object for the assay of cardiac glycosides. Pickering in 1893 first studied the embryonic chick heart for the detection of digitalis. He used embryos between 60 and 75 hours and showed that such hearts were similar to those of adult mammals in their response to digitalin and strophanthus. In 1932 Paff dissected the hearts from chick embryos and immersed them in solutions containing cardiac glycosides. Using the occurrence of arrhythmia as the end point he was able to detect as little as 10 μg per milliliter of ouabain and 1 μg per milliliter of digitoxin. Lehman and Paff (1942) studied the method in more detail and developed a precise technique for the assay of digitalis on this preparation.

Friedman and Bine (1947) used duck hearts which they found to be ten times more sensitive to lanatoside C than were those of the chick. They were able to detect lanatoside C at a dilution of 0.05 μg per milliliter. Friedman and associates (1949) used this method to estimate digitoxin and lanatoside C (Bine *et al.*, 1952) in rat urine. Wright (1960), working in our laboratories, described the use of the embryonic chick heart in studies of the metabolism of cardiac glycosides, and concentrations of digitoxin of 0.1 μg per milliliter, digoxin 0.3 μg per milliliter, and lanatoside C 1 μg per milliliter gave good results. A bath containing 0.05 ml was used and by placing the isolated embryonic chick hearts in the solution one after another it was possible to obtain complete assays with much less than 0.5 μg of these substances available from chromatographic eluates.

1. The Isolated Embryonic Chick Heart

The technique described by Lehman and Paff (1942) is reliable and efficient and is probably the best method presently available for the biological estimation of cardiac glycosides. The procedure is as follows.

Fertile hen eggs from purebred hens, which have all been laid on the same day, are incubated as soon as possible after laying; although a delay of several days has still resulted in satisfactory assays being performed. An incubator set at 39° ± 0.5°C is required, but it is particularly important that there be no temperature difference from one group of eggs to another. The incubation period lies between 46 and 48 hours, but the exact duration depends upon the development of the embryo and is judged from the state of development of the heart itself.

After using this method for many years the authors consider that the conditions of incubation are of extreme importance, and it has been our experience that commercial egg incubators are inadequate for this purpose. Since access to a large hot-room was available, a system was developed, which consisted of a vertical shaft from floor to ceiling carrying wire mesh shelves approximately 3 feet square each capable of carrying sufficient eggs in open trays for one day's assays. The shaft and shelves were slowly rotated at 1 revolution in several minutes. In this way all eggs were exposed to the same temperature zone. Remarkably uniform results have been obtained with this method and this is

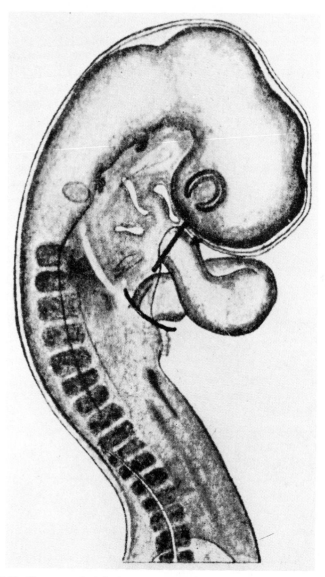

Fig. 2.16. The removal of the heart from the chick embryo. The black lines show the position of the cuts required to isolate the heart before transferring it to the observation bath (Lehman and Paff, 1942).

partly due to a reliable supply of eggs from a reputable and interested hatchery. The eggs are placed in the incubator in batches, of such a size that each can be used within one hour, at hourly intervals. Trays of 30 eggs prove quite convenient. After 46 hours the appropriate batch of eggs is removed and the embryonic hearts are dissected out. In these laboratories this is done in a tray approximately 2 × 5 cm constructed in Lucite and heated by circulating water at 39°C through a jacket surrounding the tray.

The embryo is first removed from the egg by cutting an oval window in the shell with scissors and snipping out the embryo as shown in the diagram of Fig. 2.16 from Lehman and Paff's paper. The embryo is then transferred to the heated tray and the tubular heart is dissected out with the aid of a binocular dissecting microscope of × 20 magnification. The dissection and assay are performed in Tyrode's solution of the composition shown in Table 2.4.

Table 2.4
Composition of Tyrode's Solution

NaCl	8 gm
KCl	0.2 gm
$CaCl_2$	0.2 gm
$MgCl_2 \cdot 6H_2O$	0.1 gm
NaH_2PO_4	0.05 gm
$NaHCO_3$	0.3 gm
Glucose	1.0 gm
Distilled water	To 1 liter

This must be prepared freshly each day and should have a pH of 7.4.

Figure 2.17 shows three hearts which illustrate the degree of uniformity to be sought. Only the heart shown as *B* is suitable for the assay.

Dissection is actually extremely simple and unskilled technicians can be trained to perform the assay in an hour or two. The most suitable instruments are cataract knives which have been ground down to small blades about 5 × 2 mm. A platinum wire mounted in a handle and hammered into a spatulate end is used to pick up the dissected hearts.

The assay is performed in a heated circular cavity about 5 mm diameter and 2 mm deep into which a drop of the solution to be assayed, prepared in Tyrode's solution, is placed. It is convenient to use a projection microscope as shown in Fig. 2.18 if these assays are to be performed on any scale as it is far less fatiguing than concentrating on direct vision. Three hearts may be transferred together from the dissection tray to the assay solution and observed together.

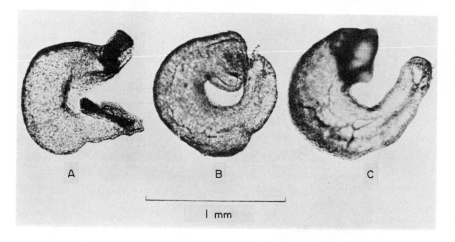

Fig. 2.17. The selection of embryonic chick hearts for uniformity for assay purposes. That shown in the center, B, is of a satisfactory degree of development. Hearts which resemble A and C are insufficiently or overdeveloped and should be discarded (Lehman and Paff, 1942).

At first the hearts beat quite regularly and by observing suspended particles the solution can be seen streaming through the tubular structure with each beat. After some time, depending upon the concentration of the cardiac glycoside, block appears between the primitive atrium and ventricle or the heart may miss beats completely. The time from the immersion of the hearts in the test solution to the appearance of the AV block is measured with a stopwatch and recorded. The hearts are then discarded and a further three hearts used. A total of 24 hearts should be used for each solution of glycoside. A fresh drop of solution should be used for each group of three hearts although when material is very scarce the same solution has been used for 12 hearts and it seems that no appreciable change in the solution takes place throughout this time. This is particularly desirable when testing

Fig. 2.18. Projection microscope used in the authors' laboratory for studies on the embryonic chick heart. The micromanipulator is used to position recording electrodes for electrocardiographic studies.

chromatographic eluates and enables a complete assay to be performed with 0.2–0.5 ml of solution.

Figure 2.19 shows the relationship between the time for AV block to appear and the concentration of cardiac glycoside. It will be seen that this is substantially linear when the log time is plotted against log concentration and the time for AV block lies between 3.5 and 11 minutes. The slope of the dose-response curve varies from day to day and two dilutions of each solution should be used to establish this and should be so arranged that block occurs at 4–5 minutes with the weaker and 9–10 minutes with the stronger solution.

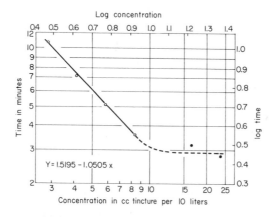

Fig. 2.19. A dose-response curve relating the time to produce block in the embryonic chick heart to the concentration of tincture of digitalis. Suitable concentrations of a cardiac glycoside for assay purposes should result in heart block between 3.5 and 11 minutes after the drug was applied to the heart (Lehman and Paff, 1942).

Lehman and Paff investigated the effect of temperature on the slope of the dose-response curve and showed that this is doubled for a 5°C rise in temperature. They suggested using a temperature of 37.5°C although constancy of temperature is far more important than the absolute value. In this connection it is worth mentioning that overheating may occur if the hearts are observed by focused incident light, and similarly during the dissection process the microscope lamp should give a broad beam and a heat filter should be used.

The precision of the method as used by Lehman and Paff was such that fiducial limits of approximately ± 15% ($P = 0.95$) could be ob-

tained on groups of 12 hearts for each of the two doses of standard
and test preparations, a total of 48 hearts for a single assay, and 24
hearts for each additional assay performed at the same time and using
the same figures for the standard.

Figure 2.20 shows dose-response curves for digitoxin, digoxin, and
lanatoside C obtained by Wright (1955). Owing to the small range of

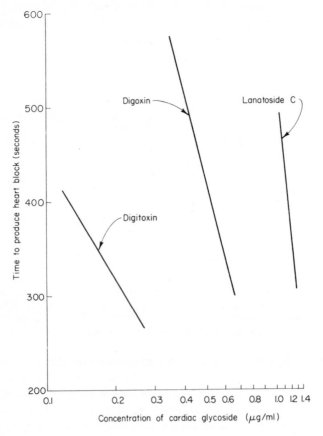

Fig. 2.20. Dose-response curves obtained upon the embryonic chick heart for three
different cardiac glycosides in pure form. The curves are substantially parallel for
digitoxin, digoxin, and lanatoside C although the potencies of the three drugs differ
over a wide range. Owing to the steepness of these curves it is necessary to have information from preliminary assays before appropriate dilutions can be made for the
precise estimation of unknown concentrations (Wright, 1955).

the time scale this was plotted on a linear ordinate, and the concentrations of unknown solutions were determined from standard curves of this kind established on each occasion. There is no other biological method as sensitive and specific for cardiac glycosides, and the effect of these substances on the embryonic chick heart is so characteristic that death of the hearts from other impurities or substances than cardiac glycosides is immediately apparent during the assay.

D. Methods for the Determination of the Duration of Action of the Cardenolides

The determination of the duration of action of cardenolides has been performed mainly by toxicity tests requiring large number of animals. Hatcher (1912, 1913) used this method and interpreted his results from the difference between the lethal dose determined on normal animals and that found for animals given single doses of the drug under examination at various time intervals previously. Haupstein (1927) devised a method which made use of the relationship between the rate of infusion and the lethal dose of a cardiac glycoside. With slow rates of infusion the decrease in toxicity is related to the rate of detoxication and excretion; the greater the decrease in toxicity the shorter the duration of action of the drug and vice-versa. Clinically the duration of action may be assessed from electrocardiographic records taken at various times after the administration of the drug although such information can only be accumulated from large numbers of patients over long periods of time. It is usually the result of clinical experience.

Rand *et al.* (1955) showed that when small doses of adenosine are injected intra-atrially into guinea pigs the transient heart block which ensues is greatly enhanced in the presence of cardiac glycosides. They suggested that this might be due to inhibition of adenosine deaminase by cardiac glycosides. Rand and Stafford (1956) used this method to study the duration of action of cardiac aglycones which have a markedly shorter duration of action than the parent glycosides. The adenosine block is potentiated by doses of cardenolides too small to show any observable effect on the electrocardiogram, and the degree of potentiation appears to depend on the amount of the cardenolide available to the heart. The duration of the potentiation depends consequently on the duration of action of the cardenolide.

In this technique guinea pigs are anesthetized with pentobarbitone sodium (40–45 mg per kilogram) and artificially respired. A fine polythene cannula is tied into the left auricular appendage and connected to a micrometer syringe containing a solution of adenosine in physiological saline (1–10 mg per milliliter). At regular intervals of 2 minutes a small volume, 0.001–0.01 ml, of this solution is injected, and the hearts shows cessation of beat, monitored by the electrocardiograph, for a period of approximately 1–10 seconds. Once a suitable dose (usually 10–20 μg) has been established for each guinea pig that dose is given regularly every 2 minutes throughout the experiment. The response is usually uniform and does not change by more than $\pm 20\%$ from one injection to another. When a cardiac glycoside is injected intravenously the duration of the heart block becomes greatly extended and will remain so until the effect of the glycoside has disappeared. Rand and Stafford compared digoxin and digoxigenin. A single dose of digoxin immediately increased the duration of the heart block from 5 to 15 seconds; it remained at this value for the remainder of the experiment which lasted for over 3 hours. When the aglycone digoxigenin was used the intensity of the response was shown to be dose dependent and the duration of effect of doses of 200 μg per kilogram was approximately 10 minutes, doubling when the dose was increased to 400 μg per kilogram. The results Rand and Stafford obtained gave values for the elimination rate of digoxigenin of 1.0 and 1.5 mg per kilogram per hour for these two doses which is within the range, 1.0–2.0 mg per kilogram per hour, Hoffman and Lendle (1951) found for digoxigenin using a slow infusion technique in the guinea pig. This method is particularly useful in the study of semisynthetic cardenolides having varying durations of action.

References

Abbott, B. C., and Mommaerts, W. F. H. M. (1959). *J. Gen. Physiol.* **42**, 533.

Anderson, F. F., and Craver, B. N. (1948). *J. Pharmacol. Exptl. Therap.* **93**, 135.

Bhatt, J. G., and Macdonald, A. D. (1960). *J. Pharm. Pharmacol.* **12**, 733.

Bine, R., St. George, S., and Friedman, M. (1952). *Proc. Soc. Exptl. Biol. Med.* **79**, 513.

Blinks, J. R., and Koch-Weser, J. (1963). *Pharmacol. Rev.* **15**, 531.

Boniface, K. J., Brodie, O. J., and Walton, R. P. (1953). *Proc. Soc. Exptl. Biol. Med.* **84,** 263.

Braunwald, E., Bloodwell, R. D., Goldberg, L. I., and Morrow, A. G. (1961). *J. Clin. Invest.* **40,** 52.

Brill, H. H., Cotten, M. de V., and Walton, R. P. (1949). *Federation Proc.* **8,** 16.

British Pharmacopoeia. (1963). Pharmaceutical Press, London.

Brooks, C. McC., Hoffman, B. F., Suckling, E. E., and Orias, O. (1955). "Excitability of the Heart." Grune & Stratton, New York.

Brousseau, A. C., Segelman, M. R., and Jenkins, H. J. (1957). *J. Am. Pharm. Assoc. Sci. Ed.* **46,** 468.

Burn, J. H. (1930). *J. Pharmacol. Exptl. Therap.* **39,** 221.

Cattell, McK., and Gold, H. (1938). *J. Pharmacol. Exptl. Therap.* **62,** 116.

Cattell, McK., and Gold, H. (1941). *J. Pharmacol. Exptl. Therap.* **71,** 114.

Chen, K. K. (1945). *Ann. Rev. Physiol.* **7,** 677.

Chen, K. K., and Anderson, R. C. (1947). *J. Pharmacol. Exptl. Therap.* **90,** 271.

Chen, K. K., Anderson, R. C., and Worth, H. M. (1948). *J. Pharmacol. Exptl. Therap.* **93,** 156.

Chen, K. K., Chen, A., and Anderson, R. C. (1936). *J. Am. Pharm. Assoc.* **25,** 579.

Chen, K. K., Bliss, C. I., and Brown-Robbins, E. (1942). *J. Pharmacol. Exptl. Therap.* **74,** 223.

Chen, K. K., Elderfield, R. C., Uhle, F. C., and Fried, J. (1943). *J. Pharmacol. Exptl. Therap.* **77,** 401.

Chen, K. K., Anderson, R. C., and Henderson, F. G. (1950). *Arch. Intern. Pharmacodynamie* **84,** 81.

Chen, K. K., Henderson, F. G., and Anderson, R. C. (1951). *J. Pharmacol. Exptl. Therap.* **103,** 420.

Chen, K. K., and Henderson, F. G. (1954). *J. Pharmacol. Exptl. Therap.* **111,** 365.

Chenoweth, M. B., and Koelle, E. S. (1946). *J. Lab. Clin. Med.* **31,** 600.

Clark, A. J. (1913). *J. Physiol. (London)* **47,** 66.

Cobbin, L. B. (1959). Ph.D. Thesis, University of Sydney.

Cotten, M. de V. (1953). *Am. J. Physiol.* **174,** 365.

Cotten, M. de V., and Bay E. (1956). *Am. J. Physiol.* **187,** 122.

Cotten, M. de V., and Maling, H. M. (1957). *Am. J. Physiol.* **189,** 580.

Curtin, C. C., and Nayler, W. G. (1963). *Biochem. J.* **89,** 69.

Creese, R. (1949). *J. Physiol. (London)* **110,** 450.

Cushny, A. R. (1897). *J. Exptl. Med.* **2,** 233.

Cushny, A. R. (1899). *J. Physiol. (London)* **25,** 49.

Cushny, A. R. (1910). *Heart* **2,** 1.

Cushny, A. R. (1918). *J. Pharmacol. Exptl. Therap.* **11,** 103.

Davis, J. O., Howell, D. S., and Hyatt, R. E. (1955a). *Circulation Res.* **3,** 259.

Davis, J. O., Hyatt, R. E., and Howell, D. S. (1955b). *Circulation Res.* **3,** 252.

De Salva, S., Dertinger, B., and Ercoli, N. (1955). *Proc. Soc. Exptl. Biol. Med.* **89,** 99.

Evans, C. L., and Matsuoka, Y. (1914). *J. Physiol.* **49,** 378.

Fagge, C. H., and Stevenson, T. (1865). *Guy's Hosp. Rept.* **12,** 37.

Farah, A. (1946). *J. Pharmacol. Exptl. Therap.* **86,** 101.

Farah, A., and Maresh, G. (1948). *J. Pharmacol. Exptl. Therap.* **92**, 32.

Friedman, M., and Bine, R., Jr. (1947). *Proc. Soc. Exptl. Biol. Med.* **64**, 162.

Friedman, M., Bine, R., and Byers, S. O. (1949). *Proc. Soc. Exptl. Biol. Med.* **71**, 406.

Freund, H. (1936). *Arch. Exptl. Pathol. Pharmakol.* **180**, 224.

Fuhner, H., and Starling, E. H. (1913). *J. Physiol. (London)* **47**, 286.

Furchgott, R. F. (1960). *In* "Methods in Medical Research" (H. D. Bruner, ed.), Vol. 8, p. 177. Year Book, Chicago, Illinois.

Furchgott, R. F., and Bhadrakom, S. (1953). *J. Pharmacol. Exptl. Therap.* **108**, 129.

Garb, S. (1951a). *Am. J. Physiol.* **164**, 234.

Garb, S. (1951b). *J. Pharmacol. Exptl. Therap.* **101**, 317.

Garb, S., and Chenoweth, M. B. (1949). *Am. J. Physiol.* **156**, 27.

Gazes, P. C., Goldberg, L. I., and Darby, T. D. (1953). *Circulation* **8**, 883.

Giotti, A., and Buffoni, F. (1949). *Boll. Soc. Ital. Biol. Sper.* **25**, 398.

Gold, H. (1945). *Conn. State Med. J.* **9**, 193.

Gold, H. (1946). *J. Am. Med. Assoc.* **132**, 547.

Gold, H., Cattell, McK., Otto, H. L., Kwit, N. T., and Kramer, M. L. (1942). *J. Pharmacol. Exptl. Therap.* **75**, 196.

Gold, H., Cattell, McK., Modell, W., Kwit, N. T., Kramer, M. L., and Zahm, W. (1944). *J. Pharmacol. Exptl. Therap.* **82**, 187.

Green, J. P., Gairmin, N. J., and Salter, W. T. (1952). *Am. J. Physiol.* **171**, 174.

Greiner, T. H., and Garb, S. (1950). *J. Pharmacol. Exptl. Therap.* **98**, 215.

Grossman, A., and Furchgott, R. F. (1964). *J. Pharmacol. Exptl. Therap.* **143**, 120.

Hajdu, S. (1953). *Am. J. Physiol.* **174**, 371.

Hajdu, S. (1957). *J. Pharmacol. Exptl. Therap.* **120**, 90.

Hajdu, S., and Szent-Györgyi, A. (1952). *Am. J. Physiol.* **168**, 159.

Hajdu, S., Weiss, H., and Titus, E. (1957). *J. Pharmacol. Exptl. Therap.* **120**, 99.

Hanzlik, P. J., and Stockton, A. B. (1929). *J. Pharmacol. Exptl. Therap.* **35**, 393.

Haring O. M., and Luisada, A. A. (1953). *Am. Heart J.* **46**, 276.

Hatcher, R. A. (1912). *Arch. Internal Med.* **10**, 268.

Hatcher, R. A. (1913). *J. Am. Med. Assoc.* **61**, 386.

Hatcher, R. A., and Brody, J. G. (1910). *Am. J. Pharm.* **82**, 360.

Haupstein, P. (1927). *Arch. Exptl. Pathol. Pharmakol.* **126**, 121.

Hoffman, G., and Lendle, L. (1951). *Arch. Exptl. Pathol. Pharmakol.* **212**, 376.

Houghton, E. M. (1898). *J. Am. Med. Assoc.* **31**, 959.

Houghton, E. M. (1909). *Lancet* **19**, 1174.

Issekutz, B. (1923). *Arch. Ges. Physiol.* **198**, 429.

Knaffl-Lenz, E. (1926). *J. Pharmacol. Exptl. Therap.* **29**, 407.

Knowlton, F. P., and Starling, E. H. (1912). *J. Physiol. (London)* **44**, 206.

Krayer, O., and Mendez, R. (1942). *J. Pharmacol. Exptl. Therap.* **74**, 350.

Krebs, H. A., and Henseleit, K. (1932). *Z. Physiol. Chem.* **210**, 33.

Kruta, V. (1937). *Arch. Intern. Physiol.* **45**, 332.

La Barre, J., and Garrett, J. (1955). *Arch. Intern. Pharmacodynamie* **100**, 418.

La Barre, J., Gillo, L., and Van Heerswijnghels, J. (1942). *Bull. Acad. Roy. Med. Belg.* **2**, 639.

Langendorff, O. (1895). *Arch. Ges. Physiol.* **61**, 291.

Lehman, R. A., and Paff, G. H. (1942). *J. Pharmacol. Exptl. Therap.* **75**, 207.

Leonard, E. (1957). *Am. J. Physiol.* **189**, 185.

Lock, J. A. (1963). *Brit. J. Pharmacol.* **21**, 393.

Lock, J. A. (1965). *Brit. J. Pharmacol.* **25**, 557.

Loeb, T. (1965). M.Sc. Thesis, University of Sydney.

Loubatières, A. (1948). *J. Physiol. (Paris)* **40**, 241-A.

Loubatières, A. (1950). *Montpellier Med.* **37**, 183.

Loubatières, A. (1951a). *Actualities Pharmacol. Third Ed.* 69.

Loubatières, A. (1951b). *Arch. Intern. Pharmacodynamie* **85**, 333.

Loubatières, A. (1951c). *J. Physiol. (Paris)* **43**, 517.

Luisada, A. A., Fleischner, F. G., and Rappaport, M. B. (1948). *Am. Heart J.* **35**, 348.

Maling, H. M., and Krayer, O. (1946). *J. Pharmacol. Exptl. Therap.* **86**, 66.

Meyer, O. B. (1905). *Z. Biol.* **48**, 352.

Michal, F. (1966). Personal communication.

Miles, A. A., and Perry, W. L. M. (1950). *Bull. World Health Organ.* **2**, 697.

Masuoka, D. T., and Saunders, P. R. (1950). *Proc. Soc. Exptl. Biol. Med.* **74**, 879.

Myers, F. H. (1954). *J. Appl. Physiol.* **7**, 114.

Nayler, W. G. (1961). *Australian J. Exptl. Biol. Med. Sci.* **39**, 429.

Niedergerke, R. (1956). *J. Physiol. (London)* **134**, 569.

Paff, G. H. (1932). *J. Pharmacol. Exptl. Therap.* **69**, 311.

Patterson, S. W., and Starling, E. H. (1913). *J. Physiol. (London)* **48**, 357.

Penefsky, Z. F., and Hoffman, B. F. (1963). *Am. J. Physiol.* **204**, 433.

Pickering, J. W. (1893). *J. Physiol. (London)* **14**, 383.

Rand, M. J. (1956). Ph.D. Thesis, University of Sydney.

Rand, M., and Stafford, A. (1956). *Nature* **117**, 278.

Rand, M., Stafford, A., and Thorp, R. H. (1955). *J. Pharmacol. Exptl. Therap.* **114**, 119.

Rothlin, E. (1947). *Pharm. Acta Helv.* **22**, 418.

Rothlin, E., Taeschler, M., and Cerletti, A. (1955). *Circulation Res.* **3**, 32.

Rushmer, R. F., and West, T. C. (1957). *Circulation Res.* **5**, 240.

Sciarini, L. J., Ackerman, E. M., and Salter, W. T. (1948). *J. Pharmacol. Exptl. Therap.* **92**, 434.

Shepheard, E. E., Thorp R. H., and Wright, S. E. (1954). *J. Pharmacol. Exptl. Therap.* **112**, 133.

Shigel, T., Imai, S., and Murase, H. (1963). *Arch. Exptl. Pathol. Pharmakol.* **244**, 510.

Siegel, J. H., and Sonnenblick, E. H. (1963). *Circulation Res.* **12**, 597.

Sonnenblick, E. H. (1962). *Am. J. Physiol.* **202**, 931.

Straub, W. (1931). *In* "Cardiac Glycosides," Lane Lecture. Stanford Univ. Press, Stanford, California.

Temple, D. M., Thorp, R. H., and Gillespie, R. (1966). *J. Comp. Physiol. Biochem.* **17**, 1089.

Thorp, R. H. (1949). *Brit. J. Pharmacol.* **4**, 98.

Thorp, R. H., and Watson, T. R. (1953). *Australian J. Exptl. Biol. Med. Sci.* **31**, 529.

Thorp, R. H., and Wilson, H. (1965). *Proc. 6th Intern. Conf. Med. Elec. Biol. Eng., Suppl.* **19**, Tokyo, Japan.

Trautwein, W., and Dudel, J. (1954). *Arch. Ges. Physiol.* **260**, 24.

Trevan, J. W., and Boock, E. M. (1928). *Quart. J. Pharm.* **1**, 6.

U.S. Pharmacopoeia. (1960). Sixteenth Revision. Mack Publ. Co., Easton, Pennsylvania.

Walker, J. M., Lourie, E. M., and Burn, J. H. (1950). *Brit. J. Pharmacol.* **5**, 306.

Walton, R. P., and Brodie, O. J. (1947). *J. Pharmacol. Exptl. Therap.* **90**, 26.

Walton, R. P., and Gazes, P. C. (1951). *Southern Med. J.* **44**, 418.

Walton, R. P., Cotten, M. de V., Brill, H. H., and Gazes, P. C. (1950a). *Am. J. Physiol.* **161**, 489.

Walton, R. P., Leary, J. S., and Jones, H. P. (1950b). *J. Pharmacol. Exptl. Therap.* **98**, 346.

Weeks, J. R., and Holck, H. J. O. (1943). *J. Pharmacol. Exptl. Therap.* **78**, 180.

White, W. F., and Salter, W. T. (1946). *J. Pharmacol. Exptl. Therap.* **88**, 1.

White, W. F., Belford, J., and Salter, W. T. (1948). *J. Pharmacol. Exptl. Therap.* **92**, 443.

Wright, S. E. (1955). Ph.D. Thesis, University of Sydney.

Wright, S. E. (1960). "The Metabolism of Cardiac Glycosides." Thomas, Springfield, Illinois.

CHAPTER 3

GENERAL PHARMACOLOGY
OF THE CARDIAC GLYCOSIDES

I. Introduction

The cardiac glycosides are a remarkable group of very potent drugs which, with adequate precautions to minimize K^+ depletion, can be administered with a comparatively high degree of safety over an indefinite period once the maintenance dose has been individually stabilized. The actions of this group, while slight upon the normal heart, are dramatic upon the heart exhibiting signs of failure (due to a variety of causes) or certain types of arrhythmias. Qualitatively, the actions of the group are similar, which implies a fundamental similarity in their mechanisms of action and, in the absence of evidence to the contrary, we will assume that this implication is in fact true. Quantitatively, of course, individual members of the class exhibit considerable differences in potency and duration of action. These differences may be related to minor structural variations in the molecule, which influence such variables as solubility, absorption, accessibility and strength of attachment to receptor sites, metabolic inactivation, and rate of elimination from the body.

The cardiac glycosides (see Fig. 3.1) consist of a steroid nucleus oriented so that rings B and C have the *trans*-configuration, whereas A and B and also C and D possess the *cis*-configuration (Tamm, 1963).

Attached to the steroid nucleus at the 17-position is an unsaturated lactone ring which has either 4 or 5 carbon atoms. The combination of steroid nucleus and lactone ring is known as an aglycone or genin and forms the minimum structural requirement for cardiac activity. Usually the drugs possess a series of sugar moieties attached via a glycoside linkage to the steroid nucleus at the 3-position and it is these compounds which are the true cardiac glycosides. The importance of the sugar residues was shown by Chen *et al.* (1938) who demonstrated that aglycones are usually less potent than the parent glycosides and that the time course of their action is modified so that the onset of action is more rapid but the duration of their effects is decreased. The presence of the sugar residues may allow a more prolonged duration of action by preventing the enzyme epimerase from inducing a change in the steric configuration of the hydroxyl at the 3-position, from the β to the α orientation, and thus depriving the molecule of cardiotonic activity (Repke, 1963).

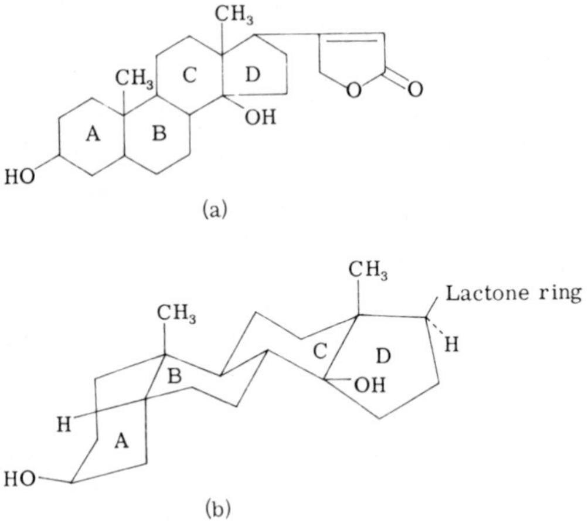

(a)

(b)

Fig. 3.1. (a) The usual representation of the structure of digitoxigenin and (b) the steric configuration of the steroid nucleus.

The most striking pharmacological actions of the cardiac glycosides are exerted upon the heart itself although the actions on the central nervous system and the kidney are also of considerable importance in the treatment of cardiac patients. These compounds act upon the failing heart to cause a marked inotropic action, and produce brady-cardia, which is partly due to indirect stimulation of the vagus (antag-onized by atropine) and when higher doses are used is also due to direct action on the myocardium (not antagonized by atropine) (Gold, 1946). The cardiac glycosides have depressant actions on the velocity of conduction of cardiac impulses and upon the excitability of the tissue, which may be put to clinical use.

In addition to actions exerted directly upon the heart, the cardiac glycosides also cause central nervous stimulation—notably nausea, vomiting, and visual disturbances such as flickering vision often accompanied by a greenish-yellow tinting of observed objects. These signs are usually regarded as the first signs of toxicity due to over-digitalization and are frequently easily corrected by adjustment of the dosage. In cardiac failure accompanied by peripheral edema, a marked diuresis is observed following administration of the cardiac glycosides. Although this may be attributed to be an effect secondary to improvement in the cardiovascular status of the patient as a result of the direct positive inotropic action of the drugs, recent evidence has shown that cardiac glycosides also have direct actions upon the kidney tubules (Orloff and Burg, 1960; Tanabe *et al.,* 1963).

Since the discovery that cardiac glycosides inhibit the active transport of Na^+ and K^+ across the red blood cell membrane (Schatzmann, 1953), study of the actions of these drugs on ion transport has been extensive and has been reviewed recently (Glynn, 1964). Inhibition of ion transport has been demonstrated in tissues other than heart muscle and red cells, and has been largely explored to determine whether or not the inotropic action of the cardiac glycosides is achieved by means of variation in ionic fluxes across the cellular membranes of the heart. This aspect of cardiac research is discussed in Chapter 4.

The heart is now recognized to consist of discrete cells and not to exist anatomically as a syncitium (Spiro and Sonnenblick, 1965). The evidence for this change of thought has resulted from the greater resolution possible when using the electron microscope rather than the light microscope to study the ultrastructure of the heart. Functionally, however, the heart behaves as a syncitium because of the low electrical impedance across the intercalated discs allowing the activation of the tissue to spread freely between cells (Woodbury, 1962). Accordingly, the study of cardiac function represents the integrated activity of many cells, and to simplify the study of drug action upon the heart many workers are turning toward the single muscle cell as a test object. To date the mode of action of the cardiac glycosides has not been satisfactorily explained but three areas of investigation have received considerable attention in an endeavor to locate the site and mechanism of action of these drugs. The cell membrane is the first region where cardiac glycosides could be assumed to act, by altering the intracellular ionic and chemical composition of the heart. The next site proceeding inward could be on the still unknown links between excitation and contraction of the cell, or, finally, upon the contractile mechanism. Action upon the contractile proteins could be envisaged as direct or indirect as, for example, by increasing the energy available for myocardial contraction from effects upon cardiac metabolism.

II. The Inotropic Actions of the Cardiac Glycosides

A. Isolated Papillary Muscle Preparations

The inotropic property of the cardiac glycosides can be demonstrated on isolated mammalian papillary muscles removed from the right ventricle as detailed in the previous chapter. The papillary muscle is a simple preparation of nearly parallel muscle fibers, which does not beat spontaneously and therefore may be stimulated electrically at a constant rate. Furthermore, the preparation is devoid of nervous and humoral influences which might modify drug actions on the heart in situ. Influences of a drug secondary to changes in the coronary circulation are excluded as the preparation is mounted in an isolated organ bath.

In recent years, the papillary muscle preparation has been used to elucidate some of the fundamental biophysical properties of cardiac muscle to allow a better description of cardiac contraction and a more complete understanding of the nature of the inotropic effects of drugs. This approach resulted from application of the knowledge of the contraction process in skeletal muscle determined from the famous experiments of A. V. Hill. Briefly, the functional behavior of a muscle may be described in terms of an active contractile unit coupled in series with an undamped passive elastic component (Hill, 1938). In this model, an isotonic contraction is represented by a shortening of the active unit without a change in length of the series elastic component, provided that a constant load is applied to the muscle fiber. In an isometric contraction, shortening of the active unit is accompanied by stretch of the series elastic component with a corresponding increase in the tension developed between the fixed ends of the muscle fiber. The nature of the series elastic component is unknown although, partly, it may involve connective tissue and tendinous material. No morphologically identified structure has been equated with the series elastic component at the present time although it is probable that it is repeated in each sarcomere.

The degree of activity of the contractile unit is described as the "active state" which is the maximal isometric tension that the contractile unit can develop, or just bear without lengthening, at a given moment, and must be measured under conditions which do not allow movement of the series elastic component. In skeletal muscle it is found that the fundamental activation of the contractile units, the "active state," reaches full intensity very rapidly and is maintained for a definite time — the plateau of full activity — and then declines to inactivity (Hill, 1949). The duration of the active state in a single twitch is too short to allow the muscle to develop full tension, and when the isometric tension curve reaches its peak, the active state has declined to about 75% of its plateau level. This is because the time lag in development of externally recorded tension depends upon the time required to lengthen the series elastic components until they exert the same tension present in the contractile units, and this time lag exceeds the duration of the active state. Consequently, the external force recorded in a single muscle twitch is below the maximum tension of which the muscle is capable. However, skeletal muscle can be tetanized so that the tension exerted externally eventually reaches that level corresponding to the full plateau of the active state and thus the intensity of the active state can be measured. Similar measurements of the active state in cardiac muscle are complicated by the inability of the heart to undergo a fused tetanic contraction because the duration of the refractory period outlasts the duration of the active state. However, recently techniques have been developed so that the active state may be determined and its time course plotted. These involve another fundamental property of muscle tissue which was described in skeletal muscle by A. V. Hill and termed the "Force-Velocity" relation.

The extent and velocity of shortening of a muscle fiber are dependent upon the imposed load on the muscle. The maximum velocity of shortening is found when the muscle is unloaded, and it diminishes in a hyperbolic fashion as the load is increased until the point where the load is exactly equal to the maximum tension which the muscle is capable of developing, and at this point the velocity of shortening becomes zero. The relationship formulated by Hill is

$$(P + a)V = b(P_0 - P)$$

or

$$(P + a)(V + b) = (P_0 + a)b$$

where P = the load; V = the velocity of shortening corresponding to the load; P_0 = maximum (isometric) tension of the muscle, and a and b are constants. The force-velocity relation in cardiac muscle has been determined and found to be essentially the same as for skeletal muscle (Abbott and Mommaerts, 1959; Edman and Nilsson, 1965). The importance of the force-velocity relation in muscular contraction is apparent, for the degree of stretch of the series elastic component depends upon the velocity of shortening of the contractile unit. Construction of force-velocity curves allows an extrapolation of the curve to the abscissa so that an estimate of the quantity of P_0 may be made which corresponds to the intensity of the active state where the velocity of shortening is zero. Details of the methods for the measurement of these parameters are given in the papers by Abbott and Mommaerts (1959) and Edman and Nilsson (1965). Recent reviews of these fundamental dynamic properties have appeared, to which the reader is directed for a further discussion (Blinks and Koch-Weser, 1963; Mommaerts and Langer, 1963; Edman, 1965).

Measurements of the active state in rabbit papillary muscle stimulated 30 times per minute have shown that the maximum intensity is reached approximately 90 msec after stimulation and is maintained at this plateau level for a further 40 msec after which it begins to decline. At this frequency of stimulation, the active state has declined to approximately 80% of the plateau level when the isometric contraction, recorded simultaneously, reaches its maximum tension after about 180 msec.

The quantification of these fundamental biophysical parameters allows a means of interpreting the inotropic actions of drugs. Theoretically a positive inotropic action can arise from a prolongation of the duration of the active state, thus allowing a longer time for development of a greater proportion of the maximum isometric tension. This type of inotropic effect has been demonstrated in skeletal muscle and is associated with no change in intensity of the active state or the force-velocity relation (Ritchie, 1954; Hill and MacPherson, 1954). A second mechanism for inotropic effects requires an increased intensity of the active state; even if the duration of the plateau and the total duration were constant, the same proportion of a greater potential tension would be realized, provided the time to reach peak isometric tension was the same. Under these circumstances the velocity of shortening would be increased irrespective of the load and therefore contraction would proceed at a greater rate. Finally, if neither the intensity nor the duration of the active state were altered but the velocity of contraction of the fiber was increased, within the available time for peak contraction a greater proportion of the active state would be reached and a greater isometric tension recorded.

It has been demonstrated recently that at a constant rate of stimulation the inotropic action of ouabain was associated with a marked increase in the maximal intensity of the active state of rabbit papillary muscles. The onset of the plateau of the active state was achieved more quickly in the presence of ouabain, but the duration was reduced and began to decline earlier. The force-velocity curve was shifted away from the origin in a parallel fashion without change in shape of the curve, which indicated that maximal shortening velocity increased proportionately to the increase in intensity of the active states (Edman and Nilsson, 1965). Edman and Nilsson believe that the fundamental mechanism of the inotropic action of ouabain is an increase in the intensity of the active state, which results in improved ability of the contractile elements to exert tension. The observed reduction of the duration of the active state limits the inotropic effect, but this latter effect of ouabain is counteracted by increased velocity of shortening resulting in a reduction of the time required for peak contraction.

Koch-Weser and Blinks (1962) agree that the inotropic action of cardiac glycosides is associated with a change in the force-velocity relationship, and that the increased contractility is not associated with increased duration of the active state of the papillary muscle. These authors did not measure changes in intensity of the active state but accepted that this was a consequence of changes in the force-velocity relation.

The same authors have developed a descriptive hypothesis to analyze the factors involved in an inotropic response. Although the hypothesis was developed initially to allow interpretation of inotropic changes following alterations in frequency of stimulation of the muscle, it can be adapted to explain differences in the dynamics of inotropic responses to cardiac glycosides and catecholamines, and also other inotropic agents. According to Koch-Weser and Blinks, the strength of an isometric heart muscle contraction is determined by three factors. The first is the strength of the "rested-state contraction," which is the strength of the contraction following a long interval between stimuli, e.g., 10 minutes. The remaining factors are the residual negative and positive effects which have accumulated as a result of previous contractions and which are designated as NIEA and PIEA (negative and positive inotropic effects of activation), respectively. Cardiac glycosides were shown to increase the contribution of the "rested-state contraction" to the total effect, without affecting the production or rate of decay of accumulated PIEA. The action of catecholamines is, however, quite different (see Chapter 6) for these drugs do not potentiate the "rested-state contraction," but instead influence the accumulation of PIEA and show a greater positive inotropic action at higher frequencies of stimulation (Koch-Weser, 1963; Koch-Weser and Blinks, 1963; see also Fig. 7.10). Unfortunately the concepts of NIEA and PIEA are a trifle vague and do not permit accurate definition. It is possible that these hypothetical effects are related to dimensions of the active state and describe changes in either its intensity or duration, or may describe changes in the force-velocity relation.

Another means of studying inotropic actions of drugs has been developed, using an index of myocardial contractility (Siegel and Sonnenblick, 1963), where the maximum rate of development of isometric tension, dp/dt, is expressed per unit of integrated systolic isometric tension (IIT). The index, $dp/dt/$IIT, can be determined for papillary muscles and also for the intact heart. In Fig. 3.2 superimposed isometric tracings from a papillary muscle are shown at different resting tensions. The maximum rate of development of isometric tension is plotted as dotted lines tangential to the isometric tension curves, and the integrated systolic isometric tension is represented as the area under the curve between the start and the peak of the contraction. The index was found to remain constant over a wide range of initial fiber lengths but could be increased by the addition of noradrenaline or increased rate of stimulation. The value of this index of contractility is claimed to lie in its ability to distinguish between increases in developed tension which are a result of increased stretch of

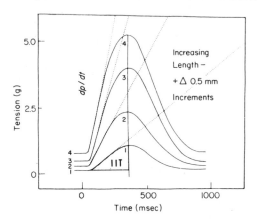

Fig. 3.2. Superimposed tracings of isometric twitches recorded from papillary muscles stimulated 60 times per minute at 22°C at increasing resting tensions imposed by increasing the diastolic length of the muscle by 0.5 mm increments. The dotted lines represent the maximum rate of development of isometric tension and IIT represents the integrated systolic isometric tension (shaded area). (From Siegel and Sonnenblick, 1963, by permission of the American Heart Association, Inc.)

the preparation (Frank-Starling effect) and those due to alterations in the velocity of shortening of the contractile unit which these authors claim to be the necessary condition for a positive inotropic effect. The main limitation of the Siegel-Sonnenblick approach is that, although they recognize the importance of alterations in the force-velocity relation, they neglect to include considerations of the active state, and in particular the situation where an inotropic response could result from a lengthening of the active state duration without alteration of either its intensity or the force-velocity relationship.

B. Intact Hearts

Superficially it is agreed that the cardiac glycosides increase the magnitude and rate of development of systolic contractions in the failing heart, and that they increase the ventricular work output of the heart. In the heart-lung preparation the cardiac glycosides increase the cardiac output without alterations of cardiac rate and slightly increase the arterial pressure. Because all the variables are easily controlled in the heart-lung preparation, it can be shown that the effects are the result of increased ventricular contractile force. In dogs with intact circulations, ventricular function curves were plotted from calculated stroke work and atrial pressures, and it has been shown that the work capacity of the hearts was increased by ouabain in doses lower than were required to produce electrocardiographic signs of intoxication (Cotten and Stopp, 1958).

A strain gauge sutured to the right ventricle of the dog heart several days before experiments with drugs allows investigation of the contractile force of the heart in situ in sedated animals. For experimental investigations, the animals were treated with atropine to abolish vagal inhibition of the heart rate and were sedated with morphine sulfate. Slow injections of cardiac glycosides resulted in increased force of contraction recorded from the strain gauge (Walton *et al.,* 1950). Usually, electrocardiographic changes were very slight before contractile force was increased and in some experiments, no electrocardiographic changes were found until after maximal inotropic effects were recorded.

Information about cardiac function is readily obtained from intraventricular pressure measurements, and this method has been in use for a considerable time. Early observations showed that strophanthin and digitalis each increased the maximum intraventricular systolic pressure and also the rate at which the pressure rose during isometric contraction (Wiggers and Stimson, 1927). The period of systolic contraction was decreased by the drugs. Because the hearts were driven at a constant rate and the arterial pressure was controlled, these results clearly indicated that an increase in ventricular contractile force resulted from administration of the glycosides. Modern experiments confirm these early observations. Under conditions of constant end-diastolic ventricular volume and mean aortic pressure the cardiac glycosides reduced the duration of total systole, the isovolumic phase where the cardiac contraction is isometric), and the ejection time in the dog heart. If we can apply the results obtained on isolated papillary muscles (Edman and Nilsson, 1965), the intact heart treated with glycosides may be envisaged as exhibiting increased intensity of the active state together with increased velocity of shortening and diminished duration of activity.

Using a canine heart in situ but isolated from the circulation by means of a cardiopulmonary bypass, the isometric portion of the cardiac cycle may be studied (Siegel and Sonnenblick, 1963). The end-diastolic volume of the left ventricle was altered by injecting known increments of fluid from a syringe into a liquid-filled balloon introduced into the chamber through the apical dimple. The heart (and other tissues of the animal) was perfused by blood from a pump at a constant flow rate, and cannulae were arranged to collect coronary and Thebesian vessel drainage and return it to the circulation. The changes in isometric pressure during contractions were measured with pressure transducers. By measuring the maximum rate of development of isometric tension, dp/dt, and the area below the rising phase of isometric contractions, IIT, the myocardial index of contractility, $dp/dt/$IIT, could be determined. As with increases in length in papillary muscles, increased initial volume produced increases in end-diastolic pressure and developed pressure. The maximum rate of pressure development and the integrated isometric tension each increased as the initial volume was increased, but, similarly to the results found in papillary muscles, the myocardial index of contractility, $dp/dt/$IIT, remained constant.

Inotropic changes were observed when the rate of stimulation of the ventricle was increased, and when noradrenaline or Ca^{++} infusions were administered. All of these inotropic situations resulted in an increase in the index of contractility. Acetyl strophanthidin produced changes which were qualitatively similar to those produced by calcium ions. Although increases in IIT occurred, they were smaller than the proportional changes in dp/dt, and the ratio increased in value. The cardiac glycoside produced its effects on contractile force without significant change in end-diastolic pressure at constant volume unless very large doses were used and then partial contracture of the muscle was observed. Thus the cardiac glycosides can produce increased contractility of cardiac muscle in situ quite independent of any change in the end-diastolic volume which results in the Frank-Starling variations in developed pressure.

Subsequently, the method has been extended and corrections applied to make estimations of the index of contractility more accurate (Siegel *et al.*, 1964). The measurement of the dynamics of cardiac function in intact closed-thorax animals is described, and measurements were also performed in human surgical patients undergoing right heart catheterization by means of intracardiac micromanometers, but the effects of cardiac glycosides were not studied in these more physiological situations.

C. Differences in Actions on Failing and Nonfailing Hearts

It has frequently been suggested that cardiac glycosides do not increase the force of myocardial contraction unless some degree of failure exists, and this belief has also been supported by numerous reports that cardiac glycosides do not increase the cardiac output in normal man or animals. There is, however, a considerable body of evidence to suggest that cardiac glycosides do in fact produce positive inotropic changes in the nonfailing myocardium. Isolated, electrically stimulated, right ventricular strips from guinea pigs suspended in bicarbonate-buffered medium do not readily develop a hypodynamic state, but the addition of ouabain $2.3 \times 10^{-7}M$ showed a positive inotropic effect which was sustained at a high level for some hours (Sanyal and Saunders, 1957). In phosphate-buffered medium, the preparations become progressively more hypodynamic, but the addition of ouabain in similar concentration at any stage of development of the hypodynamic state produced a comparable inotropic effect to that seen in nonhypodynamic muscle. The experiments of Walton *et al.* (1950), using strain gauges sutured to the right ventricles of dog hearts, showed increased force of contraction following administration of cardiac glycosides in anesthetized open-chest preparations and also in conscious dogs—neither group exhibited any sign of failure. In unanesthetized human subjects without cardiac failure, the maximum rate of increase in intraventricular pressure was increased by ouabain in experiments where changes in heart rate, end-diastolic volume, and arterial diastolic pressure were thought to have no significant effect (Mason and Braunwald, 1963).

That cardiac glycosides produce no change or even decrease cardiac output in both man and animals without cardiac failure has been well documented, and is frequently encountered in textbooks of pharmacology. However, there is some evidence to be found which suggests that the drugs have inotropic actions on the normal heart, which are obscured by other factors. For example, it was found in normal man that decreases in both systolic and diastolic size of the heart resulted from injections of cardiac glycosides, and that these were coupled with increased speed together with decreased duration of the ejection phase, which suggests that the drugs stimulate ventricular contractions (Eddleman, *et al.*, 1951; Haring and Luisada, 1953). It is probable that reduced venous return occurred as a result of peripheral actions of the glycosides and that this prevented any spectacular manifestation of increased effective work. A similar conclusion was reached in a study of the effects of cardiac glycosides on contractile force, cardiac output, and ventricular stroke work; the latter variables were not increased when there was an associated decrease in venous return (Cotten and Stopp, 1958).

It seems probable that cardiac glycosides have similar qualitative actions on failing and nonfailing myocardium, and that they produce a change leading to increased velocity of shortening of the contractile elements. We must agree that cardiac output alone is not necessarily an index of contractility of the heart as has been suggested already by Sarnoff and Mitchell (1961), and recognize that if increased cardiac output is the sole criterion of an inotropic effect of cardiac glycosides, then it will frequently be concealed because of simultaneous changes in other circulatory variables.

The effects of cardiac glycosides upon cardiac output are now thought to depend upon whether or not congestive failure is present. If no venous congestion is present as in nonfailure subjects, the heart is probably very close to optimum size and the diminished venous return resulting from increased peripheral resistance limits ventricular filling with consequent decrease in cardiac output despite enhanced contractility. The patient with cardiac failure exhibits venous congestion, but when treated with cardiac glycosides, the resultant increase in contractile force allows the heart to pump a greater volume of blood at each beat, and thus increases cardiac output. The congestive patient also has a lowered circulating blood volume due to leakage of plasma proteins and accompanying fluid from the vascular system into the tissue fluid spaces. The effect of the cardiac glycosides is primarily to increase contractility, but because of diminished circulating volume, there is a reduced volume load upon the heart on the arterial side and the stimulant action of the drugs allows contraction to provide more efficient emptying of the ventricles with every beat. The increased venous pressure associated with the failing heart causes ventricular distension with increased end-diastolic ventricular pressures. Provided that this effect is on the ascendant limb of the Starling curve, or is moved to this position by treatment with cardiac glycosides the Frank-Starling effect is also involved in increasing cardiac output, and has been discussed recently (Sarnoff *et al.*, 1964). Evidence is accumulating that the same fundamental effects of the cardiac glycosides on the contractility of cardiac muscle occur whether or not the heart is in a state of failure. Effects on cardiac output are secondary to these primary actions, and depend on the associated hemodynamic state. It has been suggested (Selzer and Kelly, 1964) that the normal subject can override the effects of cardiotonic drugs which might upset the hemodynamic balance by virtue of the intricate homeostatic regulatory mechanisms. When the circulatory dynamics are abnormal because of heart failure, drug action may help to restore optimum hemodynamic conditions, and in the case of digitalis, this is achieved principally by means of the inotropic actions of the drugs. Whether or not the peripheral circulatory actions of the cardiac glycosides contribute to the improved cardiovascular state in cardiac failure is not proved, but it would seem that their contribution is relatively minor. The paper by Selzer and Kelly provides a critical examination of available evidence and they conclude that on the basis of recent work, the same actions of digitalis are to be found in failing and nonfailing hearts. The clinical implications of the experimental data are discussed, but are out of place in this monograph.

III. The Effects of Cardiac Glycosides at the Cell Membrane

A. Actions upon the Electrical Activity of the Cell

The normal cardiac muscle cell contains approximately 180 mM K^+ and about 30 mM Na^+, whereas the tissue fluid concentrations are about 5 mM for K^+ and about 180 mM for Na^+. The electrical potential across the cell membrane is of the order of 80–90 mV, such that the interior is negative with respect to the exterior. Thus there are two forces acting which tend to drive Na^+—a concentration gradient and an electrical potential gradient. The same electrical potential gradient acts upon K^+ but is opposed by the concentration gradient which acts in the reverse direction across the membrane and hence K^+ is distributed in a state of electrochemical equilibrium. The resting membrane potential to a first approximation, is determined largely by the logarithm of the ratio of the intracellular concentration of K^+ to the extracellular, and serves to maintain the relatively high intracellular concentration. Should Na^+ leak across the membrane, the intracellular electronegativity becomes diminished and as a result K^+ diffuses passively from the cell until the opposing concentration and electrical potential gradients again become equal. However, the ratio of intracellular to extracellular K^+ is now lower than before and consequently an influx of Na^+ leads to a fall in the resting potential difference. Normally, extracellular Na^+ is excluded from the cell by the relative impermeability of the cell membrane, together with an active transport mechanism which transfers Na^+ outwardly against the direction of the concentration gradient.

Stimulation of cardiac cells produces a change in the resting electrical properties of the cell membrane. During the rising phase of the action potential the membrane suddenly becomes permeable to Na^+ which enters the cell at high speed and brings about depolarization of the membrane and in fact reverses its electrical polarity. Modern thought (reviewed by Trautwein, 1963) tends to view the increase in Na^+ permeability and entry of this ion as the activation of a Na^+-carrier system. If the resting membrane potential is high, the system is fully available for Na^+ transport, but if the resting potential is low, the availability of the carrier system is diminished. Full availability of the system is reflected by a rapid rate of rise of the action potential, and determines the extent of the overshoot of the action potential. The maximum Na^+ conductance is maintained for about 1 msec and thereafter the Na^+-carrier system becomes more and more inactivated even though depolarization is still maintained. After 10–15 msec the inactivation of the carrier system is complete, but it is gradually reactivated during repolarization when Na^+ is actively transported out of the cell probably by ATPases found in the cell membrane (see Chapter 4).

The effects of the cardiac glycosides upon the action potential and electrophysiological properties of the heart (reviewed by Hoffman and Singer, 1964) show no apparent correlation with the amplitude of the isometric contraction during the "therapeutic" phase of their action. The addition of ouabain (2×10^{-7} gm per milliliter) to a cat papillary muscle is followed by an increase in the force of contraction which can be measured within 2 minutes, and which is associated with a very small increase in the duration of the action potential. As time proceeds, a further increase in the force of contraction occurs, and the duration of the action potential becomes progressively shorter, but its amplitude is not changed (Dudel and Trautwein, 1958). Kassebaum (1963) reported the onset of inotropic effects in sheep ventricle following strophanthin prior to any observable changes (irrespective of their direction or magnitude) in the configuration of the action potential. This is illustrated in Fig. 3.3 (taken from Kassebaum, 1963), which shows superimposed recordings of action potential and isometric contractions of sheep ventricle muscle stimulated 30 times per minute.

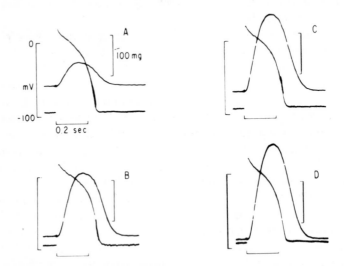

Fig. 3.3. Simultaneous recording of action potential and the course of isometric contraction in sheep ventricular muscle stimulated 30 times per minute. Panel A shows the control recordings, and panels B, C, and D show the changes in configuration recorded 20, 45, and 60 minutes after strophanthin, 10^{-6} gm per milliliter, was administered (Kassebaum, 1963).

In panel B there is a slight increase in duration of the action potential 20 minutes after administration of 10^{-6} gm per milliliter strophanthin. Similar observations have been made in isolated guinea pig auricles (Sleator *et al.,* 1964).

Thus there appears to be no correlation of variations in the shape and size of the action potential with the recorded isometric tension. More detailed studies to attempt correlation of changes in action potential configuration with variations in the active state of cardiac muscle associated with inotropic actions of various types have been suggested (Edman, 1965), as studies on skeletal muscle have indicated that there is a direct correlation between action potential duration and the length of the active state. Studies on the frog heart (Antoni *et al.,* 1962) have suggested to Edman that maximum intensity and duration of the active state are positively correlated with the duration of the action potential. This conclusion was drawn from experiments in which magnesium ions were used to produce paralysis of the heart, which seemed to be due to a decrease in duration of the action potential to such an extent that effective activation of the contractile mechanism was no longer possible. However, the ability of the heart to contract was still retained if, for example, K^+ were substituted for Na^+ in the bath. Agents which produce an increase in duration of the action potential, e.g., adrenaline and procaine amide, restored activity in the Mg^{++}-rich solution. However, both adrenaline and the cardiac glycosides act as inotropic agents and yet have opposite effects upon the action potential duration, and ryanodine which depresses contractile strength, prolongs action potential duration (Sleator *et al.,* 1964). Furthermore, agents such as acetylcholine and adenosine which produce negative inotropic actions upon cardiac muscle, each cause a diminution in action potential duration (Johnson and McKinnon, 1956). Thus we cannot agree with Edman that this correlation exists.

In toxic concentrations the cardiac glycosides produce disturbances in the configuration of the action potential which may be interpreted in terms of inhibition of the membrane adenosinetriphosphatase (ATPase) (see Chapter 4) and which are in accordance with measured variations in intracellular Na^+ and K^+ contents. The initial change in shape of the action potential in ventricular muscle is a decrease in total duration of the action potential, made up of a diminished plateau and decreased rate of repolarization. This is followed by a decrease in the magnitude of the resting potential, and the onset of this change is accelerated by high rates of contraction (Kassebaum, 1963). When the membrane resting potential is lowered, the rate of rise and the amplitude of the action potential are also decreased, and deterioration in all these parameters is progressive until finally there is cardiac arrest and inexcitability of the tissue. If the cardiac glycosides inhibit the membrane ATPase and thus slow down active outward transport of sodium during repolarization, less K^{++} will enter the cell to restore the membrane resting potential, and all the other changes observed will be consequences of this action.

B. Actions upon Rate and Rhythm

In addition to their inotropic action upon cardiac muscle, the cardiac glycosides exert important actions upon the rate and rhythm of the heart. Bradycardia is found with relatively small doses of these drugs and is thought to have two components: one is due to stimulation of the vagus nerve and can be abolished by atropine, and the other, an extravagal component more conspicuous at higher doses, presumably is due to direct action upon the myocardial pacemaker, and is atropine-resistant (Gold, 1946; McLain *et al.*, 1959).

Disturbances of rhythm are commonly seen after administration of digitalis. In dog hearts, doses of cardiac glycoside between 20 and 60% of the lethal dose have produced ectopic pacemakers. Bigeminal rhythms due to extrasystoles with constant shape and constant coupling were never observed in the electrocardiograms. Irregularities of rhythm consisted of ectopic ventricular beats, occurring singly with varying coupling, or in groups with varying shapes and in irregular sequence (Scherf and Schott, 1953). The only method known to these writers by which it is possible to produce extrasystolic arrhythmias with extrasystoles of constant shape and constant coupling following systemic administration of strophanthin, was by simultaneously administering a mixture of 25% CO_2 and 75% O_2, when ectopic tachycardia was present. A polygeminal rhythm quickly appeared and finally was converted to a true bigeminy, and was reversible on substituting air for the artificial gas mixture (Goldenberg and Rothberger, 1931). However, in studies on isolated strands of Purkinje tissue from dog hearts, digitalis or strophanthin caused arrhythmias similar to bigeminal or trigeminal contractions.

The effects of digitalis upon single myocardial cells in papillary muscles and single Purkinje cells in the conducting tissue show considerable variation. In papillary muscles, extrasystoles are always coupled to the preceding action potential; a common pattern described by Dudel and Trautwein (1958) consists of a shortened action potential followed by a depolarizing after-potential which eventually reaches a threshold value and triggers off the coupled extrasystole. The conduction system behaves differently. In Purkinje fibers, the extrasystoles appear before there is significant diminution in the duration of the action potential. Frequently the extrasystoles bear no apparent relation to the preceding contraction and may appear at any point between regular action potentials except during the absolute refractory period. Thus the appearance of extrasystoles in the intact heart following administration of digitalis is thought to represent an increase in the spontaneity of the Purkinje fibers rather than the myocardium itself. In severe digitalis intoxication, the increased spontaneous firing may occur during repolarization and result in waves of potential between -50 and 0 mV, eventually leading to ventricular fibrillation. The mechanism of these effects on rate and rhythm has not been satisfactorily explained.

IV. Antagonism of the Actions of Cardiac Glycosides

A. The Inotropic Action

The cardiac glycosides are very potent drugs and when used clinically require small doses and individual adjustment of dosage. The margin of safety is not very great and varies considerably in different patients and depends to an extent upon other adjuvant therapy, e.g., administration of potent diuretics and whether or not dietary potassium supplements are given. Obviously, it would be desirable to have antagonists to the cardiac glycosides so that toxic effects due to individual sensitivity, cumulation, or overdosage could be readily overcome. Until recent years, no antagonists to this group of drugs have been known, but there is some evidence that the inotropic actions may be overcome by aldosterone or drugs which deplete cardiac catecholamines or block their β-adrenergic actions. In the future it is possible that a clinical antagonist may be developed. Antagonism of the therapeutically beneficial inotropic action is not as important as that of the toxic arrhythmic effects of the drugs, and there is promise that these can now be overcome by several drugs to be considered in the next section.

Aldosterone has actions upon the contractility of the myocardium, which are discussed more fully in Chapter 7. It is sufficient to say here that it exerts slight positive inotropic actions on certain isolated cardiac preparations, but that these are not very pronounced. Lefer and Sayers (1965) have shown that when isolated perfused cat hearts were depressed by pentobarbitone in doses sufficient to reduce the cardiac contractile force to one half of its initial amplitude, aldosterone in doses between 3.3×10^{-8} and $10^{-7}\,M$ caused slight positive inotropic effects lasting about 20 minutes. Ouabain, $3.3 \times 10^{-8}\,M$, caused pronounced inotropic responses which were maintained for hours, but when the hearts had been pretreated with aldosterone 20 minutes prior to addition of ouabain, no inotropic response was observed in any single experiment out of a total of twenty-five, although normal responses to doses of noradrenaline were recorded. The isolated cat papillary muscle in low Ca^{++} Krebs-Henseleit solution showed similar responses, except that the inotropic response to aldosterone alone at a concentration of $10^{-7}\,M$ was hardly measurable. This concentration of the steroid completely inhibited the inotropic action of ouabain in the same molar concentration when added 20 minutes before the glycoside, which alone produced marked increase in the force of contraction. If the interval between the aldosterone and ouabain administrations was shortened or reversed so that aldosterone was added after the ouabain antagonism became progressively less marked, and if aldosterone was added at the peak of the inotropic response no antagonism was observed. Antagonism between these two drugs was not found in isolated rabbit auricles (Levy and Richards, 1963), but there were no inotropic responses recorded from this tissue with concentrations of ouabain as high as $1.7 \times 10^{-6}\,M$, which may be regarded as toxic, for the auricles exhibited contracture and marked decreases in both refractory period and excitability.

Lefer and Sayers showed that the inotropic action of ouabain was not antagonized by cortisol (hydrocortisone) in concentrations ranging between 10^{-7} and 10^{-5} M. If the action of aldosterone is due to its effects on ion transport rather than its glucocorticoid effects, then it is not surprising that cortisol was devoid of action because the latter is essentially a glucocorticoid with little mineral corticoid activity. Some actions of aldosterone and the cardiac glycosides (at least in toxic concentrations) involve ion transport across membranes, and it is possible that a competitive inhibition exists between the two molecules. However, although aldosterone and ouabain are both steroids, their resemblance to one another is not as great as may be expected from the usual manner in which their structures are drawn where no account is taken of the steric relations between the rings. In cardiac glycosides the A/B and C/D junctions both have the *cis*-configuration which tends to twist the molecule into a less planar shape, whereas in the salt-retaining steroids these two junctions are *trans* which makes the molecule more planar (Bush, 1962).

Many drugs are now recognized to exert their actions indirectly by causing liberation of noradrenaline from storage sites in the tissue (see Chapter 6), and it is not surprising that this mode of action has been suggested for the cardiac glycosides. Experiments designed to test this hypothesis have included some which involve depletion of the heart of its stored catecholamines and others where specific antagonists of the β-actions of noradrenaline (in which category the inotropic action falls) are used. Conflicting results have been reported. In papillary muscles, Tanz (1964) reported that dichloroisoprenaline (DCI) or pretreatment with reserpine reduced or abolished the ino-tropic action of ouabain depending on the doses administered, and that both treatments gave a greater response than either alone at constant dose levels. [These experiments confirmed an observation (Cairoli *et al.*, 1961) that the action of ouabain was reduced after reserpine pretreatment.] The inotropic response to Ca^{++} was retained in these experiments and Tanz concluded that ouabain acts either by releasing noradrenaline from storage sites or that its inotropic action depends upon a certain level of catecholamines in the tissue. However, on preparations of trabeculae carnae from dog hearts, the inotropic effects of ouabain were not inhibited by prior treatment of the animals with reserpine, and the conclusion drawn was that the action of ouabain did not depend upon intact stores of noradrenaline (Boyajy and Nash, 1965). In intact dogs, measurement of ventricular contractile force after ouabain with strain-gauge arches showed no significant difference from control animals in groups which were either vagotomized, denervated acutely or chronically, or pretreated with reserpine (Morrow *et al.*, 1963), and it was again concluded that intact innervation or catecholamine stores were not essential for the intropic responses to ouabain.

The conflicting reports may well result from the widespread acceptance that the action of reserpine is to deplete tissue catecholamine stores with total disregard for the fact that the drug also possesses other actions, e.g., cardiac depression (Withrington and Zaimis, 1961; Zaimis, 1964), particularly when used in high dosage, and this fact may mean that the mechanism by which the cardiac glycosides achieve their inotropic actions is impaired by reserpine. This could be the explanation for inhibition of the inotropic effect of ouabain in a molar concentration of 8.3×10^{-7} upon isolated rabbit atria, where the reserpine was administered acutely and thus could not have produced significant catecholamine depletion (Levy and Richards, 1965a). However, it has been reported that ouabain and reserpine given simultaneously enhanced arrhythmias with toxic doses of ouabain (Boyajy and Nash, 1965), which suggests that ouabain and noradrenaline released by reserpine can act together to produce increased ventricular automaticity. Furthermore it must be remembered that isolated embryonic chick hearts after 48 hours of incubation show marked inotropic responses to dilute solutions of cardiac glycosides. At this stage of development cardiac innervation has not commenced and catecholamines are not present in the tissues.

Studies with β-adrenergic receptor-blocking drugs do not provide convincing evidence for involvement of catecholamines in the inotropic responses to the digitalis glycosides. Although several observations have suggested that β-blocking agents may be of value in countering the toxic effects of cardiac glycosides on cardiac rhythm, there is no parallelism between degree of blockade and effect, and it has been claimed that in the case of pronethalol, suppression of ouabain-induced arrhythmia is achieved by a nonspecific quinidine-like action unrelated to β-blockade (Somani and Lum, 1965). Support for this claim has been supplied in a study of three β-adrenergic blocking agents, pronethalol, propranolol, and MJ-1999 [4-(2-isopropylamino-1-hydroxyethyl) methanesulfonanilide hydrochloride]. Pronethalol and propranolol were found to depress the amplitude of contractions recorded from driven rabbit atria, and high concentrations resulted in asystole accompanied by depression of the electrical properties of the tissue (Levy and Richards, 1965b). The remaining drug, MJ-1999, had about two thirds of the potency of pronethalol in blocking the inotropic effects of isoprenaline in a 3 minute pretreatment period, but was found to be devoid of direct cardiac depressant effects in 50 times the dosage. Pronethalol was shown to depress amplitude of contractions in isolated rabbit auricles in high doses and also to induce arrhythmias (Wislicki, 1964).

The dependence of the inotropic action of the cardiac glycosides upon the presence of catecholamines in cardiac tissue seems to be very unlikely. Clearly, to demonstrate whether or not any involvement is present will require some very carefully controlled experiments. Most of the work reported to date has relied very heavily upon acceptance that the primary action of a drug, or the use to which it is put in a particular experiment, is in fact the sole action of that drug. Many reports do not allow for considerations of direct depressant actions of drugs such as reserpine and β-adrenergic blocking agents upon tissues, which may have no relation to their interactions with catecholamines. In this regard the new β-receptor blocking agent MJ-1999 may be a much more valuable tool than its predecessors in this class, to determine whether or not blockade of inotropic actions of the cardiac glycosides can be achieved and also whether or not this action is dependent upon the presence of catecholamines.

A curious interaction between cardiac glycosides and noradrenaline was reported (Cotten and Cooper, 1962), in which ouabain antagonized the positive inotropic action of noradrenaline in dogs during hypothermia. Inotropic responses were measured by a strain-gauge arch sutured to the left ventricle. At normal body temperature the response to noradrenaline consisted of a smooth increase in contractile force returning to normal, but at 28°C the response became triphasic, made up of an initial brief increase in force, a secondary brief decrease, and a third prolonged increase which gradually returned to normal. Each phase was dose dependent in terms of intensity and duration. In hypothermia the animals responded to ouabain with significant increases in cardiac force, but subsequent injections of noradrenaline only produced depression of the contractile force to a degree which depended on the dose. Thus the first and third phases of the inotropic action of noradrenaline were abolished in the presence of ouabain during hypothermia whereas the second negative inotropic phase was not affected. Rewarming the ouabain-treated dogs did not restore the positive inotropic responses to noradrenaline although the negative inotropic response (phase 2) disappeared. The positive responses to noradrenaline did not begin to return for 7–9 hours and was not complete after 18 hours. These results were found when the cardiac glycoside was administered at lowered body temperature. At normal body temperature, administration of ouabain did not abolish the positive inotropic responses to graded doses of noradrenaline, and subsequent cooling to 28°C after administration of the glycoside at 37°C failed to modify the responses to noradrenaline. Explanation of these unexpected results is purely speculative at present. It was suggested that the blockade during hypothermia indicates that these two drugs influence some common mechanism at lowered body temperatures, in contrast to their actions in animals at normal body temperature. However, the mechanism of response to noradrenaline in hypothermia must either be modified or be entirely different from normal, because of the appearance of its triphasic nature. The fact that only the positive components of noradrenaline responses were blocked by ouabain in hypothermia suggests that the negative inotropic action is mediated in a different manner from the positive.

B. The Arrhythmic Action

The cardiac glycosides are used therapeutically in low doses because of their high potency, and usually patients are individually stabilized for long-term treatment of the failing heart. The margin of safety is low and care must be exercised in the use of the drugs, especially when potent diuretics are employed to hasten the excretion of associated edema fluid. Many modern diuretics tend to deplete the K^+ content of the body, and unless this effect is countered by an adequate simultaneous administration of supplementary K^+, the cardiac glycosides may precipitate arrhythmic attacks. Alternatively, the digitalizing dosage may be reduced to prevent disturbances of the cardiac rhythm. The arrhythmias may be regarded as toxic actions of the cardiac glycosides which are exerted directly upon the heart tissue, and which are independent actions unrelated to their therapeutic or inotropic effect. As the principal danger of over-digitalization is the precipitation of ventricular fibrillation it is important that antidotes to the toxic arrhythmias be developed. Until recent years however, there have been no drugs available for this purpose other than K^+, but reports are accumulating of attempts to study antagonism of the arrhythmias by treatment with other drugs.

In intact animals K^+ was shown by Loewi to antagonize the toxic action of digitalis as early as 1917. Recently the interaction between ouabain and K^+ has been studied in isolated sheep Purkinje fibers (Müller, 1963), a tissue in which Dudel and Trautwein (1958) showed that digitalis-induced extrasystoles appeared before any significant change in the duration of the action potential. Müller used ouabain in $2 \times 10^{-7} M$ concentration and found that after 1 hour, the drug caused accelerated repolarization, small diminution in the resting potential, and decreased rate of rise and amplitude of the action potential. These effects were reversed by perfusing the tissue with twice the usual K^+ concentration. High concentrations of ouabain ($5 \times 10^{-5} M$) caused rapid appearance of enhanced automaticity and other toxic signs which were antagonized within 2–3 minutes by supernormal K^+ concentration. Under these conditions, perfusion with elevated K^+ concentration had to be maintained for about 10 minutes after exposure to ouabain was discontinued, before reverting to Tyrode's solution with the usual K^+ concentration if toxic signs were not be reappear. Changes in the electrical potentials were minimal when ouabain perfusion was commenced in Tyrode's solution containing twice the usual K^+ concentration. The effects of elevated serum K^+ levels in man upon the changes in the electrocardiogram and ectopic beats induced by digitalis glycosides were reported over twenty years ago (Sampson *et al.,* 1943), and further observations have been made concerning the disturbances of AV conduction and ectopic rhythms (Bettinger *et al.,* 1956; Somlyo, 1960).

The mechanism by which K^+ antagonize these arrhythmic effects of the cardiac glycosides is probably via the Na-K-activated ATPase system, now thought to be the carrier system for the transport of Na^+ and K^+ ions. Cardiac glycosides must be extracellular to inhibit the enzyme, at least in squid giant axons (Caldwell and Keynes, 1959), and extracellular K^+ is necessary to activate the ATPase. There is a strong suggestion that competition between the cardiac glycosides and K^+ occurs at the extracellular side of the heart muscle membranes. If this is so, the deleterious effects of digitalis upon the electrical properties of the cardiac cell membrane would be diminished (see Chapter 4).

Among other drugs investigated for their abilities to antagonize the arrhythmic actions of the digitalis glycosides, perhaps the most surprising is heparin. It was shown that large doses of heparin, 10–20 mg per kilogram, partly or completely suppress the arrhythmia and bradycardia and allow the inotropic action of large intravenous doses, 0.08–0.1 mg per kilogram, of ouabain in dogs (Loubatières et al., 1963). The possible explanations for this unexpected result which were offered were: (a) heparin and ouabain formed a chemical complex which resulted in inactivation of the glycoside; (b) heparin might displace ouabain from binding sites on the cardiac muscle fibers; (c) by direct action on the contractile proteins heparin could free them from ouabain; or (d) by virtue of its strong electronegative charge heparin might bind K^+ extruded from the cells by toxic doses of ouabain. The latter explanation seems to be the least fanciful in terms of modern knowledge about the cardiac glycosides and their interactions with K^+. It would be interesting to repeat this work and to see whether heparin antagonists such as toluidine blue or protamine sulfate could restore the toxic actions of ouabain by displacing allegedly bound K^+.

The biological polypeptides have also received attention as anti-arrhythmic agents. Synthetic oxytocin has been reported to slow AV conduction and to reduce ventricular excitability, possibly due to lengthening of the refractory period; an action similar to that of quinidine (Brodeur and Beaulnes, 1963); however, the indications for digitalis overdosage in human patients were limited. Further study showed that synthetic oxytocin in concentrations ranging from 50 to 300 mU per milliliter prevented the occurrence of atrial and ventricular arrhythmias induced by electrical stimulation, changes in ionic concentrations, or chloroform and adrenaline administration in the rabbit. However, once arrhythmia had been established, oxytocin was less effective in terminating the episode. In a large dose, 1 Unit per kilogram synthetic oxytocin was very effective in preventing death from ventricular fibrillation induced by combined administration of chloroform and adrenaline to dogs, and a similar result was found for lysyl-

8-vasopressin (Beaulnes *et al.*, 1964). The quinidine-like action attributed to oxytocin (Brodeur and Beaulnes, 1963) was shown to be due to the chlorobutanol in the vehicle normally used with the drug. Oxytocin did not prove to be useful in treating fibrillation induced by ouabain (Varma *et al.*, 1963).

Beaulnes and his colleagues studied synthetic valyl-5-angiotensin II amide for anti-arrhythmic properties and concluded that it was effective in preventing chloroform-adrenaline-induced ventricular fibrillation. Recently angiotensin has been studied as an antagonist of ouabain-induced arrhythmias in perfused hearts of cats and guinea pigs and shown to prevent irregularities, particularly extrasystoles, in doses of 1–5 μg. When ouabain was infused into guinea pigs at the rate of 1.39 μg per kilogram per minute, the animals developed rhythm disturbances within 20–30 minutes, and then the infusion was stopped. If the group was not treated with angiotension, the arrhythmias gradually became converted to ventricular fibrillation and death occurred in all cases within 5–20 minutes after the ouabain infusion was stopped. The other group of six was given angiotensin at the rate of 1–10 μg per kilogram per minute when the irregularities commenced and the ouabain infusion was stopped. In all animals sinus rhythm was restored within 17–30 minutes and the total doses of angiotensin required ranged between 16.6 and 140 μg. Angiotensin was stopped and no further occurrence of arrhythmia was observed during the following 4 hours. Angiotensin alone infused at the rate of 10 μg per kilogram per minute for 20 minutes caused bradycardia and occasional extrasystoles but these effects disappeared upon cessation of the infusion (Türker, 1965).

As in the case of the inotropic actions of the cardiac glycosides, there has been speculation as to whether or not intact adrenergic mechanisms must be present for the arrhythmic action of the cardiac glycosides, and divergent results have been published. One group claims that there is no significant difference in the dose of ouabain necessary to produce multiple ventricular premature contractions between control animals and those which have undergone either acute or chronic cardiac denervation, vagotomy, or which have been pretreated with reserpine (Morrow *et al.*, 1963). However, the functional refractory period of the AV conduction system was prolonged, and these workers concluded that although arrhythmic (and inotropic) doses of ouabain appeared to be independent of autonomic innervation and myocardial catecholamine stores, the prolongation of the AV refractory period by ouabain depends upon autonomic innervation. It has been suggested that the effects of ouabain on the functional refractory period in isolated rabbit left auricles are the result of two opposing factors (Govier, 1965): (*a*) release of noradrenaline which tends to decrease the refractory period, and (*b*) a direct action of ouabain which tends to increase the refractory period. Govier points out that a further factor applies in the intact animal where vagal stimulation occurs after ouabain, with release of acetylcholine which again tends to decrease the refractory period.

In contrast to Morrow and his colleagues, other workers do not agree that reserpine has no effect on the doses of cardiac glycosides required to produce arrhythmias. Erlij and Mendez (1964) found that pretreatment with reserpine or acute surgical denervation elevated the mean lethal dose of ouabain or digitoxin required to produce death by ventricular fibrillation. Similarly, Boyajy and Nash (1965) reported that pretreatment of dog trabeculae carnae with reserpine gave protection against ouabain-induced arrhythmias. When administered simultaneously, the two drugs caused enhanced arrhythmias, which was interpreted to mean that noradrenaline being released by the reserpine in combination with ouabain caused increased ventricular automaticity. The previous remarks (see preceding section) concerning the difficulties in interpreting results obtained with the aid of reserpine apply equally well to the results of Erlij and Mendez, who used a large dose of reserpine (3 mg per kilogram) administered over 2 or 3 days prior to the experiments depending on whether dogs or cats were used. The direct cardiac depressant effect of reserpine which would have undoubtedly been present, could thus elevate the dose of ouabain required to produce ventricular fibrillation, when compared with the control group, and still be entirely independent of the state of the catecholamine stores. The results obtained after acute denervation are more difficult to explain and because they are in conflict with those of Morrow *et al.* (1963), it is clear that more work is required to clarify this point.

The use of β-adrenergic blocking drugs to provide protection against cardiac glycoside-induced arrhythmias suggests at first sight that this action of the digitalis drugs involves some interaction with stored noradrenaline in the cardiac tissue. Pronethalol increased the dose of cardiac glycosides required to produce extrasystoles, prevented fibrillation, and increased the lethal dose of the cardiac glycoside (Sekiya and Vaughan Williams, 1963a), and even after fibrillation had been induced, restored normal rhythm. DCI also showed similar behavior. Erlij and Mendez (1964) also reported the increase in mean lethal dose of ouabain and digitoxin after treatment with pronethalol in cats and dogs. In eight human patients intravenous pronethalol suppressed ventricular and atrial ectopic rhythms, and provided that the administration was slow, side effects were not marked (Taylor *et al.,* 1964).

It is now known that pronethalol and propranolol have direct cardiac depressant actions, and that these actions are independent of the β-adrenergic blocking property which is the most striking feature of these drugs. It was shown that pronethalol possessed anti-arrhythmic properties against arrhythmias induced by ouabain and acetyl strophanthidin (Lucchesi, 1964). Previous administration of pronethalol altered the ability of the heart to develop automatic foci when exposed to toxic concentrations of the cardiac glycosides, and the more common features of toxicity were cardiac arrest or slow ventricular rhythms. Lucchesi suggested that the drug possessed an anti-arrhythmic action in addition to its β-blocking action.

A quantitative comparison of pronethalol, disopyramide, and quinidine showed that the three drugs behaved similarly in their effects upon isolated rabbit auricles, raising electrical threshold, and reducing amplitude of contraction, conduction velocity, and maximum rate of stimulation which the atria could follow (Sekiya and Vaughan Williams, 1963b). The resting potential and duration of the action potential were little affected by any drug, but the rate of rise of the action potential and the degree of overshoot were reduced by all three. Thus it was concluded that interference with depolarization of the membrane is an essential feature of anti-fibrillatory activity, and "that some of the actions of pronethalol may not be directly related to its action in blocking β-receptors." Similarly, pronethalol and propranolol were shown to differ from another β-blocking drug, INPEA,* in that they had a quinidine-like action which would suppress ventricular

---

* D-(−)-1-(4′-Nitrophenyl)-2-isopropylaminoethanol hydrochloride.

tachycardia following ouabain, whereas INPEA had only β-adrenergic blocking properties (Somani and Lum, 1965).

Recently pronethalol has been resolved into its dextro(+)- and levo(−)-optical isomers, and it has been reported that the (−)-isomer has 40 times the β-adrenergic blocking activity of the (+)-isomer (Howe, 1963). It has been shown that the (+)-isomer can block the arrhythmic effects of toxic doses of cardiac glycosides and is equi-effective as the racemic mixture of the isomers (Lucchesi, 1965). Ventricular fibrillation resulting from combined isoprenaline + U 0882 administration was not blocked by (+)-pronethalol, although the more potent β-receptor blocker, *dl*-pronethalol, was effective. Thus, there appears to be little doubt that the protective action of some β-adrenergic blocking agents against arrhythmias due to the cardiac glycosides is not in fact due to their β-blocking property, but rather to an additional action of these compounds. The involvement of catecholamines in the toxic actions of the cardiac glycosides must be very slight if indeed it does exist at all, and we would suggest that experiments described where reserpine has been alleged to provide protection from arrhythmia might require a different interpretation than depletion of these substances from the myocardium.

References

Abbott, B. C., and Mommaerts, W. F. H. M. (1959). *J. Gen. Physiol.* **42**, 533.

Antoni, H., Engstfeld, G., Fleckenstein, A., and Klein, H. D. (1962). *Arch. Ges. Physiol.* **275**, 507.

Beaulnes, A., Panisset, J.-C., Brodeur, J., Beltrami, E., and Gariepy, G. (1964). *Circulation Res.* **15**, Suppl. II, 210.

Bettinger, J. C., Surawicz, B., Bryfogle, J. W., Anderson, B. N., and Bellet, S. (1956). *Am. J. Med.* **21**, 521.

Blinks, J. R., and Koch-Weser, J. (1963). *Pharmacol. Rev.* **15**, 531.

Boyajy, L. D., and Nash, C. B. (1965). *J. Pharmacol.* **148**, 193.

Brodeur, J., and Beaulnes, A. (1963). *Rev. Can. Biol.* **22**, 275.

Bush, I. E. (1962). *Pharmacol. Rev.* **14**, 317.

Cairoli, V., Reilly, J., and Roberts, J. (1961). *Federation Proc.* **20**, 122.

Caldwell, P. C., and Keynes, R. D. (1959). *J. Physiol. (London)* **148**, 8P.

Cattell, McK., and Gold, H. (1938). *J. Pharmacol.* **62**, 116.

Chen, K. K., Robbins, E. B., and Worth, H. (1938). *J. Am. Pharm. Assoc. Sci. Ed.* **27**, 189.

Cotten, M. de V., and Cooper, T. (1962). *J. Pharmacol.* **136**, 97.

Cotten, M. de V., and Stopp, P. E. (1958). *Am. J. Physiol.* **192**, 114.

Dudel, J., and Trautwein, W. (1958). *Arch. Exptl. Pathol. Pharmakol.* **232,** 393.
Eddleman, E. E., Willis, K., Greve, M. J., and Heyer, H. E. (1951). *Am. Heart J.* **41,** 161.
Edman, K. A. P. (1965). *Ann. Rev. Pharmacol.* **5,** 99.
Edman, K. A. P., and Nilsson, E. (1965). *Acta. Physiol. Scand.* **63,** 507.
Erlij, D., and Mendez, R. (1964). *J. Pharmacol.* **144,** 97.
Glynn, I. M. (1964). *Pharmacol. Rev.* **16,** 381.
Gold, H. (1946). *J. Am. Med. Assoc.* **132,** 547.
Goldenberg, M., and Rothberger, C. J. (1931). *Z. Ges. exptl. Med.* **79,** 705.
Govier, W. C. (1965). *J. Pharmacol.* **148,** 100.
Haring, O. M., and Luisada, A. A. (1953). *Am. Heart J.* **46,** 276.
Hill, A. V. (1938). *Proc. Roy. Soc.* **B126,** 136.
Hill, A. V. (1949). *Proc. Roy. Soc.* **B136,** 399.
Hill, A. V., and MacPherson, L. (1954). *Proc. Roy. Soc.* **B143,** 81.
Hoffman, B. F., and Singer, D. H. (1964). *Progr. Cardiovascular Diseases* **7,** 226.
Howe, R. (1963). *Biochem. Pharmacol.* **12,** *Suppl. Abstr. 2nd. Intern. Pharmacol. Meeting, Prague, 1963,* p. 85.
Johnson, E. A., and McKinnon, M. G. (1956). *Nature* **178,** 1174.
Kassebaum, D. G. (1963). *J. Pharmacol.* **140,** 329.
Koch-Weser, J. (1963). *Biochem. Pharmacol.* **12,** *Suppl. Abstr. 2nd. Intern. Pharmacol. Meeting, Prague, 1963,* p. 190.
Koch-Weser, J., and Blinks, J. R. (1962). *J. Pharmacol.* **136,** 305.
Koch-Weser, J., and Blinks, J. R. (1963). *Pharmacol. Rev.* **15,** 601.
Lefer, A. M., and Sayers, G. (1965). *Am. J. Physiol.* **208,** 649.
Levy, J. V., and Richards, V. (1963). *Arch. Intern. Pharmacodynamie* **146,** 363.
Levy, J. V., and Richards, V. (1965a). *J. Pharmacol.* **147,** 205.
Levy, J. V., and Richards, V. (1965b). *J. Pharmacol.* **150,** 361.
Loewi, O. (1917). *Arch. Exptl. Pathol. Pharmakol.* **82,** 131.
Loubatières, A., Sassine, A., and Bouyard, P. (1963). *Compt. Rend. Soc. Biol.* **157,** 340.
Lucchesi, B. R. (1964). *J. Pharmacol.* **145,** 286.
Lucchesi, B. R. (1965). *J. Pharmacol.* **148,** 94.
McLain, P. K., Knise, T. K., and Redick, T. F. (1959). *J. Pharmacol.* **126,** 76.
Mason, D. T., and Braunwald, E. (1963). *J. Clin. Invest.* **42,** 1105.
Mommaerts, W. F. H. M., and Langer, G. A. (1963). *Ann. Rev. Med.* **14,** 261.
Morrow, D. H., Gaffney, T. E., and Braunwald, E. (1963). *J. Pharmacol.* **140,** 236.
Müller, P. (1963). *Cardiologia* **42,** 176.
Orloff, J., and Burg, M. (1960). *Am. J. Physiol.* **199,** 49.
Reiter, M., and Schöber, H. G. (1965). *Arch. Exptl. Pathol. Pharmakol.* **250,** 9.
Repke, K. (1963). *Proc. 1st Intern. Pharmacol. Meeting, Stockholm, 1961,* Vol. 3, pp. 47–70.
Ritchie, J. M. (1954). *J. Physiol. (London)* **126,** 155.
Sampson, J. J., Albertson, E. C., and Kondo, B. (1943). *Am. Heart J.* **26,** 164.
Sanyal, P. H., and Saunders, P. R. (1957). *Proc. Soc. Exptl. Biol. Med.* **95,** 156.
Sarnoff, S. J., Gilmore, J. P., Wallace, A. G., Skinner, N. S., Mitchell, J. H., and Daggett, W. M. (1964). *Am. J. Med.* **37,** 3.
Sarnoff, S. J., and Mitchell, J. H. (1961). *Am. J. Med.* **30,** 747.

Schatzmann, H. J. (1953). *Helv. Physiol. Acta* **11,** 346.

Scherf, J., and Schott, A. (1953). "Extrasystoles and Allied Arrhythmias," pp. 276–277. Heinemann, London.

Sciarini, L. J., Ackerman, E. M., and Salter, W. T. (1948). *J. Pharmacol.* **92,** 432.

Sekiya, A., and Vaughan Williams, E. M. (1963a). *Brit. J. Pharmacol.* **21,** 462.

Sekiya, A., and Vaughan Williams, E. M. (1963b). *Brit. J. Pharmacol.* **21,** 473.

Selzer, A., and Kelly, J. J. (1964). *Progr. Cardiovascular Diseases* **7,** 273.

Siegel, J. H., and Sonnenblick, E. H. (1963). *Circulation Res.* **12,** 597.

Siegel, J. H., Sonnenblick, E. H., Judge, R. D., and Wilson, W. S. (1964). *Cardiologia* **45,** 189.

Sleator, W., Furchgott, R. F., de Gubareff, T., and Krespi, V. (1964). *Am. J. Physiol.* **206,** 270.

Somani, P., and Lum, B. K. B. (1965). *J. Pharmacol.* **147,** 194.

Somlyo, A. P. (1960). *Am. J. Cardiol.* **5,** 523.

Spiro, D., and Sonnenblick, E. H. (1965). *Progr. Cardiovascular Diseases* **7,** 295.

Tamm, C. (1963). *Proc. 1st Intern. Pharmacol. Meeting, Stockholm, 1961,* Vol. 3, pp. 11–26. Pergamon Press, Oxford.

Tanabe, T., Tsunemi, I., Abiko, Y., and Iida, S. (1963). *Proc. 1st Intern. Pharmacol. Meeting, Stockholm, 1961,* Vol. 3, pp. 233–238. Pergamon Press, Oxford.

Tanz, R. D. (1964). *J. Pharmacol.* **144,** 205.

Taylor, R. R., Johnson, C. I., and Jose, A. D. (1964). *New Engl. J. Med.* **271,** 877.

Trautwein, W. (1963). *Pharmacol. Rev.* **15,** 277.

Türker, K. R. (1965). *Experientia* **21,** 707.

Varma, D. V., Melville, K. I., and Silver, M. D. (1963). *Arch. Intern. Pharmacodynamie* **145,** 440.

Walton, R. P., Leary, J. S., and Jones, H. P. (1950). *J. Pharmacol.* **98,** 346.

Waugh, W. H. (1965). *In* "Muscle," Proc. Symp. Univ. Alberta, Edmonton, Alberta, 1964. pp. 253–266. Pergamon Press, Oxford.

Wiggers, C. J., and Stinson, B. (1927). *J. Pharmacol.* **30,** 251.

Wislicki, L. (1964). *Arch. Intern. Pharmacodynamie* **152,** 69.

Withrington, P., and Zaimis, E. (1961). *Brit. J. Pharmacol.* **17,** 380.

Woodbury, J. W. (1962). *In* "Handbook of Physiology," Section 2, Vol. 1, p. 237. Am. Physiol. Soc., Washington, D.C.

Zaimis, E. (1964). *Ann. Rev. Pharmacol.* **4,** 365.

CHAPTER 4

BIOCHEMICAL BASES FOR THE MODE
OF ACTION OF CARDIAC STIMULANT DRUGS

I. Introduction

A great deal of published work has been directed toward the elucidation of the mechanism of the inotropic action of the cardiac glycosides; considerably less work deals with this action of the catecholamines, and very little work concerns other cardiotonic substances.

The outstanding property of the cardiac glycosides is their highly selective stimulant action on the myocardium whereas the catecholamines exhibit a spectrum of other interesting properties of which this is only one. The cardiotonic alkaloids are at present of no clinical importance and it is natural that they should have attracted far less interest. Cardiotonic substances from animal tissues have not yet been obtained in pure form in any appreciable quantity and not very much is known about them beyond the fact that they exist and can stimulate the failing heart. Their mode of action has yet to be studied in detail.

Our present knowledge of the mode of action of cardiac stimulants very much resembles a jigsaw puzzle at an early stage of assembly. A few pieces link together in one corner, quite a number in another, a few of the central pieces are beginning to fall into place but the picture itself has not yet emerged. We lack the valuable guide of an illustration on the box! There are too, a number of aspects of this study which give the impression that parts of a different jigsaw puzzle may have got into our box. By this we refer to the large amount of evidence for the actions of the cardiac glycosides on Na^+ and K^+ fluxes at the cell membrane which appears to be more closely related to the toxic actions of these drugs than to their myocardial stimulant action. How relevant observations on the effects of catecholamines or caffeine on skeletal muscle are to the central problem also remains to be seen but it is clear that the puzzle is attracting many players and each year several additional pieces fall into place. A great many experiments are described in

103

which ouabain, or some other active cardiotonic drug, produces a well-defined dose-response relationship and yet very few of these include a similar substance, such as dihydroouabain, in which the cardiotonic activity has been greatly reduced by molecular changes while still retaining close physicochemical similarity with the more active substances. In this field a few "grants-in-aid" could be very profitably spent repeating older experiments with inactive congeners.

Each time the heart beats and the individual muscle cells contract, a sequence of events takes place any one of which may offer a locus of action of a cardiotonic drug. These are (1) the depolarization of the cell membrane and the accompanying ionic redistribution which determines the action potential of each cell and collectively the electrocardiogram, (2) a mechanism by which the depolarization of the cell membrane is transmitted from the membrane to the contractile proteins within the cell, (3) a stage in which the contractile elements of the muscle cell are caused to telescope and the cell to contract, and (4) a process which reverses the contraction of the myofibrils and leaves them receptive for the next cycle. None of these stages is simple and they may each involve many biochemical reactions, a few of which we are beginning to understand. Any hypothesis we may propose today to explain inotropic action may be completely outdated as additional fundamental knowledge on the biochemistry and physiology of cardiac muscle is accumulated.

II. The Actions of Cardiotonic Drugs at the Cell Membrane

A. Ionic Changes

The cardiac cell membrane, in common with that of cells generally, separates a high concentration of K^+ inside from a low concentration outside and the reverse applies to Na^+. There is thus a concentration gradient of K^+ from inside out and a concentration gradient of Na^+ from outside in. There is also an electrical potential gradient of some 80–90 mV negative inside the cell when the extracellular fluid is regarded as zero potential. In the case of Na^+ both gradients tend to draw these ions into the cell but for K^+ the electrical potential gradient and the concentration gradient are acting in opposite directions, and between contractions of the cell the K^+ ions are in equilibrium. At rest the cell membrane is comparatively impermeable to Na^+ since if this were not so these ions would instantaneously equilibrate in concentration with those in the extracellular fluid by Na^+ influx. There is an "active transport" mechanism which extrudes Na^+ from the cell and acts in opposition to the electrical and concentration gradients. Much experimental evidence has been adduced to show that cardiac glycosides affect the active Na^+ transport although it is uncertain whether this plays a significant role in the cardiotonic action of these substances. When Na^+ enters the cell the retaining forces on the K^+ are reduced and K^+ leaves the cell, and hence any inhibition of active transport of Na^+ will also result in an increased efflux of K^+. At the initiation of the action potential the membrane is depolarized and even hyperpolarized so that Na^+ rushes into the cell and K^+ flows out. The active transport system then extrudes Na^+ and K^+ returns. This process takes place during the plateau phase of the action potential and hence any inhibition of active transport of Na^+ will prolong the time for the ionic changes to revert to the resting state. In the 1930's Harrison and co-workers studied the K^+ content of cardiac muscle in congestive failure (Harrison *et al.*, 1930; Calhoun *et al.*, 1930), and showed that a postmortem analysis of skeletal and cardiac muscle of patients dying in congestive heart failure revealed lower K^+ levels than from those who died from other causes. These authors believed that excessive cardiac work led to a loss of K^+ and that this might have been a cause of the cardiac failure.

Calhoun and Harrison (1931) showed that the hearts from dogs which had been digitalized with toxic doses, when analyzed after death, contained less K^+ than did those from control dogs which had not been treated with digitalis. Those given therapeutic human doses did not show a significant decrease in the K^+ content of the heart. The idea that the therapeutic action of digitalis might be the result of the reduction of intracellular K^+ or a decrease in K^+ influx was proposed by Hajdu and Leonard (1959), but it now seems very probable that any correlation with such ionic changes is to be found only with "toxic" doses of the glycosides.

In studies upon the isolated guinea pig auricle, Klaus *et al.* (1962) showed that digitoxigenin had a biphasic action upon ion exchange at the cell membrane. Small doses caused increased K^+ influx, a decrease in Na^+ content but no change in K^+ efflux. When larger "toxic" concentrations were employed the reverse effect was observed. There was increased K^+ efflux, an accumulation of intracellular Na^+, and a fall in K^+.

Similar results have been reported by Lee and co-workers (1961) for high concentrations of cardiac glycosides on the cat papillary muscle but these workers observed no ionic changes with smaller "therapeutic" concentrations. When such experiments are carried out over long periods of time and pieces of cardiac muscle are soaked in physiological saline containing high concentrations of ouabain, active ion transport is clearly inhibited since the intracellular K^+ falls and Na^+ rises until the normal ionic content within the cell is almost completely reversed, (Page *et al.,* 1964). The concentration of cardiac glycoside, ouabain, used in these experiments was high, $10^{-5} M,$ whereas a clear positive inotropic action is seen with ouabain in concentrations of $10^{-7} M$ or even $10^{-8} M$. When the concentration of ouabain was reduced to $10^{-6} M$ inhibition of active Na^+ transport was still observed but increasing the external K^+ concentration reversed this effect and abolished the inhibitory action of ouabain (Page, 1964).

Schatzman (1953) showed that cardiac glycosides inhibited transport of Na^+ and K^+ across the red cell membrane. Similarly it is now known that the cardiac glycosides inhibit active transport of these ions in many other tissues including heart and other muscular tissues, bladder, kidney, and nerve. It seems probable that the cardiac glycosides must be on the extracellular side of the membrane in order to inhibit Na^+ movements, for when injected into the giant axon of the squid, ouabain had no effect on Na^+ transport (Caldwell and Keynes, 1959). Continued work mostly with red blood cells has shown that the active transport of Na^+ and K^+ across cell membranes is a process requiring energy and this is derived by splitting off the terminal high-energy phosphate of adenosine triphosphate (ATP), by the membranes, but only if K^+ is available at the extracellular surface, and both Na^+ and Mg^{++} are available at the intracellular surface (Glynn, 1962; Whittam, 1962; Whittam and Ager, 1962).

B. The Inhibition of Sodium-Potassium-Activated Adenosinetriphosphatase (ATPase)

It has recently been shown that particulate enzymes, transport

ATPases, can be isolated from many tissues and that they are capable of splitting ATP to provide the necessary energy for active cation transport. This was first shown by Skou (1957, 1960) who found such an ATPase in the microsomal fraction of crab nerve and showed it to be responsible for Na^+ and K^+ transport. Post *et al.* (1960) and Dunham and Glynn (1961) showed that this enzyme also occurs in the erythrocyte membrane and is related to cation transport. Bonting and associates (1961) found the enzyme to be widely distributed in animal tissues. They found varying degrees of activity in 29 tissues from the cat and in the human retina, ciliary body, and erythrocytes. These workers suggested that it should be named Na-K ATPase since this distinguishes it from other ATPases and points to its presumed role in active cation transport. To support the concept that an ATPase is the substance involved in the active transport of Na^+ and K^+, it is interesting to note that there is reasonable correlation between the activity of the enzyme and the amount of ion transfer that occurs in different tissues (Bonting and Caravaggio, 1963). As had been shown by the previous workers, Bonting *et al.* (1961) found ouabain to be inhibitory in all their preparations and Ca^{++} in many of them. They suggested that the tissues they examined could conveniently be arranged into five groups on the basis of their absolute Na-K ATPase activity. A table of these results is reproduced in Table 4.1.

The concentration of ouabain required to produce 50% inhibition of these ATPase preparations was found to be $3 \times 10^{-7} M$ which agrees reasonably with the values of Post *et al.* (1960), Dunham and Glynn (1961), and Repke (1965). The effect of Ca^{++} varied from tissue to tissue, stimulation as well as inhibition being observed. They found that Na-K-activated ATPase from heart and striated muscle was inhibited by Ca^{++} whereas that from aorta and smooth muscle of gastric origin was stimulated. These authors pointed out that certain ATPases such as mitochondrial ATPase, muscle ATPase, and Na-K ATPase are normally depressed by calcium whereas that of myosin is stimulated. Since these enzymes may occur in different combinations in different tissues the resulting effect of Ca^{++} on whole tissue homogenates is expectedly variable. The chemical structural requirements for cardiac glycoside activity both as inotropic agents and as pump ATPase inhibitors are similar (Repke and Portius, 1963; Glynn, 1964), and it has been suggested that Na-K-activated ATPase is the receptor for cardiac glycosides (Portius and Repke, 1962; Repke, 1963). Subsequently, an analysis of the inhibitory activities of 62 compounds upon transport ATPase has resulted in a suggested chemical mode of action of the cardiac glycosides with the enzymes (Portius and Repke, 1964). The active grouping in the cardiac glycosides is thought to be a

Table 4.1

Groups of Cat Tissues According to
Na-K ATPase Activity[a,b]

Group	Activity (mmoles/gm/hr)	Tissues
I	>0.5	Gray matter
II	0.5–0.2	Kidney medulla, retina, white matter, kidney cortex
III	0.2–0.02	Optic nerve, lung, choroid plexus, spleen, aorta, adrenal, liver, choroid, ciliary body, sciatic nerve, kidney papilla, heart muscle, striated muscle, iris sphincter, stomach mucosa
IV	0.02–0.001	Submaxillary gland, corneal epithelium, corneal endothelium, stomach muscle, superior cervical ganglion, sclera, whole cornea, lens capsule and epithelium
V	<0.001	Erythrocytes, corneal stroma, whole lens, lens capsule, lens fiber, vitreous, adipose tissue, serum

[a] The tissues in each group are ranked according to decreasing activity.
[b] From Bonting *et al.* (1961).

carbonyl group in conjugation with a C=C double bond located in the lactone ring. Because the carbonyl group is electronegative, it acts as a proton acceptor and can therefore build up a hydrogen bond with a hydroxyl group of the phosphoric acid residue in the phosphorylated enzyme intermediate. The hydrogen bonding of the inhibitory cardiac glycoside to the active center of the enzyme prevents access of K^+ to the phosphorylated enzyme which is K^+ dependent. The single hydrogen bond permits free rotation of the cardiac glycoside molecule so that the correct face of the steroid nucleus comes into close relationship with the complementary enzyme surface. Hydrocarbon residues now can make stronger hydrophilic attachments to the enzyme. The function of the sugar residues on the molecules is described as supportive, and they prevent nonspecific binding to proteins, thereby allowing a more rapid and complete bonding to the enzyme receptor.

The Na-K-activated ATPase from the membrane-sarcotubular fraction of guinea pig heart muscle has been prepared partially purified and shown not to be associated with nuclei, mitochondria, or myofibrils (Krespi *et al.,* 1964). The concentration of strophanthin-K required to produce 50% inhibition of the enzyme *in vitro* was $10^{-6} M,$ which is in good agreement with the figure of 2×10^{-7} gm per milliliter of ouabain to produce a rapid inotropic action on cat papillary muscle (Dudel and Trautwein, 1958) when one takes into account that strophanthin-K possesses about 40% of the biological activity of ouabain.

Bonting and co-workers (1964) studied the effect of the cardiotonic alkaloids, erythrophleine and cassaine, on the Na-K ATPase of several different tissues of cats and rabbits and found inhibition with high concentrations, $10^{-4} M,$ of erythrophleine. They found both ouabain and cassaine to be far more potent inhibitors of Na-K ATPase, and these two drugs were of comparable activity. The general shape of the inhibition curves was similar for all three drugs and there was in each case stimulation of Na-K ATPase with very low concentrations of the drugs, and although this effect was small in magnitude it was statistically significant for all three drugs. Such stimulation has also been observed by Repke (1963, 1965) for the aglycone digitoxigenin, digitoxin, dihydrodigitoxin, and several other cardiac glycosides. It is certainly a real phenomenon but its significance is not at present understood. Possibly it is associated with inotropic action and the inhibitory effect at higher concentration with the impairment of conduction which these drugs produce. Charnock and Post (1963) have studied the inhibition of Na-K ATPase by ouabain and found that this takes place in two stages, the first stage resulting in the formation of an intermediate phosphorylated compound and being a process which is activated by Na^+. This is unaffected by ouabain. The second stage is K^+ activated and completes the hydrolysis of this intermediate substance to adenosine diphosphate (ADP). This stage is completely inhibited by ouabain. The authors suggest that ouabain competes for K^+ in this reaction and inhibits the phosphorolysis by displacing K^+ at receptors on the enzyme at the outside of the cell membrane. The Na^+ activation of the first stage of this reaction is thought to take place at the inside of the membrane.

At the present state of our knowledge it is very difficult to correlate the action of cardiac glycosides in inhibiting Na-K ATPase with the effects they produce on the action potential at the cell membrane.

Inhibition of Na-K-activated ATPase results in an intracellular increase in Na^+ and a decrease in K^+. These are changes which "can hardly fail to be detrimental to cellular function" (Page, 1964). It is not surprising therefore, that many observations disagree with the hypothesis that the *therapeutic* action of digitalis might be causally related to reduction of intracellular K^+ brought about by reduced influx of this ion (Hajdu and Leonard, 1959). It is true that in digitalis poisoning there is a gain in Na^+ and a loss of K^+ from the heart, but the combined evidence tends to confirm that during the positive inotropic action of these drugs there is either no loss of K^+ (Lee *et al.,* 1961; Tuttle *et al.,* 1961) or sometimes even a slight gain (Hagen, 1939). The loss of K^+ found when toxic effects of the glycosides are observed has been shown to result from inhibition of K^+ influx (Farah and Witt, 1963).

Woodbury and Hecht (1952) described the spike of the action potential as first being increased and then decreased in amplitude by cardiac glycosides, the positive overshoot disappears and the action potential spike may fail to reach zero potential. Dudel and Trautwein (1958) showed also that the rate of rise of the action potential falls and, after a transient increase in the total duration, there is marked shortening of the action potential due to a decreased repolarization time. These effects appear to be the reverse of those which would be expected from the action of cardiac glycosides first stimulating and then inhibiting Na-K ATPase. It is clear that the action of cardiac glycosides at the cell membrane are complex, but the shortening of action potential duration may be the result of inhibition of active transport resulting in an accumulation of K^+ at the outside of the cell membrane which is known to shorten the duration of the action potential (Weidmann, 1956).

It is interesting to note that the major actions of the cardiac glycosides upon the membrane action potentials show similarities with those of adenosine which also causes a decreased rate of rise, decreased amplitude, and decreased duration of the action potential (Hollander and Webb, 1957; Johnson and McKinnon, 1956). Adenosine causes no positive inotropic effects but is synergistic with the cardiac glycosides with respect to their "toxic" actions. In the presence of subtoxic concentrations of cardiac glycosides adenosine precipitates the characteristic arrhythmias and conduction derangements which are to be seen in the guinea pig when toxic doses of cardiac glycosides are administered. Similarly the heart block which results from intra-atrial injection of adenosine is greatly prolonged by the cardiac glycosides. Both these effects have been extensively investigated by Rand *et al.* (1955a,b), and there is some evidence from work in our laboratories that these effects are unrelated to the stimulant action of drugs on myocardial contractility. The preliminary effects of cardiac glycosides in increasing the amplitude of the action potential and lengthening its duration are similar to those of caffeine described by de Gubareff and Sleator (1965) and of the catecholamines described by Furchgott *et al.* (1960) (see p. 210).

The effects of caffeine and adenosine are mutually antagonistic both on contractility and on the changes in shape and duration of the action potential (de Gubareff and Sleator, 1965) in the guinea pig atrium. This provides further evidence which suggests the possible importance of the initial phase of stimulation of Na-K ATPase activity in association with the positive inotropic effect of cardiotonic drugs. In addition to their direct action on ion transport the cardiac glycosides increase the membrane resistance (Dudel and Trautwein, 1958). The fact that in the therapeutic action of the cardiac glycosides the cation balance is often little changed or influenced positively (Farah and Witt, 1963; Clarke and Mosher, 1952; Tuttle *et al.*, 1962) may therefore be due to a variety of other factors.

Recently Erjavec and Adamic (1965) have compared the cardiotonic potencies, cardiotoxic potencies, and Na-K transport-inhibiting activity of a series of cardiac glycosides and this included the cardiotonic alkaloid ivorine. There was no clear correlation between the three effects although the concentrations for 50% Na-K transport inhibition seemed more related to the toxic potency ratios than to the cardiotonic ones.

Further work with other cardiotonic drugs, particularly those which lack the strong chronotropic effects of the digitalis group, is likely to throw some light on this problem but it seems highly probable that the actions of the cardiac glycosides on ionic fluxes at the cell membrane are not the fundamental mechanism responsible for their positive inotropic effects.

III. The Role of Calcium Ions as a Link between Membrane Excitation and the Contractile Mechanism

A. The General Effects of Calcium Ions on Contractility

It has been known for many years that many of the properties of the cardiac glycosides can be imitated by alterations in Ca^{++} concentration surrounding cardiac muscle cells. As early as 1915 A. J. Clark showed that the action of digitoxin on the isolated frog heart depends upon the presence of Ca^{++} in the perfusion fluid. It was also shown by Ransom (1917) that reduction of Ca^{++} caused a reduction of contractility in the frog heart and that this hypodynamic state was reversed by strophanthin. Otto Loewi (1918) considered that digitalis sensitized the heart to Ca^{++} and a number of workers have described synergism between digitalis and Ca^{++} by which the lethal dose of the former is reduced in the presence of increased concentrations of the latter.

Over a range of concentrations of Ca^{++}, 0.45–1.8 mM, ouabain in a concentration of 5×10^{-8} M produced similar increases in contractility in isolated rabbit left auricles, but with a higher concentration range of Ca^{++}, 1.8–7.2 mM, the positive inotropic effect of ouabain was significantly decreased (Farah and Witt, 1963). When higher concentrations of ouabain were used the toxic effects became more rapidly apparent in higher concentrations of Ca^{++} than with low. It was shown therefore that both the therapeutic and the toxic effects of ouabain in the mammalian auricle were potentiated by high Ca^{++} concentrations. Farah and Witt (1963) pointed out that it is possible that the digitalis glycosides may have actions of their own in addition to a major action via Ca^{++} so that it does not follow that the effects of digitalis and Ca^{++} need to be identical. This can also be interpreted to mean that if Ca^{++} is the mediator of the therapeutic action of digitalis then the additional toxic properties and side effects which digitalis exhibits should extend beyond the actions of Ca^{++} and the cardiac actions of Ca^{++} might be expected to be more restricted than those of digitalis.

The effects of digitalis and Ca^{++} upon the resting membrane potential and action potential of cardiac muscle exemplify this point, since in therapeutic concentrations neither digitalis nor Ca^{++} have any appreciable effects on either parameter but larger concentrations of digitalis produce the characteristic shortening of the action potential and decrease rate of rise (Weidmann, 1955; Dudel and Trautwein, 1958). This effect is probably due to other biochemical actions of digitalis not mediated by Ca^{++}. Further dissimilarities are seen in the actions of cardiac glycosides inhibiting Na-K ATPase and reducing K^+ influx into erythrocytes as well as increasing K^+ loss from muscle cells, actions which are not shown by high Ca^{++} concentrations.

An increase in extracellular Ca^{++} increases intracellular Ca^{++} and there is competition between Ca^{++} and Na^+ at the cell membrane (Willbrandt and Koller, 1948; Luttgau and Niedergerke, 1958). An accumulation of Na^+ inside the cell causes competition with the transport of Ca^{++} out of the cell and an accumulation of Ca^{++} within it. There is, however, evidence that the Ca^{++} uptake of cardiac muscle is uninfluenced by nontoxic concentrations of cardiac glycosides although toxic concentrations increase the uptake of Ca^{45} (Harvey and Daniel, 1952; Thomas *et al.*, 1958; Farah and Witt, 1963). It seems likely therefore that the depolarization of the cell membrane mobilizes Ca^{++} inside it without influencing the total content of Ca^{++} in the muscle or producing a measurable efflux or influx of Ca^{++}. The cardiac glycosides may influence this action inside the membrane with therapeutic doses and only produce gross changes in Ca^{++} fluxes with much larger doses which produce toxic effects. Much evidence is accumulating that this could well be the case. We have no *in vitro* indication of how mobilization of Ca^{++} is brought about although we have clear evidence of Ca^{++} uptake by both skeletal and cardiac muscle fibrils. Likewise we have no knowledge of the mechanism which triggers off the Ca^{++} release at the commencement of excitation-contraction coupling.

B. The Fine Structure of Cardiac Muscle and Recent Work on the Significance of the Relaxing Factor

Our knowledge of the structure of cardiac and skeletal muscle has been greatly advanced in recent years as a result of extensive electron microscope studies, and a fine description of the general anatomy of the muscle fiber is given by Franzini-Armstrong (1964) in a paper at a symposium on the relaxing factor of muscle. The basic arrangement appears to be common to both skeletal and cardiac muscle. Striated muscle fibers consist of bundles of fibrils separated by interfibrillar spaces, the whole being enclosed in an excitable membrane, the sarcolemma. Under the electron microscope the interfibrillar spaces are seen to contain several organelles some of which, mitochondria for example, are common to all cell types and have a reasonably understood function. There are, however, two distinct systems unique to muscle: the sarcoplasmic reticulum and the transverse tubular system. Their functions are not certain but there is a growing mass of data which makes it reasonable to postulate that they link excitation at the cell membrane to the contractile fibrils. The sarcoplasmic reticulum is a closed membranous system whereas the tubular system is a derivative of the sarcolemma the function of which is probably to conduct excitation into the interior of the fiber. In some muscles the tubular system appears to be open to the exterior but in others, such as frog skeletal muscle, such an opening cannot be readily demonstrated. It appears that the tubular system in this species may be closed at its periphery but if a membrane exists which closes the system it may well be a selective barrier for ions and have quite different properties from the remainder of the sarcolemma. The sarcolemma delimits the fiber and at every Z line penetrates into it to form a tubule. This is well illustrated in the photograph of Fig. 4.1. from Franzini-Armstrong (1964).

Similar tubules have been described in the heart muscle of many vertebrates (for references see Franzini-Armstrong, 1964). There is evidence from the observations of Huxley and his colleagues (Huxley, 1959; Huxley and Straub, 1958; Huxley and Taylor, 1958a,b) that local depolarization of the sarcolemma produces local contraction only when it occurs at the level of a Z line, that these tubules are probably the central element of the conduction mechanism into the fiber. On either side of the Z line are lateral sacs at the level of the I band, which form a continuous system across the fiber. The sacs communicate to the sarcoplasmic reticulum which runs longitudinally among the fibrils for the length of each A band. This gives continuity

Fig. 4.1. Longitudinal section through the segmental muscles of the black mollie (*Mollienesia* sp.) fixed in glutaraldehyde. The section is just tangential at one point to a myofibril and thus provides a face view of the sarcoplasmic reticulum (SR). The sarcolemma borders, at the right side of the photograph, the periphery of the fiber and can be followed (arrow) as it penetrates at the Z line-level between the larger "terminal sacs" of the SR to form the T (T) system. Strands of cytoplasm, remnants of the connections with the adjacent fiber, penetrate within the T system (Gl, glycogen). The line indicates 1 μ. Photograph by Dr. K. R. Porter (Franzini-Armstrong, 1964).

from the tubule across and around each fiber as well as longitudinally between the fibrils. The continuity from one sarcomere to the next is interrupted by the tubular system at each Z line. The sarcoplasmic reticulum thus seems an ideal system for holding active substances and for their release and distribution throughout the fiber.

The sarcoplasmic reticulum is a closed membranous space and it is probable that the relaxing factor which is composed of, or found in, membrane-limited vesicles derives from the breakdown of the sarcoplasmic reticulum or tubular system. Careful examination reveals that the two systems are connected, the lateral sacs being scalloped in such a way as to imply bridge-like structures joining the tubular and sarcoplasmic reticular systems.

Hasselbach (1963) and Nagai *et al.* (1960) have shown that the relaxing factor binds Ca^{++} and concentrates it inside the vesicles and lowers the concentration of Ca^{++} below that essential for the contraction-coupled actomyosin ATPase activity. Honig and Stam (1964) have discussed the relaxing system of cardiac muscle which has been shown (Honig *et al.*, 1962) to consist of both a particulate and soluble relaxing component. In skeletal muscle the particulate relaxing system consists of fragments of the sarcotubules but in cardiac muscle the sarcotubules are far less abundant than they are in skeletal muscle but mitochondria are very plentiful. When the relaxing factor is prepared from cardiac muscle both the sarcotubules and the mitochondria give rise to vesicles, and although the latter are usually larger and less elongated they cannot easily be distinguished by electron microscopy. When cardiac grana are incubated with ATP the soluble relaxing substance is formed which can be separated by ultracentrifugation or by gel filtration; it has been shown by Stam and co-workers (1963) that the cardiac relaxing substance is produced by fragmented sarcotubules rather than from the mitochondria. The most important difference between the particulate and soluble relaxing substances of cardiac muscle is that the soluble relaxing substance is unaffected by Ca^{++} when assayed by means of myofibrillar ATPase. Concentrations of Ca^{++} greater than 1 mM depress myofibrillar ATPase directly, but the action of the soluble relaxing substance was constant irrespective of the Ca^{++} concentration and simply produced an additive depression so that this substance obviously must act in a different way from chelation of Ca^{++}. This soluble relaxing system obviously cannot enhance the role of the sarcoplasmic reticulum in excitation-contraction coupling, for which Ca^{++} has been shown to play an essential part, and Honig and Stam (1964) suggest that it modifies contractile strength in cardiac muscle rather than initiating relaxation. They suggest that its role is comparable with that of an attenuator whereas the particulate system can be likened to an on-off switch in an electrical analogy.

Although the vertebrate heart responds to excitation in an all-or-none manner it can be influenced in its force of contraction by adrenergic drugs and autonomic mediation. Sonnenblick (1962) has shown that noradrenaline increases the rate of tension development in isometric recording and the velocity of shortening in isotonic recording. These changes in rate must be reflections of the rate of force-generating chemical reactions such as the hydrolysis of ATP by actomyosin ATPase. Honig and Stam (1964) sought such an effect of adrenergic drugs on cardiac myofibrillar ATPase since it had been shown that the stimulant effects of adrenergic substance were not directly the result of an effect on intermediary metabolism (Ellis, 1952). They found that adrenaline in a concentration of $10^{-5} M$ was without effect on myofibrillar ATPase activity but it became a stimulant when added to fibrils previously exposed to the cardiac relaxing substance. At $10^{-6} M$ adrenaline concentration there was a 24% increase in the myofibrillar ATPase activity when this had been depressed by the relaxing substance. Noradrenaline and isoprenaline also enhanced ATPase activity in the presence of relaxing substance but were inactive when it was absent. They concluded that the stimulation of cardiac contractility by the sympathoadrenal system could be due to a diminution of inhibition produced by the soluble relaxing substance, and they suggest that this relaxing substance may be the adrenergic intracellular receptor for tension development in cardiac muscle and provide the mechanism for alterations in contractile force produced by adrenergic drugs.

Podolsky and Costantin (1964) have made some very interesting observations on the regulation of contraction and relaxation of skeletal muscle by Ca^{++}. They used frog muscle fibers from which the sarcolemma had been removed and applied solutions of Ca^{++} directly to the fiber by means of a micropipette. By recording the local contraction of the fibers by cinematography they were able to show that contraction could be triggered by the local application of Ca^{++} and that finer changes in the striation pattern could be shown in the absence of the sarcolemma suggesting that Ca^{++} release followed membrane depolarization. They showed also that a very powerful Ca^{++} sink exists in muscle fibers and reduces the concentration of Ca^{++} available to the fibrils. The concentrations of Ca^{++} applied were 300 times greater than that necessary to elicit a local contraction and when the area of contraction was observed it was seen to be still very localized indeed, and it in no way approached the area which could be predicted by simple diffusion to comprise the zone bounded by a threshold Ca^{++} concentration. This work provides the first evidence for a Ca^{++} sink in the muscle fiber which governs the time course and distribution of Ca^{++} released intracellularly as a consequence of membrane depolarization. Although the majority of investigations on excitation-concentration coupling in muscle have been made using skeletal muscle a number of studies on cardiac muscle made recently seem generally to indicate that the differences between the two are of detail and are often quantitative rather than qualitative. Fanburg (1964) has studied the role of Ca^{++} in skeletal muscle and heart muscle and has shown that in both it behaves in an essentially similar manner. The main difference found between skeletal and cardiac subcellular preparations in this study was that cardiac extracts soon lose their ability to accumulate Ca^{++} whereas skeletal muscle preparations retain this activity for much longer periods; the rate and total accumulation of Ca^{++} were also less for cardiac preparations.

C. The Interrelation of Calcium Ions and Cardiotonic Drugs

Waugh (1962a,b) has discussed the role of Ca^{++} in the contractile excitation of vascular smooth muscle by adrenaline and considers that this process is independent of electrical depolarization of the cell membrane, since it occurs in arterial muscle completely depolarized by the substitution of potassium sulfate for sodium chloride in the extracellular fluid. Calcium ions, however, are essential for adrenaline excitation whether or not the muscle is electrically polarized. Adrenaline appears therefore to increase the cell permeability to Ca^{++} in some nonelectrical manner. Since Ca^{++} stabilizes cell membranes and a deficiency leads to increased permeability to other ions, Waugh suggests that in vascular smooth muscle adrenaline triggers an increase in membrane permeability to Ca^{++} and secondarily the movements of other ions produce electrical depolarization. Four findings are cited by Waugh (1962a) in support of Ca^{++} as a transmitter of membrane excitation to the contractile muscle proteins in vascular muscle. (1) Perfusion with a fluid containing ethylenediaminetetraacetic acid (EDTA) immediately prevents contraction of arterial muscle by either elevated K^+ or adrenaline. The rapidity of this action points to extracellular chelation of Ca^{++} as the cause. (2) Contractions already produced by K^+ or adrenaline are promptly inhibited or abolished by EDTA. (3) Calcium given with adrenaline immediately restores the contractions abolished by EDTA. (4) When the extracellular Ca^{++} is high enough to produce vascular contraction both adrenaline and K^+ greatly augment this so that the Ca^{++} which has entered the cells appears to activate the contractile process in vascular smooth muscle. It may be that the excess of intracellular Ca^{++} acts in the same way as it does in skeletal or cardiac muscle by inhibiting relaxing factor although in blood vessels the relaxing factor system has not yet been demonstrated. In the discussion of this work (Waugh, 1965) mention is made of Ca^{++} uptake being reduced in tissues such as the guinea pig taenia coli where adrenaline causes relaxation. In the vascular system, however, sites such as coronary smooth muscle, where adrenaline has inhibitory action, have not yet been studied with respect to associated Ca^{++} uptake.

Further interesting contributions to our knowledge of the role of Ca^{++} in arterial smooth muscle have been made by Hinke (1965) who has suggested that vascular muscle may contain two Ca^{++} fractions both of which are bound to the cell membrane. One is loosely bound and easily released by Ca^{++} changes outside the cell and by changes in membrane permeability. It is also suggested that it is released by high K^+ concentrations which induce contraction. The second Ca^{++} fraction is more tightly bound and is released after the first by noradrenaline. It is postulated that this second fraction is not removed by reduction of the external Ca^{++} to zero but is removed by EDTA. The binding of this fraction may not be influenced by the external Na^+ or by the electrical polarization of the membrane, whereas the loosely bound fraction is easily mobilized as a result of membrane depolarization. This is an interesting hypothesis and if a similar scheme could be shown in cardiac muscle it could suggest that cardiac glycosides might free the loosely bound form with small inotropic concentrations which appear to activate the cation pump mechanism and some part of their stimulant action could be caused in this way.

At the present time there is little experimental data concerning the action of cardiac glycosides in relation to the relaxing factor or to Ca^{++} in this connection. The studies of Lee (1961), however, appear to be particularly relevant. He has shown that glycerol-histidine-extracted heart muscle fibers contract with ATP and that if the relaxing factor is present the contraction is enhanced by ouabain. If the extraction is prolonged the relaxing factor appears to be lost and such fibers no longer contract in response to Ca^{++} and the ATP contraction is no longer sensitive to ouabain. The lack of response to Ca^{++} is thus an indicator of the loss of the relaxing factor, and ouabain may well act by mobilizing Ca^{++} from the fibers which then inhibits the relaxing factor and causes an inotropic effect.

Lüllman and Holland (1962) and Klaus and Kuschinsky (1962) have shown that during the positive inotropic action of ouabain a small increment of Ca^{45} uptake occurs. The total tissue Ca^{++} content does not change however. There is therefore a small increase in Ca^{++} exchange during cardiac glycoside stimulation which would fit in well with the observations of Lee just discussed.

Recently Lee and his colleagues have published additional observations which pinpoint Ca^{++} uptake by cardiac sarcoplasmic reticulum as a mechanism influenced by the cardiac glycosides. In a review of the present status of cardiac relaxing factor, Lee (1965) discussed the differences between preparations from skeletal and cardiac muscle and reported preparations from dog myocardium equally active in Ca^{++} uptake with that found for skeletal muscle extracts. Prior to this report cardiac preparations were insufficiently active for the Ca^{++} pump mechanism of sarcoplasmic reticulum to be generally accepted as an adequate mechanism for muscular relaxation in the heart. The major difference between the two, Lee asserts, is that for rapid Ca^{++} uptake, heart muscle requires a potentiating agent as well as the ATP-generating system whereas the latter alone suffices in skeletal muscle. The rate of Ca^{++} uptake by cardiac sarcoplasmic reticulum was only a little less than half that required to cause relaxation *in vivo,* and in view of the difficult experimental techniques such agreement is reasonable and may well be improved as more elegant methods are developed. Lee, in the same paper, also described the release of Ca^{++} from a preparation of cardiac sarcoplasmic reticulum and re-uptake when stimulation ceased, thus completing the *in vitro* demonstration of "excitation-contraction coupling."

The sensitivity of this system to cardiac glycosides has been investigated by Lee and Choi (1966) who found that ouabain or strophanthin optimally inhibited Ca^{++} uptake of sarcoplasmic reticulum fragments when present in a concentration of 10^{-6} M. They found also that this effect was more marked in NaCl medium than in KCl medium and suggest that the greater effectiveness of cardiac glycosides upon the failing heart may be associated with K^+ loss which has been previously discussed. In these circumstances it may be that the cardiac glycosides cause a greater release of Ca^{++} than in normal muscle and consequently a greater positive inotropic effect.

One of the most interesting features of the positive inotropic action of the cardiac glycosides is the characteristic slow onset of action, or long latent period, which they show. The inotropic effect of Ca^{++} is, on the other hand, very rapid in onset. It has been shown by several workers that the inotropic effect of the cardiac glycosides is related to the total number of beats of the heart preparation rather than to the time of exposure to the glycoside, and this has been clearly demonstrated by Moran (1963). He showed that rabbit left atria stimulated at one of four frequencies, 15, 30, 60, or 120 per minute, increased in contractile force and reached a maximum after varying intervals of time when exposed to ouabain in bicarbonate-buffered Tyrode's solution at 30°C. The time which elapsed was inversely proportional to the frequency of stimulation. The curves relating time and contractile force were sigmoid in shape and parallel. The time for half the maximum force to develop ranged from 8 minutes at 120 stimuli per minute to approximately 60 minutes at 15 per minute. When these curves were replotted in the form of the cumulative number of contractions against the contractile force all four curves superimposed very well. The number of contractions for the median cumulative response did not differ significantly. It was shown furthermore that when atria were exposed to ouabain for as long as 30 minutes without contracting, the ouabain could be washed away and practically no positive inotropic effect was observed when electrical stimulation was applied subsequently.

Similar results were obtained by Holland (1964) and the illustration of Fig. 4.2 is reproduced from his paper. With a stimulus frequency ranging from 20–180 beats per minute a total number of stimuli close to 2000 was always needed for the maximum positive inotropic effect to develop. The lack of effect with ouabain in the absence of contrac-

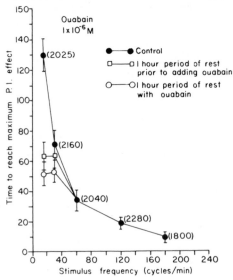

Fig. 4.2. The relationship between the frequency of stimulation and the time to reach the maximum positive inotropic effect. The figures in parentheses give the number of beats required to achieve this effect, and the vertical lines at each point give the standard error of the mean time values (Holland, 1964, by permission of the American Heart Association, Inc.)

tion is very well illustrated in Fig. 4.3 (Moran, 1963). The upper strip shows a clear staircase effect with a reduction in the frequency of stimulation before and after exposure to ouabain provided that the drug was washed away prior to electrical stimulation. The lower strip shows staircase reversal when ouabain remains in the bath.

Reiter (1963) has shown that "after-contraction" can be observed in guinea pig papillary muscles. Normally each contraction is followed by an interval of rest but by stimulating this preparation at 60 stimuli per minute in the presence of dihydroouabain a second smaller after-contraction was observed to follow the main contraction. This was seen with concentration of 8×10^{-5} M of dihydroouabain when the bathing solution contained 0.6 mM Ca^{++}. When the Ca^{++} concentration was increased after-contraction occurred more readily and with lower concentrations of dihydroouabain. In 7.2 mM Ca^{++} after-contraction was observed with 5×10^{-6} M dihydroouabain and all higher concentrations. Reiter suggested that after-contractions occur at a certain intracellular Ca^{++} concentration and that the glycoside increases this concentration. In the presence of high extracellular Ca^{++} a smaller increase suffices to produce the effect.

Gersmeyer and Holland (1963) have shown that the effect of ouabain on Ca^{++} exchange also develops in a beat-dependent manner,

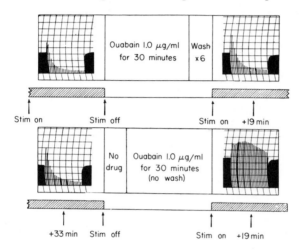

Fig. 4.3. The contraction dependency of the binding of ouabain by myocardium. In this experiment an atrium was driven at 120 per minute (represented by cross-hatched horizontal bars) with periodic brief reductions to 12 per minute. The abrupt reduction of frequency produced a typical staircase response. A control frequency-reduction test is shown in the upper left tracing. The stimulator was then turned off for 34 minutes during which time ouabain, 1 μg per milliliter, was added to the bath for 30 minutes and then washed out before the stimulator was turned on again. A frequency-reduction test performed 19 minutes after the stimulator was restarted is shown in the upper right tracing. There is no significant change in the staircase. The lower left tracing shows a test 33 minutes after the resumption of stimulation. The middle part of the lower section represents a second period of no stimulation upon exposure to ouabain—the ouabain was not washed out. Resumption of stimulation resulted in increased contractile force and reversal of the staircase 19 minutes after restarting stimulator. Repeated washings after full development of the inotropic effect failed to alter the ouabain action, although this is not shown in the figure (Moran, 1963).

and Holland (1964) has observed that isolated rabbit auricles beating in Ringer's solution which contained only one sixth of the normal Ca^{++} content show a decline in developed tension exponential with time, and as this decline proceeds Ca^{++} is lost. Such preparations when pretreated with ouabain showed a more rapid decline in contractile strength although a concomitant increased loss of Ca^{++} was not shown in these experiments. These results suggest that ouabain causes increased mobilization of Ca^{++} with each beat, which may activate the contractile elements of the muscle or perhaps inhibit relaxing factor. Adrenaline behaved in the opposite manner and prolonged the decline in contractile strength. It is difficult to explain this result but it may be significant that the soluble relaxing factor described by Honig and Stam (1964) is unaffected by Ca^{++} but inhibited by catecholamines. This is obviously a very interesting and simple technique which could be investigated with other cardiotonic substances and also with those which depress contractility.

In summary the evidence for Ca^{++} as the transmitter of excitation contraction coupling in heart muscle is mounting and there are good reasons for believing that the positive inotropic action of the cardiac glycosides may be at least partly if not primarily the result of an action at this level rather than upon active transport at the cell membrane.

IV. Cardiotonic Drugs and the Contractile Mechanism of Muscle

A. Evidence That the Cardiac Glycosides Enter the Cardiac Muscle Cell

The positive inotropic effect of cardiotonic substances, of which that of the cardiac glycosides has been the most thoroughly investigated, may be the result of action at several sites in the chain between the excitation, contraction, and subsequent relaxation of cardiac muscle. Whether there is a direct action of these drugs on the contractile proteins of muscle or whether they provide a facilitatory environment for contraction has been considered by many investigators. If cardiotonic drugs act directly on actin, myosin, or actomyosin it is to be expected that changes would be produced in the physical properties of one or more of these materials. If this action is of physiological significance then also the drug must enter the cell and not be barred by the cell membrane. This question has been studied by Waser (1962) who, by the use of autoradiography, showed that radioactive digitoxin entered the muscle fibers; Smith and Fozzard (1963) performed similar experiments with H^3-digoxin upon hearts of frogs and dogs. In each case they administered the drug until toxic effects were produced.

Conrad and Baxter (1964) used H^3-digoxin and administered nontoxic doses to dogs under anesthesia. In two of the animals they monitored the force of contraction of the right ventricle by means of a strain-gauge arch and recorded the electrocardiogram in all five dogs. They also gave H^3-digoxin to rats in a chronic fashion over 2 weeks. They took considerable care to preserve the normal intracellular architecture as far as possible and also to prevent elution of the radioisotope from the tissue sections. They related their autoradiographic observations to the changes in contractile force and showed that between ½ and 2 hours after intravenous administration of H^3-digoxin the increase in contractile force was well established and the histological sections showed intense development of silver grains in the A bands, along the cell membrane and myofibrils. Observations after shorter time intervals showed faint or no grain development, and after 4 hours the development had again decreased. The localization of H^3-digoxin in the A band was of particular interest since this is the area where actin and myosin fibrils overlap, and it has been reported (Draper and Hodge, 1949) that Ca^{++} and Mg^{++} appear to be highest in this region also.

B. The Action of Cardiac Glycosides on the Physical Properties of the Contractile Proteins of Muscle

Cardiac glycosides bind to proteins to a varying degree, and a number of papers have appeared dealing with the binding to serum albumin. It is very doubtful whether this is relevant to their action on the heart since it is a very general phenomenon shown by a great many drugs.

Waser (1963) has summarized his work on the binding of cardiac glycosides to myosin, actin, and actomyosin extracted from both skeletal and heart muscle from calves and rabbits. Actomyosin from rabbit skeletal muscle can bind approximately 1 μg of lanatoside A and rather less of K-strophanthoside per milligram of protein, and this would accord with one molecule of actomyosin accepting one molecule of the glycoside (Waser, 1956). Subsequent experiments, however, led him to repeat these studies with myosin from beef skeletal and heart muscle. The method used was to add the glycosides to the myosin and then submit the mixture to equilibration-dialysis for some days. Similar dissociation constants were obtained in both skeletal and cardiac muscle for lanatoside A and lanatoside C, but for K-strophanthoside the figure for skeletal myosin was half as great as that for the cardiac preparation (Waser, 1963). It is believed that a similar bonding process takes place in each case but that double the amount of glycoside is bound by cardiac myosin which has been reported to be a dimer of two molecular units. Waser has also described a series of experiments using both Ostwald and rotational viscometers since fibrous actomyosin has high viscosity and also exhibits marked thixotropy. Cardiac glycosides cause a decrease in relative viscosity which is often proportional to the concentration of glycoside. This parameter shows very little variation with structural changes in the glycosides, and there is no parallelism between the change in relative viscosity and biological activity. When, however, thixotropy was studied a different situation was found. Thixotropy is manifest as an apparent viscosity fall when a change in the internal structure of the protein solution is caused so that the fibrous protein molecules are dissociated one from another. This can be the result of physical agitation such as stirring or shaking. This property cannot be measured by the Ostwald viscometer since this instrument requires that the fluid being studied shall flow through a narrow-bore capillary tube, a process which in itself will produce thixotropic breakdown. The rotational viscometer, on the other hand, applies a constant shear and measures relative thixotropy as the degree of fluid coupling between two concentric cylinders one of which is continuously rotated by a small electric motor, the other being allowed to follow it until a measured torsional restraint balances the viscous coupling of the fluid between them. When Waser (1963) used this method he found that there was correlation between biological activity and the coefficient of thixotropic breakdown. The thixotropy was diminished in rough proportionality to the cat lethal dose for active glycosides. Inactive glycosides such as allocymarin, alloperiplogenin, and hexa-hydroscillaren usually enhanced the thixotropy but certainly caused no fall. Changes in thixotropy can also be produced by alterations in the ion concentration in the solution and they are probably the result of changes in the hydration of the protein molecules.

Potassium and calcium ions can also be bound to actomyosin, and Waser found that cardioactive glycosides enhanced the degree of binding in both cases whereas inactive glycosides did not. These experiments were performed with actomyosin from skeletal muscle and with myosin from heart muscle and similar results were found in each case. The effect was a marked one since with active glycosides a hundred K^+ ions were bound to the myosin molecule whereas in their absence only twelve are so bound. Similar although less marked effects were observed for Ca^{++}. Waser considers that the enhanced binding of K^+ compensates for the K^+ loss in myocardial insufficiency and counteracts a decreased K^+ transport at the cell membrane.

Binding of Ca^{++} to actomyosin has been shown to cause increased contractility by Kako and Bing (1958) on actomyosin bands; Ca^{++} also accelerates the globular to fibrous actin transformation.

In discussing Waser's (1956) observations on the binding of cardiac glycosides to actomyosin, Wollenberger (1962) calculated that 54 μg of digitoxin would be required to saturate 1 gm of dog heart if it were to combine with actomyosin as its receptor. This is a far greater concentration than has ever been detected in tissues, the figures generally lying between 2 μg per gram for the rat heart and 0.3 μg per gram in the dog (Friedman *et al.*, 1952). It appears that only few myosin molecules can be attached to cardiac glycoside molecules, and Wollenberger put this ratio at many hundred to one which makes it unlikely that myosin is a primary site of action of cardiac glycosides. He discusses this point thoroughly and concludes that the binding of cardiac glycosides to contractile proteins is probably not the basis for their therapeutic action and that the viscosity changes are also secondary.

There seems no doubt that the active cardiac glycosides can affect the contractile proteins possibly directly but certainly by increasing ionic binding. Whether this is a significant action in the therapeutic action of the cardiac glycosides is unknown, but it is possible that it is another of the multiple actions exhibited by these drugs, the concerted result of which is a positive inotropic effect.

C. Differences in the Behavior of the Contractile Mechanism in the Normal and Failing Heart

It appears that the contractile properties of the myocardial proteins of the heart differ in chronic failure from those observed in normal hearts (Benson, 1955). Actomyosin from the hearts of dogs in chronic failure gave a significantly different response upon the addition of ATP than did that from normal dogs. Benson *et al.* (1958) induced chronic congestive heart failure in dogs by the surgical production of tricuspid insufficiency and pulmonary stenosis. The operated dogs showed the characteristic signs of congestive failure and were sacrificed between 5 and 24 months after the production of the surgical lesions. Glycerol-extracted muscle fibers were prepared from trabecular muscle and stored in 50% glycerol for at least 2 weeks. Even when stored for 6 months at $-20°C$ no further changes were observed in the contractile properties of the fiber bundles. The developed tension was measured by an isometric myograph in a solution of buffer at pH 8.2 containing K^+, Cl^-, Mg^{++}, and Ca^{++} and at 25°C. ATP was added and the tension developed immediately and reached a maximum in 1–3 minutes. After the measurements the protein concentration was determined in the fibers by ultraviolet spectrophotometry. Isotonic shortening was also recorded by visual observation of the fibers in a Petri dish containing the bathing solution.

Fibers from the failing hearts consistently developed less tension, when this was corrected for protein content and resting fiber length, than did those from normal hearts. In nine observations from each group the normal fibers developed approximately 50% greater tension and the significance of the differences was better than $P=0.999$. In isotonic shortening no difference was observed between the two groups of fibers. The ATPase activity of the two groups of fibers was also studied and did not differ significantly. The work capacities of the two groups of fibers were also calculated as a function of fiber length and it was shown that the fibers from failing hearts could do less work than those from normal hearts under similar conditions.

Figure 4.4 gives the results of Benson *et al.* (1958), obtained in this study, in graphical form and illustrates the difference between the two groups of heart muscle fibers very clearly.

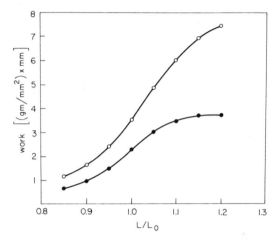

Fig. 4.4. Work as a function of fiber length in fiber bundles from normal and failing hearts. *L* is the length of the fiber bundle at which measurement was made; L_0 is the equilibrium length. O = normal myocardial fiber bundles; ● = failing myocardial fiber bundles (Benson *et al.*, 1958, by permission of the American Heart Association, Inc.)

It can be argued that studies of this kind are markedly unphysiological and this, of course, is true. The glycerol-extracted fibers do not possess a cell membrane and they are isolated from energy-providing systems present in whole muscle, but the very fact that the two groups differ only in the state of the hearts from which they were taken provides strong evidence that the difference observed is almost certainly due to the induced cardiac failure and it seems most probable that changes in the contractile proteins of which these results provide an index do occur in heart failure. Because of the long period of glycerol extraction used by Benson *et al.* (1958), it seems reasonable to assume that the relaxing factor had been lost (Lee, 1961), and therefore it is most unlikely that fibers prepared in this way would show an increased force of contraction with added cardiac glycosides.

Kako and Bing (1958) have described a study of the contractility of actomyosin bands prepared from normal and failing human hearts. They prepared actomyosin and then compressed it into bands in a

Langmuir trough. One end of the band was fixed and the other attached to the lengthened arm of a torsion balance. The movement of this arm actuated a servo system which moved the fixed end of the band in the opposite direction so that the arm of the torsion balance was kept in equilibrium. Movements of the fixed end, and the trough, were recorded with an ink-writing recorder on a moving paper chart. Shortening of the band was thus recorded at a magnification of 23 times. Actomyosin from 41 hearts was studied in this way, 12 were from patients suffering from congestive heart failure, and the remainder from those who died from causes normally regarded as unrelated to cardiac function. The experimental material was collected 1–6 hours after the death of the patient. It was shown that ATP induced contractions in the actomyosin bands and that there was a reverse relationship between the load applied to the band and the percentage shortening. The contractility of the actomyosin bands from failing hearts was significantly less than those from normal hearts.

Digoxin or calcium chloride added separately to the actomyosin band preparations did not influence their contractility whether they were prepared from normal or failing hearts. When calcium chloride and digoxin were added together however, there was increased shortening of the bands in both cases, and in the preparations from failing hearts the contractility was restored to normal. The results obtained in this study indicate that changes occur in cardiac actomyosin in the failing heart but do not, of course, permit of any speculation upon the nature of such changes. The short period of time between procuring the hearts and the performance of these experiments would be compatible with the observations of Lee (1961) that relaxing factor is essential for the action of cardiac glycosides on glycerinated fibers and that preparations left for periods of some weeks do not respond to Ca^{++} or ouabain because the relaxing factor has been lost. It is not, however, known whether the process of preparing actomyosin bands would also extract part of the relaxing factor although it seems most unlikely that it would and therefore these results are difficult to explain in this way. The extent of the stimulant effect produced, however, was far less than Lee observed in his preparations in which the relaxing factor was present.

Previous studies upon glycerinated muscle fibers have sometimes failed to show any effect of cardiac glycosides on ATP-induced contraction (Korey, 1950; Stutz *et al.,* 1954; Edman, 1953), whereas other workers have found that these drugs did enhance the speed and force of contraction of actomyosin threads (Robb and Mallov, 1953; Bowen, 1952). These discrepancies may be due to the loss of relaxing factor or other differences in the preparation of actomyosin such as the presence or absence of Ca^{++}.

In summary it can be said that there is very strong evidence that cardiac glycosides enter the cardiac muscle cell. In preparations of the contractile proteins or of glycerinated fibers the force of contraction appears to be greater if these have been taken from normal hearts than if they came from hearts in a state of failure. If preparations of glycerinated fibers are fresh a positive inotropic response can be seen with cardiac glycosides in the presence of Ca^{++}. Active cardiac glycosides enhance the binding of ions to contractile proteins and this property may supplement the action of Ca^{++}. Direct effects of cardiac glycosides on the thixotropy of protein solutions or the binding of these drugs to molecules of the contractile proteins are effects which can be observed *in vitro,* but which seem unlikely to play a significant effect in the living animal in view of the very small concentrations of these drugs which gain access to the heart.

V. Effects on Cardiac Metabolism

This chapter would not be complete without a short discussion of the influence of cardiac glycosides upon the metabolic processes in cardiac muscle. This topic has, however, been the subject of several recent reviews and the reader is referred to Wollenberger (1949, 1962), Bing (1963, 1965), Lee (1963), and Opie (1965), all of whom have given accounts of present views in this field.

It is considered by many investigators that the cardiac glycosides do not have any action which, of itself, increases the oxygen consumption of the myocardium. Any increase observed after these drugs are given is thus considered to be secondary to the increased mechanical work which they can induce (Hajdu and Leonard, 1959). When isolated tissue slices from the heart were incubated with cardiac glycosides in concentrations not much greater than the therapeutic range, increased oxygen uptake was observed by several workers. The significance of these results has been the subject of debate, however, since Bing and his colleagues studied the effect of strophanthin on coronary flow and oxygen consumption in normal and failing hearts *in vivo* and observed no change in either parameter although the work output of the failing heart was increased (Bing *et al.*, 1950). Lee and co-workers (1960) used isolated papillary muscles which were allowed to fail spontaneously and showed that ouabain caused increased force of contraction which did not parallel the time course of oxygen consumption changes. Shortly after the ouabain was added there was a period during which contractility was increasing while the oxygen consumption remained unchanged, and after the inotropic effect had passed its peak and contractility was falling a further increase in oxygen consumption was observed.

The oxygen consumption of resting cardiac muscle is usually one third or less that of the muscle when beating (Lee, 1954; Beuren *et al.*, 1958), and in tissue slices the oxygen consumption is very low compared with that of the normal heart. It is difficult therefore to assess the significance of changes in oxygen consumption of nonbeating tissues. Dinitrophenol (DNP) causes a decrease in the contractility of cat papillary muscles to about 20% of its normal value in half an hour, but during this time oxygen consumption progressively increases. It is suggested that DNP uncouples phosphorylation of ATP before this can be utilized as an energy source by the muscle since the depressant action is not antagonized by the addition of ATP (Lee, 1954). These results, however, show quite clearly that the oxygen consumption and contractile behavior of cardiac muscle are clearly separable and hence it need not be considered remarkable that the cardiac glycosides have such a clear effect on contractility whereas their action on oxygen consumption is equivocal.

It is generally accepted that the production of high-energy phosphate bonds and ATP formation is not changed in the failing heart; Lee *et al.* (1960) showed that ouabain causes very little decrease in ATP or phosphocreatine during the positive inotropic effect. There was a major loss, however, of these compounds when toxic effects were produced. Lee *et al.* (1961) suggested that during the toxic stage of ouabain action the rate of breakdown of ATP and phosphocreatine exceeds their synthesis. The rise in oxygen consumption in this stage would then be explained by the accumulation of large amounts of ADP and orthophosphate which are known to stimulate cellular respiration.

Wollenberger (1951) had observed similar effects *in vivo* and in heart-lung preparations and points out (Wollenberger, 1962) that when the levels of high-energy phosphates in the myocardium are low, ouabain causes a further fall at an early stage in the inotropic action or when present in low concentrations. These observations are insufficient to suggest that changes in high-energy phosphate levels provide a basis for the positive inotropic effect of the cardiac glycosides but they do rule out the suggestion that this action is the result of increased levels of these substances.

Cardiac glycosides have been shown to have effects upon intermediary carbohydrate metabolism. Kien (1960) has shown that they can increase the uptake of sugars by the myocardium and that the contribution which glucose makes to the total energy production of the heart is also increased (Kien and Sherrod, 1960). This appears to be the result of a change in substrate utilization since the total metabolic rate is unchanged. The changes which Kien and Sherrod (1961) observed occurred without any concomitant change in cardiac function. It has not been shown that carbohydrate metabolism is at fault in the failing heart, but Gudbjarnason *et al.* (1964) have suggested that there are changes in the myocardial enzyme patterns which cause a decrease in activity of enzymes of the Krebs cycle. Since the cardiac glycosides inhibit active cationic transport it would seem likely that sugar transport might be similarly depressed. This has in fact been shown in the case of sugar transport in the frog small intestine (Czaky *et al.*, 1961). These observations seem contrary to those of Kien and Sherrod (1960) but it may be that, as in the case of the active transport of cations, there is a dose-dependent biphasic effect in this case with increased transport at very low glycoside concentrations. Such an effect has not yet been shown experimentally.

The extraction of substrates from the failing heart has not been shown to differ from the normal (Bing and Kako, 1961), although the contractile proteins do appear to be altered (Olson, 1956, 1961). Present evidence generally supports an action of the cardiac glycosides in improving energy utilization with possibly some measure of direct action upon contractile proteins as the primary mechanism by which they produce a positive inotropic action. It seems unlikely that metabolic changes are fundamentally the cause of this action.

References

Benson, E. S. (1955). *Circulation Res.* **3**, 221.

Benson, E. S., Hallaway, B. E., and Turbak, C. E. (1958). *Circulation Res.* **6**, 122.

Beuren, A., Sparks, C., and Bing, R. J. (1958). *Am. J. Cardiol.* **1**, 103.

Bing, R. J. (1963). *Proc. 1st Intern. Pharmacol. Meeting, Stockholm, 1961* **3**, 75. Pergamon Press, Oxford.

Bing, R. J. (1965). *Physiol. Rev.* **45**, 171.

Bing, R. J., and Kako, K. (1961). *Circulation* **24**, 483.

Bing, R. J., Maraist, F. M., Dammann, J. F., Draper, A., Heimbecker, R., Daley, R., Gerard, R., and Calazel, P. (1950). *Circulation* **2**, 513.

Bonting, S. L., and Caravaggio, L. (1963). *Arch. Biochem. Biophys.* **101**, 37.

Bonting, S. L., Simon, K. A., and Hawkins, N. M. (1961). *Arch. Biochem.* **95**, 416.

Bonting, S. L., Hawkins, N. M., and Canady, M. R. (1964). *Biochem. Pharmacol.* **13**, 13.

Bowen, W. J. (1952). *Federation Proc.* **11**, 16.

Caldwell, P. C., and Keynes, R. D. (1959). *J. Physiol. (London)* **148**, 8P.

Calhoun, J. A., and Harrison, T. R. (1931). *J. Clin. Invest.* **10**, 139.

Calhoun, J. A., Cullen, G. E., Clarke, G., and Harrison, T. R. (1930). *J. Clin. Invest.* **9**, 393.

Charnock, J. S., and Post, R. L. (1963). *Nature* **199**, 910.

Clark, A. J. (1915). *Proc. Roy. Soc. Med.* **5**, 1.

Clarke, N. E., and Mosher, R. E. (1952). *Circulation* **5**, 907.

Conrad, L. L., and Baxter, D. J. (1964). *J. Pharmacol. Exptl. Therap.* **145**, 210.

Csaky, T. Z., Hartzog, H. G., and Fernald, G. W. (1961). *Am. J. Physiol.* **200**, 459.

de Gubareff, T., and Sleator, W. (1965). *J. Pharmacol. Exptl. Therap.* **148**, 202.

Draper, M. H., and Hodge, A. J. (1949). *Nature* **163**, 576.

Dudel, J., and Trautwein, W. (1958). *Arch. Exptl. Pathol. Pharmakol.* **232**, 393.

Dunham, E. T., and Glynn, I. M. (1961). *J. Physiol. (London)* **156**, 274.

Edman, K. A. P. (1953). *Acta Physiol. Scand.* **30**, 69.

Ellis, S. (1952). *J. Pharmacol. Exptl. Therap.* **105**, 381.

Erjavec, F., and Adamic, S. (1965). *Arch. Intern. Pharmacodynamie* **155**, 251.

Fanburg, B. (1964). *Federation Proc.* **23**, 922.

Farah, A., and Witt, P. N. (1963). *Proc. 1st Intern. Pharmacol. Meeting, Stockholm, 1961*, **3**, 137. Pergamon Press, Oxford.

Franzini-Armstrong, C. (1964). *Federation Proc.* **23**, 887.

Friedman, M., St. George, S., Bine, R., Byers, S. O., and Bland, C. (1952). *Circulation* **6**, 367.

Furchgott, R. F., Sleator, W., and de Gubareff, T. (1960). *J. Pharmacol. Exptl. Therap.* **129**, 405.

Gersmeyer, E., and Holland, W. C. (1963). *Am. J. Physiol.* **205**, 795.

Glynn, I. M. (1962). *J. Physiol. (London)* **160**, 80P.

Glynn, I. M. (1964). *Pharmacol. Rev.* **16**, 381.

Gudbjarnason, S., de Schriver, C., Hunn, G., and Bing, R. J. (1964). *J. Lab. Clin. Med.* **64**, 796.

Hagen, P. S. (1939). *J. Pharmacol. Exptl. Therap.* **67**, 50.

Hajdu, S., and Leonard, E. (1959). *Pharmacol. Rev.* **11**, 173.

Harrison, T. R., Pilcher, C., and Ewing, G. (1930). *J. Clin. Invest.* **8**, 325.

Harvey, S. C., and Daniel, E. E. (1952). *J. Pharmacol. Exptl. Therap.* **106**, 394.

Hasselbach, W. (1963). *Naturwissenschaften* **50**, 249.

Hinke, J. A. M. (1965). *In* "Muscle," Proc. Symp. Univ. of Alberta, Edmonton, Alberta, 1964, p. 284 Pergamon Press, Oxford.

Holland, W. C. (1964). *Circulation Res. Suppl.* **15**, 85.

Hollander, P. E., and Webb, J. L. (1957). *Circulation Res.* **5**, 349.

Honig, C. R., and Stam, A. C., Jr. (1964). *Federation Proc.* **23**, 926.

Honig, C. R., Stam. A. C., Jr., and Mahan, P. E. (1962). *Am. J. Physiol.* **203**, 137.

Huxley, A. F. (1959). *Ann. N.Y. Acad. Sci.* **81**, 446.

Huxley, A. F., and Straub, R. W. (1958). *J. Physiol. (London)* **143**, 40P.

Huxley, A. F., and Taylor, R. E. (1958a). *Nature* **176**, 1068.

Huxley, A. F., and Taylor, R. E. (1958b). *J. Physiol. (London)* **144**, 526.

Johnson, E. A., and McKinnon, M. G. (1956). *Nature* **178**, 1174.

Kako, K., and Bing, R. J. (1958). *J. Clin. Invest.* **37**, 465.

Kien, G. A. (1960). *Proc. Soc. Exptl. Biol. Med.* **103**, 682.

Kien, G. A., and Sherrod, T. R. (1960). *Circulation Res.* **8**, 188.

Klaus, W., and Kuschinsky, G. (1962). *Arch. Exptl. Pathol. Pharmakol.* **244**, 237.

Klaus, W., Kuschinsky, G., and Lüllman, H. (1962). *Arch. Exptl. Pathol. Pharmakol.* **242**, 480.

Korey, S. (1950). *Biochim. Biophys. Acta* **4**, 58.

Krespi, V., Fozzard, H. A., and Sleator, W. (1964). *Circulation Res.* **15**, 545.

Lee, K. S. (1954). *J. Pharmacol. Exptl. Therap.* **112**, 484.

Lee, K. S. (1961). *J. Pharmacol. Exptl. Therap.* **132**, 149.

Lee, K. S. (1963). *Proc. 1st Intern. Pharmacol. Meeting, Stockholm, 1961* **3**, 185. Pergamon Press, Oxford.

Lee, K. S. (1965). *Federation Proc.* **24**, 1432.

Lee, K. S., and Choi, S. J. (1966). *J. Pharmacol. Exptl. Therap.* **153**, 114.

Lee, K. S., Yu, D. H., and Burstein, R. (1960). *J. Pharmacol. Exptl. Therap.* **129**, 115.

Lee K. S., Yu, D. H., Lee, D. I., and Burstein, R. (1961). *J. Pharmacol. Exptl. Therap.* **132**, 139.

Loewi, O. (1918). *Arch. Exptl. Pathol. Pharmakol.* **82**, 131.

Lüllman, H., and Holland, W. C. (1962). *J. Pharmacol. Exptl. Therap.* **137**, 186.

Lüttgau, H. C., and Niedergerke, R. (1958). *J. Physiol. (London)* **143**, 486.

Mallov, S., and Robb, J. S. (1949). *Federation Proc.* **8**, 104.

Moran, N. C. (1963). *Proc. 1st Intern. Pharmacol. Meeting, Stockholm, 1961* **3**, 251. Pergamon Press, Oxford.

Nagai, T., Makinose, M., and Hasselbach, W. (1960). *Biochim. Biophys. Acta* **43**, 223.

Olson, R. E. (1956). *Am. J. Med.* **20**, 159.

Olson, R. E. (1961). *Am. J. Med.* **30**, 692.

Opie, L. H. (1965). *Am. Heart J.* **69**, 401.

Page, E. (1964). *Circulation* **30**, 237.

Page, E., Goerke, R. J., and Storm, S. R. (1964). *J. Gen. Physiol.* **47**, 531.

Podolsky, R. J., and Costantin, L. L. (1964). *Federation Proc.* **23**, 933.

Portius, H. J., and Repke, K. (1962). *Arch. Exptl. Pathol. Pharmakol.* 243, 335.
Portius, H. J., and Repke, K. (1964). *Arzneimittel-Forsch.* 14, 1073.
Post, R. L., Merritt, C. R., Kinsolving, C. R., and Albright, C. D. (1960). *J. Biol. Chem.* 235, 1796.
Rand, M., Stafford, A., and Thorp, R. H. (1955a). *J. Pharmacol. Exptl. Therap.* 114, 119.
Rand, M., Stafford, A., and Thorp, R. H. (1955b). *Australian J. Exptl. Biol. Med.* 33, 663.
Ransom, F. (1917). *J. Physiol. (London)* 51, 176.
Reiter, M. (1963). *Proc. 1st Intern. Pharmacol. Meeting, Stockholm, 1961* 3, 265. Pergamon Press, Oxford.
Repke, K. (1963). *Proc. 1st Intern. Pharmacol. Meeting, Stockholm, 1961* 3, 69. Pergamon Press, Oxford.
Repke, K. (1965). *Proc. 2nd Intern. Pharmacol. Meeting, Prague, 1963* 4, 65. Pergamon Press, Oxford.
Repke, K., and Portius, H. J. (1963). *Experientia* 19, 452.
Robb, J. S., and Mallov, S. (1953). *J. Pharmacol. Exptl. Therap.* 108, 251.
Schatzmann, H. J. (1953). *Helv. Physiol. Acta* 11, 346.
Skou, J. C. (1957). *Biochim. Biophys. Acta* 23, 394.
Skou, J. C. (1960). *Biochim. Biophys. Acta* 42, 6.
Smith, J. R., and Fozzard, H. A. (1963). *Nature* 197, 562.
Sonnenblick, E. H. (1962). *Federation Proc.* 21, 975.
Stam, A. C., Jr., Panner, B. J., and Honig, C. R. (1963). *Physiologist* 6, 279.
Stutz, H., Feigelson, E., Emerson, J., and Bing, R. J. (1954). *Circulation Res.* 2, 555.
Thomas, L., Jr., Jolley, W., and Grechman, R. (1958). *Federation Proc.* 17, 162.
Tuttle, R., Witt, P. N., and Farah, A. (1961). *J. Pharmacol. Exptl. Therap.* 133, 281.
Tuttle, R., Witt, P. N., and Farah, A. (1962). *J. Pharmacol. Exptl. Therap.* 137, 24.
Waser, P. G. (1956). *Cardiologia* 29, 214.
Waser, P. G. (1962). *Experientia* 18, 35.
Waser, P. G. (1963). *Proc. 1st Intern. Pharmacol. Meeting, Stockholm, 1961* 3, 173. Pergamon Press, Oxford.
Waugh, W. H. (1962a). *Circulation Res.* 11, 927.
Waugh, W. H. (1962b). *Circulation Res.* 11, 264.
Waugh, W. H. (1965). *In* "Muscle," Proc. Symp. Univ. of Alberta, Edmonton, Alberta, 1964, p. 253 Pergamon Press, Oxford.
Weidmann, S. (1955). *J. Physiol. (London)* 129, 568.
Weidmann, S. (1956). *J. Physiol. (London)* 132, 157.
Whittam, R. (1962). *Biochem. J.* 84, 110.
Whittam, R., and Ager, M. E. (1962). *Biochim. Biophys. Acta* 65, 383.
Wilbrandt, W., and Koller, H. (1948). *Helv. Physiol. Pharmacol. Acta* 6, 208.
Woodbury, L. A., and Hecht, H. H. (1952). *Circulation* 6, 172.
Wollenberger, A. (1949). *Pharmacol. Rev.* 1, 311.
Wollenberger, A. (1951). *J. Pharmacol. Exptl. Therap.* 103, 123.
Wollenberger, A. (1962). *Proc. Ciba Foundation Symp. Enzymes and Drug Action.* Churchill, London.

CHAPTER 5

CARDIOTONIC ALKALOIDS

I. Introduction

Several groups of alkaloids include substances which exhibit cardiotonic activity. This property, however, is not used significantly in therapeutics since it is in no case as specific as the action of the cardiac glycosides and is associated with many other pharmacological actions both on the heart and generally throughout the body.

The principal alkaloidal groups having cardiotonic activity include the *Erythrophleum* alkaloids which show this most clearly although these substances are too toxic to the heart to be of practical application and are also potent local anesthetics. The structures of the *Erythrophleum* alkaloids show some similarities to those of the cardiac glycosides, and there is good evidence that they act at similar receptor sites.

The *Veratrum* alkaloids show a diverse range of pharmacological properties which appear to be associated with changes in ionic permeability at cell membranes. They show cardiotonic activity but this is not seen in whole animals since it is masked by their more general properties. In isolated heart preparations however, particularly when hypodynamic, the effect is very marked.

Recently, studies have been made of the chemistry and pharmacology of a series of alkaloids from *Voacanga* species by workers in Paris and Brussels. Some of these alkaloids appear to be powerfully cardiotonic on isolated cardiac preparations and on chemically induced failure in whole animals. Pharmacological studies on these substances are very incomplete and clinical observations have so far proved disappointing.

Finally the xanthines are cardiotonic although only feebly so by comparison with other active substances. This effect, again, is of aca-

137

demic interest in so far as it may throw light on the mechanism of cardiotonic activity. The central nervous stimulation and other pharmacological properties of the xanthines overshadow the cardiotonic action.

Very little is known of the mode of action of any of these drugs and very little study has been made of synthetic congeners or chemical modifications to the molecules which could elucidate their more important features. In this chapter these groups of alkaloids are discussed but almost entirely with reference to their cardiotonic properties. Their general pharmacology and therapeutic actions are well described in the major pharmacological texts and review articles.

II. Alkaloids from *Erythrophleum* Species

A. Historical Introduction and Chemical Structure

In 1876 Gallois and Hardy isolated an alkaloid, which they named erythrophleine, from the bark of *Erythrophleum guineense,* a West African tree widely distributed in the equatorial forests. The bark is used by natives as an arrow poison or ordeal drug. Extracts are intensely colored; hence one name for the tree is "red water tree," although it has many native names and is often referred to as "sassy bark."

The related species *E. couminga* was also considered to contain erythrophleine in the leaves and seeds. Gallois and Hardy noted that the drug had a powerful digitalis-like action which was later confirmed by Harnack and Zabrocky (1882) with a sample of amorphous erythrophleine. Later Harnack (1896) repeated these observations using a purer specimen of the alkaloid. Although interest was maintained in the *Erythrophleum* alkaloids it was not until 1935 that Dalma described the isolation of the crystalline alkaloids, cassaine, cassaidine, and norcassaidine, and later Dalma (1939) isolated crystalline coumingine and coumingaine from *E. couminga.*

In 1962 La Barre and co-workers examined the alkaloidal content of *E. ivorense* and isolated in crystalline form a new alkaloid which they named ivorine.

Erythrophleine (Merck) was examined by Blount *et al.* (1940) and considered to be a pure substance, although amorphous. Upon hydrolysis they obtained crystalline erythrophleic acid and β-methylaminoethanol. Cassaine yields β-dimethylaminoethanol and cassaic acid (Faltis and Holzinger, 1939). Coumingine also is an ester of β-dimethylaminoethanol, but cassaic acid and β-hydroxyisovaleric acid are obtained upon hydrolysis. Under mild conditions coumingic acid (β-hydroxyisovalerylcassaic acid) was obtained (Ruzicka *et al.*, 1941).

Upon hydrolysis, ivorine yields ivoric acid and monomethylaminoethanol (La Barre *et al.*, 1962).

Figure 5.1 gives the structural formulas of cassaine and erythrophleine, and for comparison that of ouabain. The structure of ivorine is at present unknown.

The similarity in cardiotonic activity among the cardiac glycosides, the bufotenins, and the *Erythrophleum* alkaloids prompts an examination of their chemical structure for similarities on which their mode of action may depend.

Superficial inspection of the structural formulas* in Fig. 5.1 shows a resemblance between the polycyclic skeletons, as the diterpene structure on which the *Erythrophleum* alkaloids are based is related to the steroid structure and contains three fused cyclohexane rings corresponding to rings A, B, and C of the tetracyclic steroids. The quest for structural analogies is complicated by the fact that the *Erythrophleum* alkaloids lack most of the structural features of the cardiac glycosides and the related toad poisons which are classically regarded as essential for cardioactivity.

The stereochemistry of the steroid nucleus is important. The *cis* fusion of the C and D rings, unique to cardioactive steroids, cannot be repeated in the diterpenes which have no D rings. The methyl substituent on the diterpene C ring, however, has the α-configuration, which makes it analogous to the C-15 atom in the steroid *cis*-oriented D ring. The substituents on the diterpene C ring may be viewed as an open D ring (Fig. 5.2).

The orientation of rings B and C is always *trans*. That of rings A and B is best *cis* in the cardiac glycosides, but activity is not destroyed by

---

* For these views of possible structural considerations the authors are indebted to Dr. Diana M. Temple of the Smith Kline and French Institute in the Department of Pharmacology of the University of Sydney.

inversion at C-5, which confers *trans* orientation upon rings A and B, as in the cardiac glycoside uzarin. Its aglycone, uzarigenin, can be seen to have the same conformation as cassaine (Fig. 5.2).

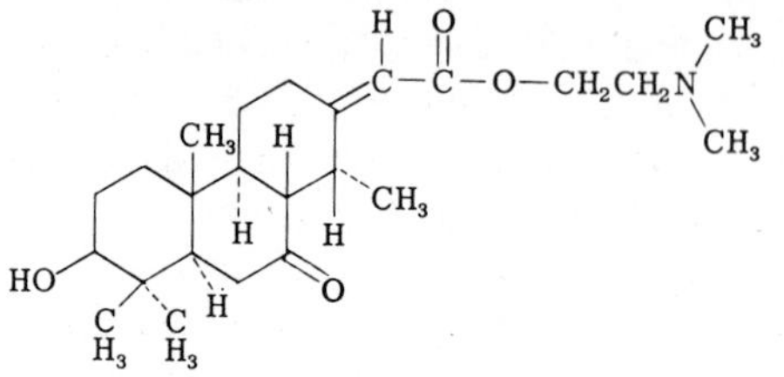

Cassaine

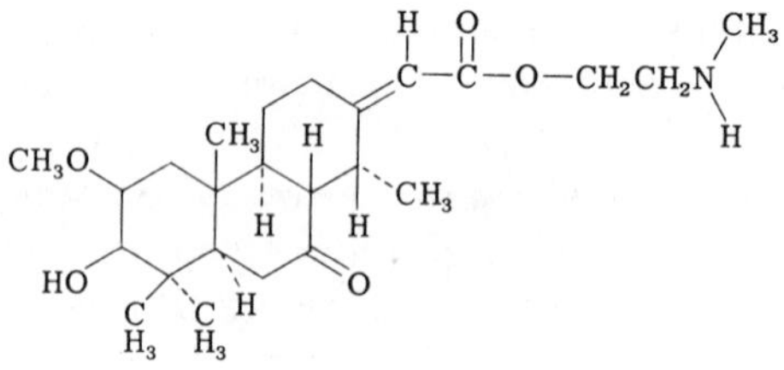

Erythrophleine

Fig. 5.1. Structural formulas of cassaine and erythrophleine in conventional style. The structure of cassaine is now well established, but the position and configuration of the ring constituents of erythrophleine are less certain.

In addition to the stereochemistry of the steroid moeity, other structural features in the cardiac glycosides which appear to be essential for their activity are the following substituents: a β-oriented unsaturated lactone ring in position 17, a 14β-hydroxyl group, and a 3-hydroxyl group which is normally β-oriented; however, the α-epimers do retain some activity. The 3β-hydroxyl group forms a glycoside link with one or more sugar molecules, and while this is necessary for sustained activity, the genins, particularly those from some bufadienolides, also show cardioactivity of short duration.

Some analogies can be found in the *Erythrophleum* alkaloids. The

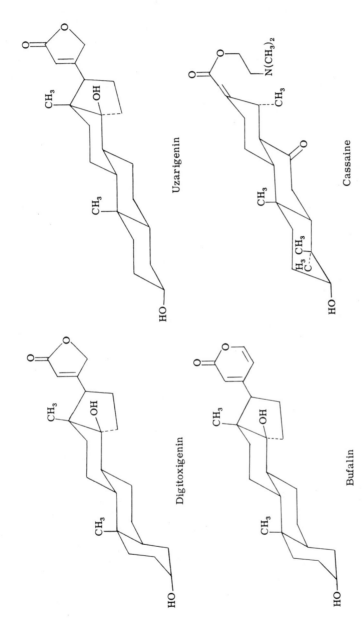

Fig. 5.2. Stereochemistry of the cardenolides and bufadienolides compared with the *Erythrophleum* alkaloids.

unsaturated ester substituent which is common to the whole series occurs in the molecule in a position comparable to the unsaturated cyclic ester (lactone) group of the cardiac glycosides, and in both cases the double bond, essential to activity, is conjugated with the ester carbonyl. The aminoethanol substituent in the *Erythrophleum* ester group is hydrophilic like the sugar substituents in the glycosides and possibly serves a similar function of increasing solubility.

The basic property in which the alkaloids differ from the cardiac glycosides depends on the presence of the aminoethanol group. The importance of the aminoethanol group is illustrated by the following facts. Hydrolysis of these alkaloids to the corresponding acids destroys their activity (Maling and Krayer, 1946). La Barre (1961) found that esterification of the alkaloid voacamine with dimethylaminoethanol enhances its activity; Ruzicka *et al.* (1941) esterified bile acids with diethylaminoethanol to give slight digitalis-like activity in spite of the profound differences between the steroid functions of digitalis and the bile acids. Acetylation and propionylation of hydroxyl groups in cardenolides show that ester groups themselves enhance cardio-activity.

The 14-hydroxyl group of the cardiac glycosides, the β-orientation of which is determined by the *cis* fusion, has no parallel in the *Erythrophleum* alkaloids. Recently, however, there has been some doubt about the essential nature of this hydroxyl substituent since the finding of cardiotonic activity in bufadienolides such as cinobufagin and marinobufagin in which the 14β-hydroxyl is replaced by the $14\beta-15\beta$-epoxide ring.

The 3β-hydroxyl group present in the *Erythrophleum* alkaloids is directly comparable with the 3β-hydroxyl group of the cardiac aglycones. Also present in both series is the β-methyl substituent between rings A and B. The two methyl substituents in ring A of cassaine and the ketone group in ring B may perhaps be regarded as diterpene characteristics having no direct bearing on the cardioactivity of the molecule, in the same way that the hydroxyl substituents of ouabain or the aldehyde group of cymarin are not essential to cardiotonic activity.

Despite some important differences there would seem to be sufficient structural resemblance between these two groups to explain their comparable activity on heart muscle. It seems likely that both groups act by affecting the balance of cation transport, perhaps by way of the enzyme adenosinetriphosphatase (ATPase). The observation by Bonting and associates (1964) that ouabain and erythrophleine have parallel inhibitory action on Na-K-activated ATPase, reversed in both cases by K^+ but not by Mg^{++}, prompts the speculation that a similar association may occur between *Digitalis* and *Erythrophleum* compounds and the carrier system.

Portius and Repke (1964a,b) proposed that ionic transport ATPase is a digitalis receptor, and they suggested a structural basis for the activity of a series of compounds which inhibit ATPase. The effective group for binding to the receptor is alleged to be a carbonyl group conjugated with a double bond as in the digitalis lactone ring and the *Erythrophleum* side chain. This group is presumed to form a hydrogen bond with a hydroxyl group in the phosphorylated enzyme intermediate, thus preventing access of K^+. The steroid and diterpene ring structures were described as fixing groups. The distance between the carbonyl oxygen and the 3-hydroxyl group was measured in stereomodels and shown to be approximately 12 Å in many active inhibitors. Compounds tested by Portius and Repke for percentage inhibition of the enzyme included cardenolides and bufadienolides, some steroid hormones, and *Erythrophleum* and *Veratrum* alkaloids.

The possible mechanism of a sodium pump involving Na-K-activated ATPase bound to a cell membrane was discussed by Opit and Charnock (1965). They alleged that ouabain inhibits the decomposition, which is normally stimulated by K^+ but not by Na^+, of a phosphorylated enzyme-protein complex. A conformational structural diagram depicted ouabain with a hydrophilic surface which could form hydrogen bonds with the protein-ATPase membrane surface.

B. Pharmacology

Power and Salway (1912) fractionated extracts of the bark of *E. guineense* and they described the properties observed by Sir Henry Dale who noted continuous vomiting in dogs and a marked slowing of the heart. The alkaloid which Power and Salway isolated produced similar effects to the crude extract: 1 mg caused cardiac slowing, 2 mg a more marked effect with convulsions and death in half an hour. Dale reported a rise in blood pressure and typical digitalis-like action in pithed cats.

Chen *et al.* (1936) compared the effects of intravenous infusion of erythrophleine sulfate with those of a number of cardiac glycosides and showed that the electrocardiographic changes induced in the cat were similar. Prolongation of the P-R interval was seen together with AV dissociation and ectopic rhythm finally followed by systolic arrest. Nausea and vomiting occurred with erythrophleine, and the mean lethal dose for cardiac arrest was 0.37 mg per kilogram compared with 0.33 mg per kilogram for digoxin and 0.12 mg per kilogram for ouabain. It was also shown that the effects of erythrophleine are persistent since a smaller second dose, given 1–7 days after a first emetic dose, was required to cause cardiac arrest than in animals not previously given the drug. Perfusion into frogs via the inferior vena cava cause AV dissociation and systolic arrest; again this is similar to the action of the cardiac glycosides.

Chen *et al.* (1938a) compared the activity of several *Erythrophleum* alkaloids with respect to the cat cardiac arresting dose, the emetic dose, and the local anesthetic effect in guinea pigs. Coumingine was shown to be the most potent of the alkaloids, erythrophleine next, and coumingaine, norcassaidine, cassaine, homophleine, and acetyl cassaine were weaker in that order.

It had been noted that the toad is more resistant to the cardiac glycosides than the frog. Chen *et al.* (1938b) compared ouabain, cymarin, and coumingine by determining the lethal doses in the toad, *Bufo valliceps,* and the frog, *Rana pipiens.* They found the toad to be 77 times less sensitive to ouabain, 167 times less sensitive to cymarin, and 58 times less sensitive to coumingine, again supporting a similarity of action between coumingine and the cardiac glycosides.

The *Erythrophleum* alkaloids have been examined for their effect on the heart-lung preparation in dogs by Maling and Krayer (1946) using cassaine, norcassaidine, erythrophleine, and coumingine. They found that they all have a characteristic positive inotropic effect which resulted in improved work output of the heart and they also showed effects upon heart rate and the development of cardiac irregularities. Differences were observed in the ratio of the minimum dosages leading to cardiac irregularities to those which produced a positive inotropic effect. In the normal heart norcassaidine, cassaine, and erythrophleine caused a decrease in the diastolic volume of the ventricles without any marked change in systemic output. When failure was present, either naturally occurring or induced by the addition of a barbiturate to the blood, these alkaloids increased the systemic output nearly to the value before the onset of failure. The onset of the inotropic effect was not immediate but reached a maximum after 5 to 15 minutes and the effect was of long duration, 30–45 minutes. Norcassaidine was more potent than cassaine or erythrophleine although positive inotropic effects were observed with all three alkaloids with concentrations of approximately 0.5 mg per liter in blood. With erythrophleine the concentration of the alkaloid required to produce full restoration of performance in the failing heart was very close to that causing cardiac irregularity. Coumingine also, although more potent than the other alkaloids, required doses very near to those producing irregularities in order to give a full inotropic effect. On the electrocardiogram toxic doses of the alkaloids caused slowing of the heart, a prolonged P-R interval, and AV block. There was increased excitability of the ventricles since ectopic beats were often seen. The irregularities were persistent and continued until the end of the experiments. In these experiments Maling and Krayer also included erythrophleic acid but they found this to be inactive both on cardiac performance and the electrocardiogram even with doses up to 61 mg per liter of blood.

Wedd and Blair (1951) pointed out that Maling and Krayer's demonstration that the predominant effect of *Erythrophleum* alkaloids was to decrease diastolic volume and their opinion that this was not considered to be adequate evidence that the *Erythrophleum* alkaloids were digitalis-like in congestive failure indicated that differences between the two groups of drugs should be further studied. Using isolated turtle auricle strips, Wedd and Blair found that slowing or arrest could result for up to 1 hour after the drug was given. The strips showed diastolic shortening which was irreversible and some lengthening of the refractory period. Since they considered that the criteria for cardiac glycoside activity was a shortening of the refractory period without impairment of contractility, this impairment with the *Erythrophleum* alkaloid, coumingine, showed that this drug could not be considered as showing characteristic cardiac glycoside activity.

Krayer and his colleagues concluded that the ester nature of the *Erythrophleum* alkaloids was essential for the cardiac activity, and examinations were later made (Farah and Krayer, 1946; Krayer *et al.*, 1946) of the effects of β-dimethylaminoethanol, β-methylaminoethanol, and related substances on the heart-lung preparation. All three substances were shown to produce a positive inotropic effect but doses between 60–800 mg per liter were needed. These bases did not produce an effect upon heart rate neither did they show a latent period of onset as was seen with the cardiac glycosides or the *Erythrophleum* alkaloids.

Uhle and colleagues (1956) studied a series of closely related synthetic alkanolamine esters in order to ascertain the structural elements responsible for the much greater action of the *Erythrophleum* alkaloids compared with dimethylaminoethanol on the failing heart. They used the dog heart-lung method and showed that esters of succinic, glutaric, pimelic, and adipic acids had a positive inotropic effect five to ten times greater than that of dimethylaminoethanol. Dimethylaminoethyl pimelate appeared to be the most active member of the dibasic acid series. In a typical experiment 10 mg gave an effect comparable with that produced by 34 mg of dimethylaminoethanol which on a molar basis gives a ratio of 0.052 of the ester to 0.380 milliequivalents of the base. Out of 26 synthetic esters examined in this series, only 4 showed clear activity and two doubtful activity.

The pharmacology of ivorine has been investigated by La Barre *et al.* (1962), and it has been shown to have very strong cardiotonic properties. On the isolated rabbit auricle it was shown that a similar cardiotonic effect was produced with 0.5 μg of ivorine sulfate or with 0.06 mg of digitoxin. La Barre *et al.* (1955) showed that aminophylline, presumed to be due to its ethylenediamine content, enhanced the potency of digitoxin or strophanthin on the isolated auricle. This effect was not observed with ivorine and aminophylline, and the authors attribute this to greater ease of penetration into the muscle due to the methylaminoethanol in the ester composition of ivorine, whereas molecules of cardiac glycosides penetrate more readily in the presence of aminophylline. In cats in which a critically low blood pressure had been produced by intravenous administration of a barbiturate, ivorine produced a marked analeptic effect on the circulatory system with a dose of 2 μg. Emesis in pigeons is produced only with very large doses of ivorine and appears not to exhibit this effect to any significant extent.

The acute toxicity in guinea pigs determined by continuous intravenous injection after the manner of the usual assay for digitalis preparations was found to be 6 mg per kilogram compared with 2.4 mg per kilogram for digitoxin. No clinical reports appear to be available due to shortage of pure ivorine for this purpose.

C. Mode of Action of *Erythrophleum* Alkaloids

Flacke (1959) studied the antagonism of the veratrine response of the frog sartorius muscle by cardiac glycosides and *Erythrophleum* alkaloids and showed that the latter caused changes in this response similar to those produced by cardiac glycosides. When veratrine is applied to the frog sartorius muscle it causes after-contraction follow- ing the twitch resulting from electrical stimulation. If cardiac glyco- sides are applied before the veratrine the after-contraction develops for the first few stimulation periods after veratrine application but instead of being maintained this response decreases progressively and may even be completely abolished with appropriate concentrations of the glycosides. This action was first observed by Krayer and George (1951) and was shown to be produced by the cardiac glycoside group as a whole and by bufotoxin (Arora, 1953). This antiveratrine effect paralleled the positive inotropic action, and Arora suggested that it involves similar stereochemical configurations in the cardiac glycoside molecules. Cassaine, cassaidine, erythrophleine, coumingine, and acetylcassaine all antagonized the veratrine response to varying de- grees in concentrations of the order of 1 : 100,000 to 1 : 300,000.

Dimethylaminoethanol had only a weak antiveratrinic effect in con- centrations of 1 : 3000 whereas cassainic acid and cassaidinic acid were inactive. Dimethylaminoethyl pimelate was more potent and produced almost complete abolition of the response in a concentration of 1 : 20,000. These results parallel very closely the positive inotropic effects of these drugs. It seems very probable that the site of action of these *Erythrophleum* alkaloids and related compounds is largely at the cell membrane and is probably the result of changes in ionic permea- bility qualitatively similar to those shown to occur with the cardiac glycosides (discussed in Chapter 3).

Further support of the idea that the *Erythrophleum* alkaloids act in a manner similar to that of the cardiac glycosides at the cell membrane is given by the work of Bonting and co-workers (1964). They studied the inibition of Na-K-activated ATPase *in vitro* by *Erythrophleum* alkaloids. A digitalis-sensitive Na-K-activated ATPase system was first described by Skou (1957, 1960), and Bonting *et al.* investigated erythrophleine and cassaine in comparison with ouabain on Na-K-activated ATPase of rabbit brain, kidney, ciliary body, and cat choroid plexus. Erythrophleine inhibited the enzyme completely at $10^{-4}M$ concentration, and cassaine inhibited it by 86%. The inhibition curves had the same general shape as that for ouabain which was of a similar order of potency. The inhibition curves which these workers obtained are given in Fig. 5.3.

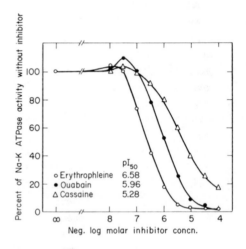

Fig. 5.3. Inhibition curves of rabbit brain Na-K ATPase for ouabain, erythrophleine, and cassaine. The negative logarithms of the half-maximal inhibition concentrations are listed in the bottom left corner (Bonting *et al.*, 1964).

A very interesting observation was that all three drugs stimulated the Na-K-activated ATPase system with much smaller concentrations, and this has also been noted by Repke (1963) in studying the influence of cardiac glycosides on Na-K-activated ATPase from guinea pig cardiac muscle (see Chapter 4).

Evidence is thus accumulating that the mode of action of the positive inotropic properties of the *Erythrophleum* alkaloids may be fundamentally similar to that of the cardiac glycosides especially with respect to the chronotropic effects of the latter.

As is to be expected from their ester structure they do show quite potent local anesthetic activity and in fact cassaine sulfate has been used as a dental local anesthetic. It would be of considerable interest to study the inotropic actions of analogs of the acids to which other basic side chains were attached with possibly a closer stereochemical similarity to the cardiac aglycones. These alkaloids and particularly synthetic analogs are clearly worthy of further study.

III. The *Veratrum* Alkaloids

A. Sources and Alkaloids

The *Veratrum* alkaloids are glyco- and ester-alkaloids obtained from plants of the Liliaceae; the principal sources are *Veratrum album,* the white hellebore; *Veratrum viride,* the green hellebore; *Schoenocaulon officinale,* the cevadilla or sabadilla, and *Zygadenus venesosus.* The occurrence, isolation, and chemical properties of the *Veratrum* alkaloids have been described in a review by Prelog and Jeger (1953), and Table 5.1, reproduced from this work, gives the names of the alkaloids, their alkamines, and the esterifying acid or sugar.

Veratrosine was isolated from *Veratrum viride* and it also occurs in *Veratrum album* where it is accompanied by pseudojervine. Cevadine is the most abundant alkaloid in *Schoenocaulon officinale* and has been termed veratrine. The name veratrine also has been used for the total alkaloids of *Schoenocaulon.* Veratridine is the second alkaloid quantitatively, in this species. Protoveratridine, germerine, germidine, protoveratrine, and neogermitrine have all been found in either *Veratrum album* or *Veratrum viride,* or both. From *Zygadenus venenosus* germine, zygadenine, and two ester alkaloids, veratroylzygadenine and vanilloylzygadenine have also been isolated, and from *Veratrum eshcholtzii* a further new alkaloid, escholerine, has been obtained.

B. Pharmacology

1. General Properties

The alkaloids from *Veratrum album* and *Veratrum viride* are hypotensive as a result of general vasomotor inhibition of central origin together with reflex bradycardia and inhibitory vasomotor reflexes from the carotid sinus, aorta, and pulmonary artery. The latter con-

5. Cardiotonic Alkaloids

stitutes the well-known Bezold-Jarisch reflex. Veratrum does not interfere with the hypertensive response to adrenaline or sympathetic stimulation and hence shows no adrenolytic or sympatholytic properties. The tertiary ester alkaloids have a weak digitalis-like action on the

Table 5.1

The Composition of the Glyco- and Ester-Alkaloids of *Veratrum*
and of Related Genera[a]

Glycoalkaloid	Alkamine	Sugar
Veratrosine	Veratramine	D-Glucose
$C_{33}H_{49}O_7N$	$C_{27}H_{39}O_2N$	
Pseudojervine	Isojervine	D-Glucose
$C_{33}H_{49}O_8N$	$C_{27}H_{39}O_3N$	

Ester-alkaloid	Alkamine	Acid
Cevadine	Cevagenine or Cevine	Angelic
$C_{32}H_{49}O_9N$	$C_{27}H_{43}O_8N$	
Veratridine	Cevagenine or Cevine	Veratric
$C_{36}H_{51}O_{11}N$	$C_{27}H_{43}O_8N$	
Protoveratridine	Germine	D-(−)-α-Methylbutyric
$C_{31}H_{49}O_9N$	$C_{27}H_{43}O_8N$	
Germerine	Germine	D-(−)-α-Methylbutyric
$C_{37}H_{59}O_{11}N$	$C_{27}H_{43}O_8N$	(+)-α-Oxy-α-methylbutyric
Germidine	Germine	Acetic,
$C_{34}H_{53}O_{10}N$	$C_{27}H_{43}O_8N$	D-(−)-α-Methylbutyric
Neogermitrine	Germine	2 Moles Acetic,
(Alkaloid A)	$C_{27}H_{43}O_8N$	D-(−)-α-Methylbutyric
$C_{36}H_{55}O_{11}N$		
Germitrine	Germine	Acetic,
$C_{39}H_{61}O_{12}N$	$C_{27}H_{43}O_8N$	D-(−)-α-Methylbutyric,
		(+)-α-Oxy-α-methylbutyric
Protoveratrine	Protoverine	Acetic,
$C_{39}H_{61}O_{13}N$	$C_{27}H_{43}O_9N$	D-(−)-α-Methylbutyric,
		(+)-α-Oxy-α-methylbutyric
Veratroylzygadenine	Zygadenine	Veratric
$C_{36}H_{51}O_{10}N$	$C_{27}H_{43}O_7N$	
Vanilloylzygadenine	Zygadenine	Vanillic
$C_{35}H_{49}O_{10}N$	$C_{27}H_{43}O_7N$	
Escholerine	Protoverine	Acetic,
$C_{41}H_{63}O_{13}N$	$C_{27}H_{43}O_9N$	α-Methylbutyric

[a] From Prelog and Jeger (1953).

myocardium with positive inotropic effects followed by tachycardia and arrhythmias. This probably is insignificant with clinical doses. The alkaloids from *Schoenocaulon officinale,* cevadine and veratridine, produce a characteristic prolonged contracture of skeletal muscle, the Bezold effect, and stronger cardiotonic actions on the isolated heart. The pharmacology of the *Veratrum* alkaloids has been reviewed by Krayer and Acheson (1946); this work still constitutes the main source of general reference on these drugs.

2. Cardiotonic Effects

As early as 1903, Straub observed increased force of contraction with veratrine applied to the isolated heart of *Aplysia limacina*. Studies on the isolated frog heart by Ransom (1917) and McCartney and Ransom (1917) showed that veratrine in the absence of Ca^{++} caused an increase in the amplitude of ventricular contraction. This has been confirmed by Richter (1940) who showed that if the Ca^{++} content of the perfusion fluid is reduced to one third the normal value veratrine will completely restore the contraction of the heart to normal.

Krayer *et al.* (1944) perfused frog hearts with a solution containing one half the normal Ca^{++} content and showed that the pure alkaloids veratridine or protoveratrine were both capable of restoring the normal cardiac output without changing the rate or causing arrythmias. Concentrations of the order of 1×10^{-7} were used. The alkamine base, cevine, was much less potent and a concentration of 2×10^{-4} was necessary to restore the heart.

A number of the early investigators studied the effects of the *Veratrum* alkaloids on the mammalian heart and in all cases veratrine produced a marked increase in the amplitude of contraction.

In 1942 Krayer and Mendez showed that veratrine, the mixed alkaloids of *Schoenocaulon officinale,* had a digitalis-like effect upon the heart-lung preparation in the dog, and Moe and Krayer (1943) continued these studies using pure veratridine and the alkamine base cevine which is derived from it. Using the denervated heart-lung preparation of the dog in a state of failure, either spontaneously occurring or produced by the use of pentobarbitone, it was shown that the failure was reversed by veratridine. Very little effect was seen in preparations in which failure was absent. The pure alkaloid veratridine was slightly more powerful than the mixed alkaloids, veratrine. Cevine was very much less active having a therapeutic potency smaller than 1/3000 that of veratridine.

Veratric acid was also tested and no effect was observed in doses up to 100 mg whereas the smallest effective dose of veratridine was 0.05 mg in a blood volume of approximately 800 ml. It was shown that the ester structure was essential for the cardiac action and that the alkamine or acid was ineffective. Krayer and Mendez (1942) made the point that unless the heart is in a failing state, the positive inotropic effect is not seen and no consistent effects on rate, mean arterial pressure, systemic output, coronary flow, or pulmonary arterial pressure were seen in the dog heart-lung preparation with doses even as high as 0.5 mg of veratrine although there was a slight decrease in right and left auricular pressures, and the increase in pressure caused by raising the venous reservoir was smaller than that in the absence of veratrine. They found that veratrine was capable of restoring quite severe heart failure causing marked increase in systemic output, increased coronary flow, decreased auricular pressure, and a marked reduction in the size of the heart. The reduction of diastolic volume could have been partly due to a diminution of the resistance of the pulmonary circuit caused directly by the drug and the resultant fall in pulmonary arterial pressure. Krayer *et al.* considered that the pulmonary arterial pressure changes could have been fully accounted for by the positive inotropic action on the heart alone and that decreased pulmonary resistance was not a major factor.

Protoveratrine, the most potent of the veratrum alkaloids, produced a positive inotropic effect in the heart-lung preparation with as little as 0.005 mg (Krayer *et al.*, 1944), and when a dose of this substance fails to produce a positive effect a dose of veratridine is still effective. The site of action of these two drugs would therefore appear to be somewhat different.

3. Mode of Action

Veratrine produces a characteristic contracture of frog skeletal muscle after electrical stimulation of a single twitch, and this effect is influenced by a number of agencies which affect muscular contraction.

The contracture is diminished by increased extracellular K^+ and increased by Ca^{++} although high doses abolish it altogether.

This "veratrine response," as it is often termed, was antagonized by cardiac glycosides (Arora, 1953) and by *Erythrophleum* alkaloids and was considered by Bacq (1939) to be the result of the alkaloid sensitizing the muscle to K^+ since after bathing frog skeletal muscle in a 1×10^{-7} concentration of veratrine the muscle contracted to dilutions of KCl which ordinarily were without effect. The action of veratrine on motor nerve fibers resembled its effect upon muscle, and Shanes (1951) has shown that the loss of K^+ during stimulation of the frog sciatic nerve was doubled in the presence of veratrine.

IV. Alkaloids from *Voacanga* Species

A. Sources and Chemistry

Two species of *Voacanga, Voacanga africana* and *Voacanga chalotiana,* have been studied as sources of cardiotonic alkaloids. These are bushes or small trees which belong to the Apocynaceae and are indigenous to Africa. Janot and Goutarel (1955a,b,c, 1956) isolated several different alkaloids in crystalline form, and their pharmacology has been described by Quevauviller *et al.* (1955). La Barre and Gillo (1955) isolated two other alkaloids which they named voacangine and voacanginine, but the latter proved to be the same as voacamine isolated previously. La Barre and Gillo (1956) isolated voacaline, and Martin *et al.* (1960) isolated a further new alkaloid voachalotine from *Voacanga chalotiana.* The six alkaloids now known are summarized in Table 5.2 [from the review of La Barre (1961)] together with their melting points.

B. Pharmacology

The pharmacology of voacamine, voacaline, and voachalotine has been described by La Barre (1961) although there is here a concentration on cardiotonic properties, a general examination does not appear to have been published.

1. Voacamine

There is increased amplitude of contraction of the isolated rabbit auricle after the addition of voacamine, and it was shown that 0.1 mg of voacamine sulfate produces an effect similar to 0.06 mg of digitaline (digitoxin).

Table 5.2
The Alkaloids from *Voacanga africana*[a]

Alkaloid	Empirical formula	Melting point
Voacangine	$C_{22}H_{28}O_3N_2$	137–138°
Voacamine	$C_{44}H_{50}O_6N_4$	219–221°
Voacaminine	$C_{44}H_{50}O_6N_4$	240–242°
Vobtusine	$C_{21}H_{20}O_3N_2$	286°
Voacaline	$C_{41}H_{50}O_6N_4$	280–285°
Voachalotine	$C_{22}H_{26}O_3N_2$	223–224°

[a] La Barre (1961).

It is not possible to be certain of the concentration of the drug since the capacity of the bath is not stated although a 50 ml bath is referred to in other similar experiments. The effect was reversed after two or three washes and it apparently was more easily removed than digitoxin from the heart muscle. If the drug was left in contact with the muscle the effect persisted for at least 45 minutes. In the cat anesthetized with chloralose, doses of 50 mg per kilogram did not produce cardiac slowing unlike digitalis. It has been suggested that voacamine also has the property of depressing vagal centers since it produces a similar decline in sensitivity to that of small doses of barbiturates. Voacamine sulfate was also shown to act synergistically with strophanthin with a marked increase in the bradycardia produced by the latter.

2. Voacaline

Voacaline was shown to be approximately equipotent with voacamine in its cardiotonic action but at the same time was much less toxic. It is claimed to be very long acting on the heart but readily removed on washing.

3. Voachalotine

Voachalotine is of approximately the same potency as voacamine on the isolated rabbit auricle but it differs in the degree to which it is fixed to the heart muscle. Voachalotine required a considerable number of washes to reverse its effect. When voachalotine was incubated at 37°C in horse serum for half an hour no cardiotonic effect was seen on the isolated auricle, and it is interpreted that this alkaloid binds very readily to proteins and hence produces such a persistent cardiotonic effect.

When cats were anesthetized with chloralose and given a slow intravenous injection of a large dose of pentobarbitone until the blood pressure fell to 20 mm Hg, a dose of 10 mg per kilogram of voachalotine produced an immediate cardiac stimulant effect and a rise of blood pressure. Since the dose of pentobarbitone was given over a very short period of time a number of animals would survive a fall of blood pressure of this order as soon as the depressant drug had become more widely dispersed throughout the body. In a study of analeptic drugs Thorp (1947) studied this effect and used continuous intravenous infusion of a barbiturate to induce circulatory collapse over several minutes. This would appear to be a preferable technique. This effect was also seen with voacamine but the voachalotine effect was stronger.

The intravenous toxicity of these alkaloids was determined by intravenous infusion in guinea pigs over a period of 12–15 minutes together with electrocardiographic recording. The values obtained were between 60 and 350 mg per kilogram and it was found that these alkaloids are less toxic than digitaline (digitoxin) or strophanthin where the doses in the same experimental series were 2.5 and 0.9 mg per kilogram, respectively. Since the cardiotonic doses on the isolated auricles were very similar it was suggested that these alkaloids have a far higher "coefficient of efficacy" than digitalis (La Barre, 1961). No measurements of cardiotonic effects in whole animals appear to have been made and therefore such a conclusion would appear to need further justification.

4. Voacaminate of Dimethylaminoethanol

La Barre and Gillo (1960) formed a compound of dimethylaminoethanol and voacamine on the analogy of the importance this group has in the activity of the *Erythrophleum* alkaloids. The resulting substance was readily water-soluble and appeared to be of similar cardiotonic activity to voacamine but to have a persistent action like voachalotine. It was also bound by horse serum in a similar manner.

The compound did not exhibit pressor effects nor did it show any central nervous sedative action in unanesthetized dogs. In the anesthetized cat with the blood pressure reduced to a critical level with pentobarbitone there was a powerful analeptic effect which was considered to be due to its cardiotonic action.

Fish *et al.* (1960) also have studied the chemistry of the *Voacanga* alkaloids, and in a discussion after this paper it was reported that several workers had been unable to show the cardiotonic effects reported by La Barre (1961). Samples of voacamine, voacangine, and voacorine prepared by Dr. Poisson have been examined in our laboratories on the isolated guinea pig auricles and upon the cat papillary muscles, and no significant cardiotonic effects were observed with concentrations up to 10^{-5} gm per liter. When the concentration was increased to $4–6 \times 10^{-5}$ gm per liter the guinea pig auricle preparation was depressed.

Clinical studies by Percheron (1959) with several of the alkaloids of *Voacanga* have been rather disappointing but it is clear that this group of alkaloids should receive further study.

V. The Xanthines, Purines, and Nucleotides

A. The Effects of the Xanthines on Cardiac Contractility

The xanthines, caffeine, theophylline, and theobromine, act on the heart and blood vessels both directly and by virtue of central nervous action. These drugs exhibit a number of reasonably distinct actions. With small doses the most predominant effect is that of increased excitability of the central nervous system resulting in wakefulness and stimulation of the medullary centers. With larger doses reflexes are enhanced and tetanic convulsions may ensue. Vasodilatation is observed from a direct action on the blood vessels and cardiac stimulation is seen with increased heart rate and force of contraction. These effects are the result of action upon the musculature of the heart and blood vessels, and analogous effects are also seen on skeletal muscle which exhibits increased contractility progressing to spasm and rigor. These substances are also diuretics which is a result of the interaction of several different mechanisms.

Caffeine is the most potent central nervous stimulant of the three common xanthines; theobromine and theophylline show stronger peripheral effects and less central stimulant actions. In very large doses in experimental animals caffeine produces a characteristic contracture of skeletal muscle which has been the subject of study for the information it has yielded on the mechanisms of muscular contraction although it is not of clinical significance.

The study of the xanthines has been most frequently pursued using caffeine as the typical member, presumably since this is the active alkaloid in so many beverages whereas theophylline and theobromine are much less common. Consequently the properties of theophylline and theobromine have been less thoroughly documented. Pilcher (1912) studied the action of caffeine on the isolated heart and found that intravenous injection was without effect with doses less than 10 mg per kilogram. Between 10 and 20 mg per kilogram there was an increase in heart rate and amplitude and a rise of blood pressure. Doses larger than this caused progressively a fall in blood pressure and toxic effects on the heart with decreased amplitude, increased diastolic volume, and decreased amplitude of contraction. Upon intravenous injection of small doses of caffeine there is a temporary depression of the myocardium followed by a rise of blood pressure as the local concentration lessens and myocardial stimulation takes place. Heathcote (1920) extended these studies by investigating the effects of caffeine, theobromine, and theophylline on the hearts of frogs and rabbits.

Theophylline, in a 1 in 1500 concentration, produced a brief decrease in the amplitude of contraction in the isolated frog heart followed by a well-marked and sustained increase in amplitude until the preparation was washed with fresh Ringer's solution. An increased rate of beating was also observed. The lower limit of dilution of any of the three xanthines was between 1 in 5000 to 1 in 10,000 and recovery on washing was complete. A 1 in 5000 dilution of either caffeine, theobromine, or theophylline produced in the isolated rabbit heart in the Langendorff preparation a marked increase in amplitude of contraction and acceleration but the effect of theobromine on the amplitude was the most pronounced of the three and was observed with dilutions of 1 in 40,000 at which concentration caffeine was without effect. Theophylline was the second drug in order of activity. All three drugs increased coronary flow but caffeine was the weakest in this respect and theobromine was the most active.

Cheney (1935) also has studied the effects of caffeine on heart muscle using spontaneously beating sinoauricular strips from the large bullfrog, *Rana catesbiana,* and has showed that in concentrations of 1 in 4000 to 1 in 500 there was increased amplitude of contraction without any other effects upon the tissue initiating cardiac activity.

The action of caffeine in producing contracture of skeletal muscle has been studied by Axelsson and Thesleff (1958) and by Frank (1962), and it has been shown that this process is intimately associated with the intracellular Ca^{++} concentration. If skeletal muscle is kept for a time in Ca^{++}-free solution the contracture, which can be induced by K^+, disappears. Such a muscle, however, will still give a contracture in a solution containing caffeine but upon repeating the contracture responses will become less and less until after four or five such tries contracture is no longer seen. When the muscle from this experiment is placed in a solution containing Ca^{++} the contracture response is restored. Caffeine causes increased efflux of Ca^{++} from skeletal muscle when placed in Ca^{++}-free solutions (Bianchi, 1961), and the same applies to the muscle of the toad ventricle (Nayler, 1963). These results are consistent with the hypothesis put forward by Frank (1962) that caffeine releases Ca^{++} from a binding site in the muscle, extracellular Ca^{++} not being needed to support the caffeine contracture of skeletal muscle but to replace the loss of Ca^{++} from the cellular binding sites.

De Gubareff and Sleator (1965) investigated the actions of caffeine on the isolated atria of guinea pigs and studied the interaction of this substance with Ca^{++} and adenosine. Since it seemed probable that at least part of the cardiotonic action of caffeine might be due to the release of noradrenaline, the studies were also made upon atria taken from animals previously depleted of noradrenaline by the administration of reserpine.

Both the normal and reserpinized atria responded with increased contraction in solutions containing caffeine until a concentration of 2.5 m*M* was reached after which the amplitude of contraction declined (isotonic recording), and the developed tension in isometric

recording behaved similarly. Action potentials showed little change in
the rate of rise but showed a progressive increase in the duration of the
plateau with increasing concentrations of caffeine. This increase continued with concentrations of caffeine high enough to depress the contractile response. These results are shown in Fig. 5.4. The differences

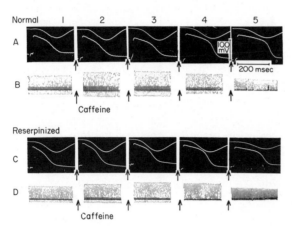

Fig. 5.4. The effects of caffeine on the action potentials of normal (A and B) and reserpinized (C and D) left atria of guinea pigs; caffeine was added stepwise (at arrows) at
concentrations of 0.25, 1.5, 2.5, and 5.0 mM to all preparations. A, (upper trace), isometric contractions (tension increase downward); (lower trace), transmembrane action
potentials (AP). Each AP in the row was from a different impalement and different cell.
The minute uncontrolled differences in the impalement are responsible for the differences
of AP height. B, isotonic contractions; C, isometric contractions and AP's (as in A); D,
isotonic contractions (de Gubareff and Sleator, 1965).

between normal and reserpinized atria were small and could be explained by individual variations from one preparation to another. There
was certainly no strong evidence that the enhanced responses in the
normal atria were the result of noradrenaline release. When experiments were made in different ionic concentrations of Ca^{++} it was found
that caffeine increased the contractility in solutions of normal (2.5 mM)
or low (0.25, 0.83 mM) concentrations of Ca^{++} but was purely depressant at high (7.5 mM) concentration. The concentration of caffeine
at which the effect changed from a stimulant to a depressant one increased as the Ca^{++} concentration was reduced.

Upon changing the frequency of stimulation from 1 per second to 1 per 10 seconds a decrease in the force of contraction is seen in the normal atria. In high concentrations (7.5 mM) of Ca^{++} the force of contraction is maintained or even increased when the frequency of stimulation is slowed. The concentration of caffeine in these experiments would have been strongly depressant at the normal stimulation rate (1 per second) in the presence of this increased Ca^{++} concentration.

Adenosine produces effects on cardiac muscle which resemble those of acetylcholine: the duration of the action potential is markedly reduced and the contractility is reduced or even abolished. The effects of acetylcholine are rapidly reversed by atropine whereas those of adenosine are unaffected. Caffeine, however, reverses the effects of adenosine and restores the atrium to its normal state but caffeine is without effect on the response to acetylcholine. These responses are similar both in normal and reserpinized atria. Figure 5.5. shows the results of such an experiment.

In discussing their work de Gubareff and Sleator came to the conclusion that the release of noradrenaline is certainly not the primary mode of action of caffeine for which they gave a number of reasons. The effects of adrenaline and caffeine on the action potential are qualitatively different: adrenaline causes a very great increase in contraction strength whereas with caffeine the increase is never more than 45%. The effects of caffeine on the action potential are greater than would result from a maximal dose of adrenaline or noradrenaline and with procedures known to release noradrenaline the effects of added noradrenaline can be duplicated up to concentrations which will double the contractility of the muscle.

The antagonism between adenosine and caffeine could be explained by their structural similarity since the nucleotides adenosine monophosphate (AMP), 3',5'-cyclic AMP, adenosine diphosphate (ADP), and adenosine triphosphate (ATP) act like adenosine on the atria and are also antagonized by caffeine. The shortening of the action potential plateau by adenosine is probably the result of inhibition or abolition of the decrease in K^+ conductance which occurs at the time so that adenosine increases K^+ conductance and caffeine does the reverse.

The interaction of caffeine and Ca^{++} can probably best be explained by postulating that caffeine releases bound Ca^{++} and may also change the sensitivity of a receptor site for Ca^{++} so that in low concentrations of Ca^{++} some local Ca^{++} release takes place and this is sufficient for augmented contraction to occur. With high concentrations of Ca^{++} depression of contractility is seen in the absence of caffeine when the Ca^{++} concentration is still further increased; both observations being compatible with caffeine increasing the sensitivity to Ca^{++}.

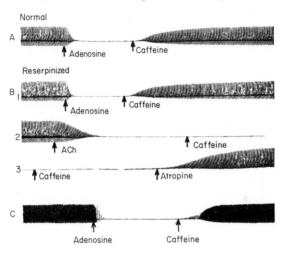

Fig. 5.5. Effect of caffeine on guinea pig atria treated with adenosine and acetylcholine (ACh). Arrows indicate times of addition of each substance. A. Normal left atrium stimulated 1 per second under standard experimental conditions, isotonic contraction. At arrow 0.1 mM adenosine was added. After full effect, 1.5 mM caffeine was added. B. Reserpinized left atrium isotonically contracting. (1) After full effect of 0.07 mM adenosine, 1.5 mM caffeine is applied. (2) Same atrium as in B_1 after washing out adenosine and caffeine. Physostigmine, 1.5×10^{-3} mM, is present and 4.4×10^{-5} mM ACh is added to produce full effect. Then 1.5 mM caffeine is added. (3) Caffeine concentration increased to 2.5 mM. After 5 minutes 1.5×10^{-3} mM atropine is added. C. Reserpinized right atrium spontaneously contracting (isotonically). Adenosine at 0.1 mM reduced the frequency about 50% and depressed contractile strength about 98%. Caffeine, 1 mM, antagonized both chronotropic and inotropic effects of adenosine (de Gubareff and Sleator, 1965).

These explanations can, of course, only be regarded as suggestive. There is room for much further study on Ca^{++} fluxes in cardiac muscle under the influence of caffeine, and it is important to know how the Ca^{++} inflow and outflow is affected by adenosine. It may well be, as suggested by de Gubareff and Sleator, that the effects of adenosine in this respect may be the reverse of those of caffeine, and increased binding and lowered sensitivity to Ca^{++} may take place.

B. Cardiac Activity of the Purines, Nucleosides, and Nucleotides

Adenosine and its phosphorylated derivatives have very strong pharmacological activity and many studies have been reported of their action on the heart. Drury and Szent-Györgyi (1929) first reported heart block in guinea pigs, hypotension, and the inhibition of intestinal motility. Adenosine, AMP, ADP, and ATP have actions on the cardiovascular system which are qualitatively similar. Generally their action on the heart is similar to that of acetylcholine since they cause slowing and in some species cessation of beat, but unlike acetylcholine these effects are not blocked by atropine (Johnson and McKinnon, 1956).

Most investigators have agreed that adenosine has a negative inotropic and chronotropic effect (Schaedel and Schlenk, 1948; Hollander and Webb, 1957; Angelakos and Glassman, 1961, 1965; Buckley et al., 1961), but some workers have reported an increase in heart rate and cardiac output. (Rowe et al., 1962.) A complex action, both stimulant and depressant, on the isolated frog heart has been described (Sheikon, 1946), and Cook et al., (1958) found increased force of contraction in the isolated frog ventricle. Hollander and Webb (1957) indicated that there are differences between the different nucleosides since they found that adenosine and inosine reduce the contractility of rat atria whereas guanosine was without effect.

Similar differences were found by Buckley et al. (1959) who investigated the actions of a number of nucleosides on left ventricular failure in isolated dog hearts. They found that adenosine and cytidine were negatively inotropic, whereas guanosine, inosine, thymidine, and uridine were positively inotropic and restored left ventricular function to its control level. These workers drew attention to the relationship between chemical structure and inotropic action (see Table 5.3) and showed that a positive effect was associated with nucleosides in which a hydroxyl group was found in position 6, whereas those in which there was an amino substituent in this position were depressant to cardiac muscle.

In a second paper (Buckley, et al., 1961) they extended the study to the purine and pyrimidine bases of the nucleosides and also used rabbit

Table 5.3: Relationship between Chemical Structures and Inotropic Action in the Purines, Pyrimidines, and Nucleosides

Compound	R	Substituents in position			Inotropic action	Ref.[a]
		2	6	Others		
Purine base						
Adenosine	D-Ribose	H	NH$_2$		−	a
Adenine	H	H	NH$_2$		−	b
Guanosine	D-Ribose	NH$_2$	OH		+	a
Guanine	H	NH$_2$	OH		+ +	b
Deoxyguanosine	2-Deoxy-D-ribose	NH$_2$	OH		±	c
6-Thioguanosine	D-Ribose	NH$_2$	SH		+ +	c
Inosine	D-Ribose	H	OH		+ +	a
Hypoxanthine	H	H	OH		+ +	b
Xanthine	H	OH	OH		+ +	b
Caffeine	H	OH	OH	1,3,7-CH$_3$	+ +	b
6-Chloropurine	H	H	Cl		−	b,c
Pyrimidine base						
Cytidine	D-Ribose	OH	NH$_2$		−	a
Cytosine	H	OH	NH$_2$		−	b
Uridine	D-Ribose	OH	OH		+ +	a
Uracil	H	OH	OH		+ +	b
Thymidine	2-Deoxy-D-ribose	OH	OH		+	a
Thymine	H	OH	OH	5-CH$_3$	+ +	b
Orotic acid	H	OH	OH	4-COOH	+ +	b
Alloxan	H	OH	OH	4,5-OH	+ +	b
4-Carboxy-pyrimidine	H	H	H	4-COOH	− +	b
Pyrimidine	H	H	H		+	b

+ Strong positive inotropic action; ± Feeble or doubtful positive or negative inotropic action; − Strong negative inotropic action.

[a] References: (a) Buckley *et al.* (1959); (b) Buckley *et al.* (1961); (c) Rosenblum and Stein (1964).

hearts which were not in failure to establish whether the inotropic effect was to be observed only in the failing heart. The range of compounds studied was also further extended. These results are summarized in Table 5.3.

The bases and the nucleosides were found to have inotropic effects in the nonfailing rabbit heart similar to those found in the failing dog or rabbit hearts with the exception of thymine and thymidine. Because of the varying force of contraction and degree of failure from one heart to another no accurate quantitative comparisons could be made but from the structure-activity standpoint the expression of the inotropic effect as either positive or negative was adequate. The thymine and thymidine inconsistency may in fact have arisen from this difficulty. Compounds with a second hydroxyl in another position as well as at C-6, xanthine, 5-hydroxyuridine, barbituric acid, and alloxan, gave no consistently positive effects but the methylated xanthine, caffeine, was clearly positive in all cases. The authors concluded that a hydroxyl in position 6 was essential for positive inotropic actions in both the purines and the pyrimidines and that effects of the bases and their nucleosides run parallel.

Rosenblum and Stein (1964) studied the positive inotropic effects of guanosine on isolated atria of guinea pigs, rabbits and rats in an attempt to ascertain the mechanism of this action. They suggested that there are two classes of purine nucleosides exhibiting positive or negative inotropic effects and they chose guanosine as typical of the former group. Rat atria showed a clear positive inotropic effect with fairly high concentrations of guanosine, 10^{-4}–10^{-3} moles per liter, but a negative effect with low concentrations (3.16×10^{-5} moles per liter). Previous addition of atropine to the bath had no effect on the response to low or high concentrations.

In animals depleted of catecholamines by previous administration of reserpine, guanosine produced only a negative inotropic effect with all concentrations. Repletion of the noradrenaline stores restored the biphasic action of guanosine. Cocaine was next used to block catecholamine release and there was possibly a reduction of the positive inotropic effect of guanosine. Noradrenaline added to the bath after guanosine produced a significantly greater response than when the same amount was added alone. When atria were exposed to guanosine and washed the subsequent addition of tyramine to the bath produced a smaller response than when the same concentration was added to atria not pretreated with guanosine. These findings provide very strong evidence that the positive inotropic effect of the 6-OH purines is the result of the release of endogenous noradrenaline. The positive inotropic effect was observed with auricular tissues of man, rabbit, rat, and guinea pig.

It appears therefore that guanosine acts by releasing noradrenaline from sites similar to those acted upon by tyramine and it may also sensitize the tissue of the atrium to noradrenaline or it may inhibit the destruction of this substance.

In the light of this work and the clear structural relationships shown by Buckley *et al.* (1959, 1961), it seems reasonable to agree to the hypothesis that there are two classes of cardioactive purines, pyrimidines, and nucleosides, and although they are all fundamentally depressant to cardiac muscle those which have a C-6 OH substituent release noradrenaline the effect of which reverses this depression so that a positive inotropic action results. Sometimes a negative inotropic action is seen with such compounds in doses too small to release significant amounts of noradrenaline.

References

Angelakos, E. T., and Glassman, P. M. (1961). *Proc. Soc. Exptl. Biol. Med.* **106,** 762.

Angelakos, E. T., and Glassman, P. M. (1965). *Arch. Intern. Pharmacodynamie* **154,** 82.

Arora, R. B. (1953). *J. Pharmacol. Exptl. Therap.* **108,** 26.

Axelsson, J., and Thesleff, S. (1958). *Acta Physiol. Scand.* **44,** 55.

Bacq, Z. M. (1939). *Arch. Intern. Pharmacodynamie.* **63,** 59.

Bianchi, C. P. (1961). *J. Gen. Physiol.* **44,** 854.

Blount, B. K., Openshaw, H. T., and Todd, A. R. (1940). *J. Chem. Soc.* **1,** 286.

Bonting, S. L., Hawkins, N. M., and Canady, M. R. (1964). *Biochem. Pharmacol.* **13,** 13.

Buckley, N. M., Tsuboi, K. K., and Zeig, N. J. (1959). *Circulation Res.* **7,** 847.

Buckley, N. M., Tsuboi, K. K., and Zeig, N. J. (1961). *Circulation Res.* **9,** 242.

Chen, K. K., Chen, A. L., and Anderson, R. C. (1936). *J. Am. Pharm. Assoc.* **25,** 579.

Chen, K. K., Hargreaves, C. C., and Winchester, W. T. (1938a). *J. Am. Pharm. Assoc.* **27,** 9.

Chen, K. K., Hargreaves, C. C., and Winchester, W. T. (1938b). *J. Am. Pharm. Assoc.* **27,** 307.

Cheney, R. H. (1935). *J. Pharmacol. Exptl. Therap.* **54,** 213.

Cook, M. H., Greene, E. A., and Lorber, V. (1958). *Circulation Res.* **6,** 735.

Dalma, G. (1935). *Ann. Chim. Appl.* **25,** 569.

Dalma, G. (1939). *Atti. Congr. Intern. Chim., 10th Congr., Rome, 1938.*
de Gubareff, T., and Sleator, W. (1965). *J. Pharmacol. Exptl. Therap.* **148**, 202.
Drury, A. N., and Szent-Györgyi, A. (1929). *J. Physiol. (London)* **68**, 213.
Faltis, F., and Holzinger, L. (1939). *Ber.* **72**, 1443.
Farah, A., and Krayer, O. (1946). *Federation Proc.* **5**, 177.
Fish, F., Newcombe, F., and Poisson, J. (1960). *J. Pharm. Pharmacol.* **12**, 41T.
Flacke, W. (1959). *J. Pharmacol. Exptl. Therap.* **125**, 49.
Frank, G. B. (1962). *J. Physiol. (London)* **163**, 254.
Gallois, N., and Hardy, E. (1876). *J. Pharm. Chim.* **24**, 25.
Harnack, E. (1896). *Arch. Pharm. Berl.* **234**, 561.
Harnack, E., and Zabrocky, R. (1882). *Arch. Exptl. Pathol. Pharmacol.* **15**, 404.
Heathcote, R. St. A (1920). *J. Pharmacol. Exptl. Therap.* **16**, 327.
Hollander, P. B., and Webb, J. L. (1957). *Circulation Res.* **5**, 349.
Janot, M.-M. and Goutarel, R. (1955a). *Compt. Rend. Acad. Sci.* **240**, 1719.
Janot, M.-M. and Goutarel, R. (1955b). *Compt. Rend. Acad. Sci.* **240**, 1800.
Janot, M.-M. and Goutarel, R. (1955c). *Compt. Rend. Acad. Sci.* **241**, 986.
Janot, M.-M. and Goutarel, R. (1956). *Compt. Rend. Acad. Sci.* **242**, 2981.
Johnson, E. A., and McKinnon, M. G. (1956). *Nature,* **178**, 1174.
Krayer, O., and Acheson, G. H. (1946). *Physiol. Rev.* **26**, 383.
Krayer, O., and George, H. W. (1951). *J. Pharmacol. Exptl. Therap.* **103**, 249.
Krayer, O., and Mendez, R. (1942). *J. Pharmacol. Exptl. Therap.* **74**, 350.
Krayer, O., Farah, A., and Uhle, F. C. (1946). *J. Pharmacol. Exptl. Therap.* **88**, 277.
Krayer, O., Moe, G. K., and Mendez, R. (1944). *J. Pharmacol. Exptl. Therap.* **82**, 167.
La Barre, J. (1961). *Actualities Pharmacol.* **14**, 109.
La Barre, J., and Gillo, L. (1955). *Compt. Rend. Soc. Biol.* **149**, 1075.
La Barre, J., and Gillo, L. (1956). *Compt. Rend. Soc. Biol.* **150**, 1628.
La Barre, J., and Gillo, L. (1960). *Bull. Acad. Roy. Med. Belg.* **25**, 586.
La Barre, J., Lequime, J., and Van Heerswijnghels, J. (1955). *Bull. Acad. Med. Belg.* **20**, 415.
La Barre, J., Gillo, L., and Van Heerswijnghels, J. (1962). *Bull. Acad. Roy. Med. Belg.* **2**, 639.
McCartney, E., and Ransom, F. (1917). *J. Physiol. (London)* **51**, 287.
Maling, H. M., and Krayer, O. (1946). *J. Pharmacol. Exptl. Therap.* **86**, 66.
Martin, R. H., Pecher, J., and Defay, N. (1960). *Chem. Ind.* p. 1481.
Moe, G. K., and Krayer, O. (1943). *J. Pharmacol. Exptl. Therap.* **77**, 220.
Nayler, W. G. (1963). *Am. J. Physiol.* **204**, 969.
Opit, L. J., and Charnock, J. S. (1965). *Nature* **208**, 471.
Percheron, F. (1959). *Ann. Chim.* **4**, 303.
Pilcher, J. D. (1912). *J. Pharmacol. Exptl. Therap.* **3**, 609.
Portius, H. J., and Repke, K. (1964a). *Angew. Chem.* **14**, 1073.
Portius, H. J., and Repke, K. (1964b). *Experientia* **19**, 452.
Power, F. B., and Salway, A. H. (1912). *Am. J. Pharm.* **84**, 337.
Prelog, V., and Jeger, O. (1953). *In* "The Alkaloids" (R. H. F. Manske and H. L. Holmes, eds.), Vol. III, p. 270. Academic Press, New York
Quevauviller, A., Janot, M.-M., and Goutarel, R. (1955). *Ann. Pharm. Franc.* **13**, 423.

Ransom, F. (1917). *J. Physiol. (London)* **51**, 176.

Repke, K. (1963). *Proc. 1st Intern. Pharmacol. Meeting, Stockholm, 1961*, Vol. 3, p. 69, Pergamon Press, Oxford.

Richter, H. (1940). *Arch. Exptl. Pathol. Pharmakol.* **194**, 362.

Rosenblum, I., and Stein, A. A. (1964). *J. Pharmacol. Exptl. Therap.* **145**, 78.

Rowe, G. G., Afonso, S., Gurtner, H. P., Chelius, C. J., Lowe, W. C., Castillo, C. A., and Crumpton, C. W. (1962). *Am. Heart J.* **62**, 228.

Ruzicka, L., Dalma, G., Engel, B. G., and Scott, W. E. (1941). *Helv. Chim. Acta* **24**, 1449.

Schaedel, M. L., and Schlenk, F. (1948). *Texas Repts. Biol. Med.* **6**, 176.

Shanes, A. M. (1951). *Federation Proc.* **10**, 124.

Sheikon, F. D. (1946). *Byul. Eksperim. Biol. i Med.* **21**, 40.

Skou, J. C. (1957). *Biochim. Biophys. Acta* **23**, 394.

Skou, J. C. (1960). *Biochim. Biophys. Acta* **42**, 6.

Straub, W. (1903). *Arch. Ges. Physiol.* **98**, 233.

Thorp, R. H., (1947). *Brit. J. Pharmacol.* **2**, 93.

Uhle, F. C., Mitman, B. A., and Krayer, O. (1956). *J. Pharmacol. Exptl. Therap.* **116**, 444.

Wedd, A. M., and Blair, H. A. (1951). *Proc. Soc. Exptl. Biol. Med.* **78**, 271.

CHAPTER 6

SYMPATHOMIMETIC AMINES

I. Introduction

There has been considerable progress in our understanding of the pharmacological actions of sympathomimetic amines. Attention has been focused on fundamental studies on the origin and distribution of catecholamines in cardiac muscle and the manner in which noradrenaline particularly is stored. Much new knowledge has been derived from studies of interactions of various new drugs with noradrenaline at its storage sites, and the mechanism of action of many synthetic sympathomimetic amines can be interpreted in terms of their abilities to release stored noradrenaline. Biochemical studies are a fruitful line of investigation which holds promise of explaining the ultimate mode of action whereby noradrenaline causes inotropic responses in cardiac muscle. The account given below attempts to describe the current lines of inquiry which are evolving rapidly in this field, and it reflects the interests of the authors. No attempt has been made to provide an exhaustive coverage of the tremendous amount of literature in this field, as many aspects of the subject matter form the basis of periodical reviews.

II. The Distribution of Catecholamines in Cardiac Tissue

The catecholamines, adrenaline and noradrenaline, are found in the hearts of various species; representative figures have been collected in Table 6.1. It will be seen that the quantities in whole hearts vary according to the species and to an extent with the methods of estimation used by different workers. However, for mammals, the quantities of noradrenaline and adrenaline may be said to lie usually between 0.5–2.0 and 0.02–0.2 μg per gram, respectively. The percentage of

Table 6.1

The Distribution of Noradrenaline and Adrenaline in the Hearts of Various Species Expressed as Micrograms per Gram Tissue[a]

Tissue	Cat	Dog	Rabbit	Guinea pig	Rat	Sheep	Pig	Cow	Man
Whole heart									
Noradrenaline	0.44 (11) 0.70 (2)	1.01 (11)	1.20 (11) 0.5 (5)	1.80 (11) 0.4–1.0 (4)	0.27 (11) 0.65 (5) 0.53 (7)	0.60–1.10 (1) 0.79 (3)	0.3–0.5 (4)	0.3–0.6 (3) 0.48 (5)	0.24 (4)
Adrenaline	0.06 (11) 0.05 (2)	0.11 (11)	0.17–0.54 (4) 0.15 (11) 0.05–0.09 (4)	0.20 (11) 0.18–0.20 (4)	0.05 (11) 0.02 (5) 0.16 (7)	0.15 (3) 0.1–0.2 (11)	0.03–0.10 (4)		0.07 (4)
% Adrenaline	7	10	11 12	10 21	15 4 23	18	15		23
Right auricles									
Noradrenaline	1.24 (8)	2.7 (10) 2.64 (13)[b] 1.46 (6)[b] 1.95 (12)	3.03 (8) 1.56 (13)[b]	4.11 (8)	1.49 (8)			0.17–0.39 (3)	
Adrenaline	0.48 (8)	0.03 (12)	0.05 (8)	0.23 (8)				0.02–0.04 (3)	
% Adrenaline	4	1.5	1.6	5				9	
Left auricles									
Noradrenaline	0.61 (8)	2.3 (10) 1.46 (13)[b] 1.13 (6)[b] 1.55 (12)	1.51 (8) 1.56 (13)[b]	2.73 (8)	1.14 (8)				

Adrenaline	0.03 (8)	0.00 (12)	0.02 (8)	0.14 (8)	
% Adrenaline	5	0	1.3	5	
Right ventricles					
Noradrenaline	1.15 (8)	1.4 (10) / 0.85 (13)[b] / 0.80 (6)[b] / 0.60 (12)	1.98 (8) / 2.02 (13)[b]	1.57 (8)	0.70 (8)	0.15–0.30 (3)
Adrenaline	0.04 (8)	0.02 (12)	0.03 (8)	0.09 (8)		0.04–0.09 (3)
% Adrenaline	4	3	1.5	5		22
Left ventricles					
Noradrenaline	0.88 (8)	1.3 (10) / 0.73 (13)[b] / 0.62 (6)[b] / 0.60 (12)	1.52 (8) / 2.13 (13)[b]	1.30 (8)	0.40 (8)	0.13 (9)
Adrenaline	0.29 (8)	0.01 (12)	0.02 (8)	0.06 (8)		0.01 (9)
% Adrenaline	3	1.5	1.3	4		9

[a] The numbers in parentheses refer to the sources listed below.

1, von Euler (1954); 2, von Euler and Hellner-Björkman (1955); 3, Goodall (1951); 4, Holtz *et al.* (1951); 5, Hökfelt (1951); 6, Klouda (1963); 7, Montagu (1956); 8, Muscholl (1959); 9, Raab and Gigee (1955); 10, Shore *et al.* (1958); 11, Anton and Sayre (1964); 12, Angelakos (1965); 13, Hirsch *et al.* (1963).

[b] Total catecholamines expressed as noradrenaline equivalents.

total catecholamine (excluding dopamine as little information is available) represented by adrenaline ranges between 5 and 20% in most determinations although some lower values have been indicated, and a few higher estimates have also been made.

A very refined study of the distribution of catecholamines in the various chambers of the hearts of cats, rabbits, guinea pigs, and rats (Muscholl, 1959), revealed that in these species, the guinea pig and rabbit had rather more catecholamine in cardiac tissue than the cat or rat. This observation has been confirmed recently in whole hearts of these species (Anton and Sayre, 1964). However, in all parts of the heart in each species, the proportion of adrenaline was of the order of 3–5%. The auricles contained greater quantities of noradrenaline per gram than the ventricles, and the right side of the heart also contained greater quantities of noradrenaline than the left. Von Euler (1954, 1956) has stated that the amount of noradrenaline in different organs varies greatly but can be correlated with the extent of the sympathetic nerve supply to the organ. Thus the cow's spleen which is richly innervated contains comparatively high quantities of noradrenaline and the nerve-free placenta contains no demonstrable catecholamines. Muscholl's findings are in accordance with this correlation, and he interprets the relatively high concentration of noradrenaline in the right auricles of the species examined to the presence of adrenergic fibers supplying this region of the heart. The presence of adrenaline is usually indicative of chromaffin tissue, and the low proportion of adrenaline in the chambers of the hearts suggests that very little, if any, chromaffin tissue is present.

It is generally believed that noradrenaline in tissues exists only within nervous structures, and Hagen (1959) has stated, "There is no evidence that the catecholamines are outside the nervous tissue of these organs and until evidence of a non-nervous location is forthcoming it is probably safe to assume that the amines are within sympathetic nervous structures." Later evidence to support this belief has been derived for the hearts of mice treated with H^3-noradrenaline, and then examined radioautographically (Marks *et al.,* 1962). The radioactive noradrenaline taken up by the heart was found to become concentrated in long thin fibers less than 2 μ wide and as much as 50–100 μ long, alongside the myocardial muscle cells, and it was concluded that the site so labeled was most probably in postganglionic nerve endings. These fibers took up labeled noradrenaline rapidly and specifically — within 1–2 minutes — and the radioactivity was retained for some hours. If the adrenergic nerve endings are the storage site of this labeled noradrenaline, then it is possible that such studies may provide information on the structure of adrenergic nerve endings together with information about their distribution in cardiac tissue.

Hirsch *et al.* (1963) have also demonstrated the location of cardiac catecholamines in nervous plexi and ganglia surrounding the muscle fibers, and have correlated the catecholamine content with the number of perimysial plexi. However, they reported figures for total catecholamine content (expressed as noradrenaline equivalents) in rabbits, which suggested that the ventricles contain more catecholamine than the atria, and also that the left ventricles contain more than the right, but the mean levels are so close that the statistical significance of this latter finding would be slight.

Von Euler (1958) has drawn attention to distribution of noradrenaline in sympathetic nerves, and Falck (1962) has shown that the greatest content of the amine occurs in the terminal parts of nerve fibers. More recently, H^3-noradrenaline was found localized in small particles associated with the microsomes of heart tissue, and these are believed to represent the granulated vesicles of preterminal sympathetic nerves seen by electron microscopy (Potter and Axelrod, 1963b).

In addition to noradrenaline and adrenaline, a third catecholamine, dopamine, is found in cardiac tissue. In guinea pigs, rabbits, and dogs the dopamine content of the whole heart was estimated to be about 3–5% of the noradrenaline content, whereas in the rat and cat, the proportion of dopamine was about 11 and 16%, respectively (Anton and Sayre, 1964). These estimations do not agree in the case of the dog with those of Angelakos (1965) who found dopamine to be present in all cardiac tissues in quantities from 15 to 30% of the noradrenaline content, with the exception of the sinoauricular node where dopamine appeared to be higher; however, the statistical significance of the estimates is doubtful. Dopamine is found in highest concentration in the region of the sinus node (Angelakos and Torchiana, 1963; Angelakos, 1965), but its distribution does not parallel that of noradrenaline elsewhere. High concentrations of dopamine in the sinus region may explain the relatively high content of noradrenaline found in the right auricle, if it is assumed that the dopamine acts as a biochemical precursor of noradrenaline. However, because dopamine has definite pharmacological actions (see below), there is the possibility that dopamine may serve a functional role in some areas of the heart in addition to acting as a metabolic intermediate in noradrenaline synthesis.

III. The Origin of Noradrenaline within the Heart

The presence of noradrenaline in cardiac tissue is attributed to synthesis within the tissue and to uptake of catecholamine circulating in the blood stream originating from "spillover" following sympathetic nervous activity in other organs or release from the adrenal medulla. Opinions differ as to the relative importance of these two sources of noradrenaline in the heart. The pattern of synthesis of noradrenaline is generally accepted as that shown in Fig. 6.1, which was originally proposed by Blaschko (1939) and Holtz (1939). Proof that this synthesis rather than alternative pathways is the correct one was established by the use of radioactive materials (Kirschner, 1959). Although the steps of the synthesis are almost universally accepted, only the enzyme dopadecarboxylase has received much study. More work is required to understand the actions of other enzymes in this synthetic pathway. The conversion of dopa to dopamine occurs in the cytoplasm (Schümann, 1958), and the resulting dopamine is either stored as such in the cytoplasmic granules or is converted to noradrenaline by the enzyme dopamine β-oxidase, which is present in cytoplasmic granules (Udenfriend and Wyngaarden, 1956; Demis et al., 1956; Goodall and Kirschner, 1958; Potter and Axelrod, 1963c). It has been suggested that noradrenaline is also stored in granules in the cells, or in some types of cells, converted to adrenaline by a methylating enzyme present in the cytoplasm (Kirschner and Goodall, 1957), and then stored in granules.

The scheme outlined in Fig. 6.1 was originally propounded for synthesis of catecholamines in the adrenal medulla, but it is now generally accepted to occur as far as the stage of noradrenaline in sympathetic postganglionic nerve endings located in other organs. In recent years the biosynthesis of noradrenaline from radioactive dopamine added to the blood perfusing the isolated dog heart has been described (Chidsey et al., 1963c). Analysis of noradrenaline one hour later showed that between 1.4 and 10.8% of noradrenaline was formed from the dopamine, with a greater turnover in ventricles than in auricles. The isolated dog hearts in these experiments were not able to synthesize noradrenaline from labeled tyramine. Isolated perfused guinea pig hearts were shown to synthesize noradrenaline from radioactive tyrosine at a rate of 0.03–0.05 μg per gram per hour, which was comparable to the estimated rate of conversion *in vivo* (Spector *et al.,* 1963b).

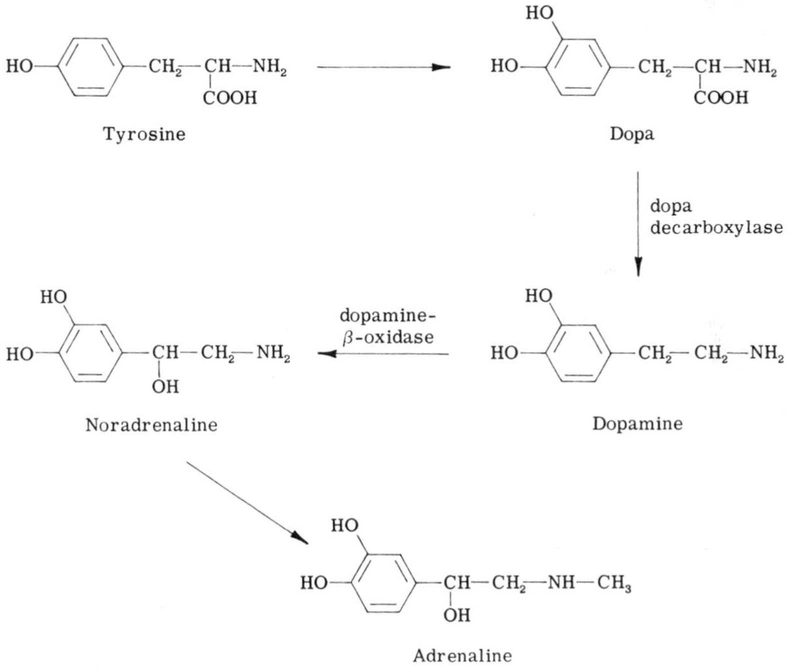

Fig. 6.1. The synthesis of catecholamines from tyrosine.

When guinea pig hearts were perfused with solutions containing varying concentrations of tyrosine, dopa, or dopamine, it was found that all precursors increased the rate of synthesis of noradrenaline and its concentration in the perfusate. Tyrosine in concentrations less than 5×10^{-4} M resulted in the greatest rate of synthesis of noradrenaline – 0.2 μg per gram per hour, and it was concluded that conversion

of tyrosine to dopa must therefore be the rate-limiting step in noradrenaline biosynthesis (Levitt *et al.,* 1965).

While not discounting the major importance of the synthetic route
summarized in Fig. 6.1, Creveling *et al.* (1962) suggested that there
was a possibility that noradrenaline could be synthesized from tyramine, which has been shown to be present in tissues of certain mammals (Spector *et al.,* 1963a). This is a view at variance with that ex-
expressed by Hagen and Welsh (1958), who claimed that tyramine and
tyrosine decarboxylase do not normally occur in mammalian tissues.
Creveling and his associates fed radioactive tyramine to rats for 5
days, and radioactive noradrenaline was successfully isolated from
urine along with normetanephrine. It may be that the rat differs from
other mammals in its ability to handle tyramine and use it as a precursor for noradrenaline. Spector and his associates showed that
tyramine occurred principally in central nervous tissue and that
heart and most other peripheral tissues either contained no tyramine
or less than 0.5 μg per gram, which was the limit of sensitivity of their
method of detection.

Opinions differ concerning the relative importance of cardiac synthesis of noradrenaline and its extraction from the circulating blood in
accounting for the presence of this substance in the heart. In their
experiments on perfused guinea pig hearts. Spector *et al.* (1963b)
claimed that to account for the quantity of noradrenaline in the normal
heart, the synthetic process was entirely adequate and that thus it was
not necessary to postulate that the amine was extracted from the blood.
Using isolated perfused canine hearts, Chidsey and colleagues (1963b)
showed that when the circulating blood was labeled with H^3-noradrena-
line, the extraction during a single circuit through the coronary vascular
bed reached the very high figure of 74%. The isotopic material was
readily released from storage sites and between 75 and 88% was
metabolized by catechol-*O*-methyl transferase before reaching the
coronary venous sinus blood. Using noradrenaline labeled with C^{14}
the rat heart was shown to extract approximately 20% from the circulating pool, and the remainder was synthesized (Kopin and Gordon,
1963). Uptake and binding contribute to the inactivation of circulating
noradrenaline (Stromblad and Nickerson, 1961). Injections of adrenaline or noradrenaline increase the quantities of catecholamine in the
heart and salivary glands, and, as chronic denervation prevented this

increase, the site for storage is probably located within the sympathetic nerves. A study based on the kinetics of disappearance of H^3-noradrenaline from the hearts of guinea pigs, rats, and mice indicated that noradrenaline is continually formed at a constant rate. The estimated rates of synthesis were given in micrograms per gram per hour: mouse, 0.12; guinea pig, 0.17; and rat, 0.06 (Montanari *et al.*, 1963).

It has been suggested that a pumping mechanism operates continuously to transfer catecholamines inwardly across the cell membrane up to the concentration where outward diffusion is just balanced (Shore, 1962). Thus the degree of uptake of exogenous catecholamines may depend on the saturation of cellular stores, and when large doses of catecholamines are employed, inward diffusion may operate in addition to a concentrating mechanism to supersaturate the stores beyond the normal physiological capacity. Iversen and Whitby (1962) have shown that the uptake mechanism was more important at low doses than at high doses where the tissue-concentrating mechanism appears to become saturated. The same concentrating mechanism may well serve uptake of both adrenaline and noradrenaline, for when combined doses of these amines were administered, there appeared to be competition for entry into intracellular storage sites. H^3-Noradrenaline was capable of entering rat cardiac tissue to increase the total tissue content and it also exchanged with the endogenous noradrenaline, although a large portion of the total pool, 75%, exchanged very slowly if at all. Considerations of rates of uptake led to the suggestion that noradrenaline could be taken up into at least two different intracellular pools and that diffusion played an insignificant role in these processes (Iversen, 1963). Similarly, H^3-adrenaline was also taken up by isolated perfused rat hearts at two rates. The initial rate of uptake was rapid and satisfied Michaelis-Menton kinetics with $K_m = 1.4 \times 10^{-6}\ M$, and had a half time between 3 and 5 minutes. The slow component of uptake had a half time of 20–30 minutes. Competition for entry into the heart existed but noradrenaline was taken up at a faster rate than adrenaline provided concentrations of the catecholamines were less than 1 μg per milliliter of perfusion fluid (Iversen, 1965a).

When the concentrations of catecholamines in the perfusion fluid exceeded 1 μg per milliliter another type of uptake process occurred (Iversen, 1965b). Both adrenaline and noradrenaline were taken up initially in satisfaction of Michaelis-Menton kinetics with K_m values

51.6 × 10^{-6} *M* and 252 × 10^{-6} *M*, respectively (corresponding to concentrations of 9.5 and 42.6 μg per milliliter). At these higher concentrations of catecholamines, the process was described as "Uptake 2" whereas at concentrations below 1 μg per milliliter, the process was described as "Uptake 1." In contrast to Uptake 1, Uptake 2 favored adrenaline rather than noradrenaline and showed no stereospecificity for (+) or (−) isomers. Catecholamines taken up by Uptake 2 were rapidly washed out of the heart when catecholamine-free fluid was perfused, but even after prolonged washing the contents remained at about 2 μg per gram. Both of these uptake processes were associated with sympathetic nerve fibers in the heart.

Although Uptake 2 did not operate at low concentrations of catecholamines in the perfusion fluid, the process was found to be readily distinguishable from Uptake 1 by various interactions with other drugs and metabolites of catecholamines.

The structural requirements for both uptake processes were determined from a study of inhibitory effects of some forty-eight sympathomimetic amines (Burgen and Iversen, 1965). In summary, affinity for Uptake 1 was increased by phenolic hydroxyl groups in positions 3 and 4 and by α-methylation, but was decreased by β-hydroxylation, N-substitution, or O-methylation. Affinity for Uptake 2 was influenced by these structural variations in a manner contrary to that of Uptake 1.

Recently, the importance of cardiac innervation has been studied in relation to the synthesis and uptake of catecholamines in the heart. After bilateral cervical sympathectomy the content of cardiac noradrenaline in dogs showed a rapid decrease for 4 to 7 days followed by a slower decrease for the following 14 days and remained at low levels for up to 50 days (Kimata, 1965). No change in the content of dopamine or dopa was observed after this operation and it was concluded that noradrenaline cannot be synthesized or accumulated following sympathetic denervation, but dopamine may be synthesized by cardiac muscle.

Comparison of normal dogs with a series of dogs whose hearts were transplanted to study the effects of denervation showed striking differences (Potter *et al.,* 1965). Normal hearts bound large quantities of C^{14}-dopamine, and both auricles and ventricles synthesized large quantities of noradrenaline. Isolated perfused normal hearts removed and bound about 56% of infused H^3-noradrenaline. Because they received more perfusion fluid, the ventricles exhibited greater uptake than the auricles and the turnover of noradrenaline was greater in these chambers. The radioactive noradrenaline was localized in particles of microsomal size, and radioautographs showed that it was found only in association with nervous structures. After nervous degeneration had occurred, transplanted hearts were found to contain about 1.2% of the normal catecholamine content and the uptake of C^{14}-dopamine was only a few percent of normal. The uptake and retention of H^3-noradrenaline was about 6% of normal; it was bound temporarily to unknown sites and rapidly released and metabolized mainly by catechol-O-methyl transferase. Potter and his co-workers concluded, therefore, that intact adrenergic innervation is very important for the synthesis and storage of noradrenaline in cardiac tissue.

In summary it would appear that the presence of noradrenaline in normal cardiac tissue depends primarily upon synthesis and to a lesser degree upon extraction from the blood. The differences in published observations may depend upon different experimental approaches, methods of measurement, and species variation. It is difficult to evaluate quantitatively the relative importance of these two processes in accounting for the noradrenaline content of the heart, because although synthesis may proceed rapidly and continuously, the rate of synthesis may not necessarily be adequate to maintain saturation of the cardiac stores when the loss due to physiological release, outward diffusion, and metabolism is totaled. According to the degree of saturation of the stores, the proportion of noradrenaline extracted from the circulating pool would be expected to vary in an inverse fashion. Clearly, much work remains to be done to quantify this problem but before a complete understanding can be achieved, it will be essential to obtain a clear picture of the nature of the cardiac stores of catecholamines.

IV. Cardiac Noradrenaline Stores

In the absence of evidence to the contrary, it is now accepted that the noradrenaline present in cardiac (and other) tissue is located within the sympathetic postganglionic nerve endings. Clearly, noradrenaline is "stored" in some manner and is capable of release from intraneuronal storage sites by activation of the sympathetic nerves supplying the heart.

It is now accepted that some sympathomimetic amines of a noncatechol nature will also bring about release of noradrenaline from its storage sites. There are other drugs which cause release of noradrenaline, without allowing it to accumulate again by synthesis, or which may block its uptake into the storage sites. Considerations of all these effects, taken together with evidence derived from studies on different pathways of metabolism of released amine, have provided strong evidence of at least two "pools" of available noradrenaline in heart tissues, and this evidence has been further supported by studies on the kinetics of uptake of perfused noradrenaline (Iversen, 1963, 1965a).

A. Pharmacological Agents Which Release Noradrenaline from the Heart

1. Reserpine

It has been known since 1955 that reserpine is capable of releasing catecholamines and 5-hydroxytryptamine from storage sites in almost all tissues, and the heart is no exception to this generalization (Bertler et al., 1956). Early studies in this field involved comparatively large doses (up to 5 mg per kilogram) of reserpine to induce tissue depletion of noradrenaline, but 24 hours after the administration of 1 mg per kilogram reserpine to cats, a state of failure exists in the heart (Withrington and Zaimis, 1961). It has been shown that smaller doses are effective if given time to act, and the likelihood of complications due to actions of reserpine at other sites is minimized. In rats, 0.1 mg per kilogram reduced cardiac noradrenaline by 96% after 6 hours (Callingham and Cass, 1962). Rabbits and guinea pigs were shown to have peripheral stores of noradrenaline almost completely depleted 24 hours after injections of 0.1 and 1.0 mg per kilogram reserpine, respectively (Crout et al., 1962). In general, these lower dose schedules of reserpine require a longer time than higher doses to achieve a given degree of depletion, but there is the advantage that animals so treated are in better physiological condition than those treated more drastically with much larger doses. Depletion of cardiac catecholamines is complete in dogs when doses of reserpine 0.1 mg per kilogram are administered intraperitoneally on each of 2 days prior to investigation (Waud *et al.*, 1958). In a series of 29 human patients without cardiac failure who were undergoing open-thorax operations, small portions of atrial appendages were removed and the noradrenaline content estimated spectrofluorimetrically was 1.82 ± 0.77 μg per gram. Five patients who had received reserpine, 0.125–1.0 mg, daily averaging a total of 21 mg over 50 days had atrial appendage levels of noradrenaline between 0.04 and 0.36 μg per gram. Thus, the use of clinical doses of reserpine in humans also causes depletion of catecholamine from the heart (Chidsey *et al.*, 1963a). Recent evidence for the depletion of noradrenaline from sympathetic neurones by reserpine has been provided by the use of the electron microscope, which reveals that nerve endings lose their usual granular content after treatment with the drug (Clementi and Garbagnati, 1964).

Experiments have been performed to locate the site of noradrenaline storage at the subcellular level (Campos and Shideman, 1962; Potter and Axelrod, 1962). Potter and Axelrod showed that noradrenaline was recovered in a fraction, described as "microsomes," containing small particles of microsomal size (see Fig. 6.2). Campos and Shide-

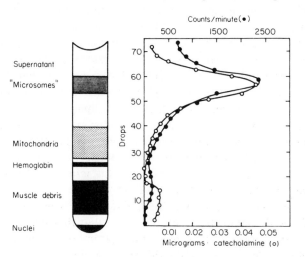

Fig. 6.2. The distribution of tritiated and endogenous noradrenaline in a homogenate of rat heart centrifuged in a sucrose gradient ranging from 0.2 to 2.2 *M* (Potter and Axelrod, 1962).

man found that after the coarse cellular debris had been removed by low speed centrifugation the catecholamines were located in a particulate fraction. When their animals were pretreated with reserpine in doses of 0.5 mg per kilogram 80 or 120 minutes prior to estimation of noradrenaline, the particulate fraction showed significant depletion. Potter and Axelrod (1963c) prepared microsomal pellets and showed that the particles contained the enzyme dopamine-β-oxidase, and sufficient adenosine triphosphate (ATP) to form a storage complex with the noradrenaline. High concentrations of reserpine, 10^{-3} M, caused release of 89% of bound noradrenaline from the storage particles.

Depletion of cardiac catecholamines by reserpine has two important consequences relating to the effects of nervous stimulation and the effects of certain drugs. The responses to cardiac sympathetic nervous stimulation are drastically reduced and may not be restored by infusions of noradrenaline. Isolated atria with intact sympathetic nerves were prepared from guinea pigs and rabbits pretreated with reserpine, and compared with similar preparations from untreated animals. The reserpinized atria showed diminished response to nervous stimulation which could not be restored by administration of noradrenaline in attempts to replete the stores (Trendelenburg, 1965). That any response to nervous stimulation is found at all may be due either to the fact that there is usually some small residual noradrenaline content in the stores following treatment with reserpine, or that the tissue may still be capable of synthesizing and releasing small quantities of the neurohumor when nervous stimulation is applied.

The responses of cardiac tissue to certain sympathomimetic drugs, e.g., tyramine, are modified by reserpine pretreatment. When catecholamines are depleted, there may be no response to tyramine in doses which are effective in the untreated animal, but infusions of noradrenaline may restore the cardiac responses to tyramine. There is a voluminous literature on tyramine which suggests that its action is due to release of noradrenaline from storage sites, and that if these are depleted by denervation or reserpine, then tyramine will give reduced or no responses depending on the degree of depletion.

Although it is now accepted that reserpine is a useful tool and that its chief value experimentally lies in its ability to deplete tissues of their catecholamines, one must be cautious that this is the only significant effect of the drug. Isolated rabbit atria showed diminished amplitude of contractions following addition of 10^{-5} M reserpine to the bath and eventually they ceased to beat entirely, even though the noradrenaline content was only slightly reduced when spontaneous beating ceased (Matsuo and Tachi, 1962). Doses of reserpine which do not deplete the catecholamine content of the toad heart have depressant actions on the isolated heart (Nayler, 1963), and large doses impair the force of contraction of the dog heart (Innes and Krayer, 1958). It seems probable that reserpine has marked toxicity upon cardiac muscle if large doses are used, and this may complicate the interpretation of results obtained when all that is desired is the depletion effect of the drug.

2. Tyramine

Tyramine has long interested pharmacologists, for although it is a sympathomimetic amine resembling adrenaline and noradrenaline in its chemical structure, its pharmacological actions differ from the catecholamines in some respects. Notably, depeletion of catecholamines from tissues, whether by denervation or by pretreatment with reserpine, results in markedly diminished responses to injections of tyramine or even complete abolition of response. These facts suggested to Burn and Rand (1958) that responses to tyramine depend upon the presence of noradrenaline in the tissues and that tyramine releases noradrenaline from tissue stores to bring about sympathomimetic effects upon the tissue.

Direct evidence that this may be the mode of action has been provided by many workers. In isolated perfused guinea pig hearts, repeated administration of tyramine was followed by gradual reduction of the noradrenaline content of the heart and gradual increase in the quantities of noradrenaline in the perfusate (Davey and Farmer, 1963). When the noradrenaline content of the hearts was reduced to about 45% of the normal level, tyramine failed to give inotropic responses. This evidence has been supported by studies in intact dogs (Chidsey *et al.*, 1962) where tyramine was administered intravenously and the noradrenaline concentration in coronary sinus blood was measured at the peak of the pressor response and found to be elevated above normal. It could be argued that tyramine released noradrenaline from sites other than the heart but it was found that tyramine infused slowly for one hour produced a small but consistent reduction of the noradrenaline content of the atrial appendage, suggesting that cardiac stores of noradrenaline are also depleted by tyramine.

The doses of tyramine used in many experiments have been criticized by Zaimis (1964) as being high and very close to toxic. She states that "even large doses of tyramine produce a limited decrease in nor stores. It is possible, therefore, that smaller, pharmacological doses do not produce a significant depletion at all." Porter and associates (1963) showed that the ability of tyramine to deplete tissue stores was very weak and short-lived when compared with reserpine. In the mouse heart, reserpine (allowed to act for 16 hours) was compared with tyramine (allowed to act for one hour). The effective tissue concentrations of the two drugs, expressed in terms of milligrams per kilogram body weight, which produced 50% depletion of cardiac noradrenaline were given as 0.05 for reserpine and 28.5 for tyramine. These authors also showed that the time taken for the cardiac noradrenaline to return from 90% depletion to 10% depletion was 20.6 days after reserpine administration and 0.7 days after tyramine administration.

The effects of reserpine depletion of noradrenaline stores upon the responses to tyramine injections has also been widely studied. In dogs treated with reserpine, tyramine administered 30 and 60 minutes later gave potentiated responses of ventricular contractile force, and the output of noradrenaline was greatly augmented at these times (Harrison *et al.*, 1963a). Because reserpine had caused no noradrenaline depletion in one hour, these results suggested that reserpine may interfere with noradrenaline at nerve endings and may facilitate the net release of the catecholamine by tyramine.

When depletion of the noradrenaline stores proceeded after treatment with reserpine, it was found that 50% depletion caused no effect on responses to tyramine in isolated guinea pig auricles, but when the stores only contained 10% of their normal noradrenaline content, responses to tyramine were reduced. Incubation with noradrenaline gave 70% restoration of responses to tyramine without giving complete restoration of noradrenaline content of the atria (Crout *et al.*, 1962). These results were recently confirmed on isolated atria from guinea pigs and rabbits, and they were compared with the effects of sympathetic nervous stimulation of the preparations. Depletion of nora-drenaline by reserpine was followed by abolition of responses to tyramine and nerve stimulation; but after reserpinized animals were given infusions of noradrenaline, the responses of isolated atria to tyramine were restored although nervous stimulation remained without effect (Trendelenburg, 1965).

Dogs given 0.1 mg per kilogram reserpine for each of 2 days prior to experiments responded with much smaller increments in cardiac contractile force (measured with a Walton=Brodie strain gauge) when given doses of tyramine than did a group of control dogs. The effect of reserpine was to reduce the mean atrial noradrenaline content from 2.08 μg per gram to 0.02 $\pm$ 0.01 ($P < 0.01$). Similarly, 8 or more days after acute cardiac denervation, another group of dogs had no detectable atrial noradrenaline and showed only slight increases in cardiac contractile force following administrations of tyramine (Gaffney *et al.,* 1962a,b). In the same series of experiments, Gaffney *et al.* also demonstrated that an infusion of noradrenaline partially restored the sensitivity of the heart to tyramine in the reserpine-treated group and restored the noradrenaline content of the heart to about 30% of normal, but a similar infusion had no effect on responses to tyramine in the denervated group. From these experiments, it was concluded that the cardiac effects of tyramine depended mainly on noradrenaline release.

Experiments have been performed upon the effects of tyramine on catecholamine distribution in subcellular fractions prepared from homogenized cat hearts which had been isolated and perfused. The homogenized material was subjected to low speed centrifugation at 2000 *g* for 5 minutes and the supernatant was then centrifuged at 105,000 *g* for one hour to provide a "particulate" sediment and a soluble supernatant. Tyramine in low concentrations, 1 μg per milliliter, perfused through the heart for 30 minutes prior to homogenization led to a depletion of catecholamines in all fractions, but higher concentrations, 10 and 100 μg per milliliter, caused greatest depletion in the "particulate" fraction (Campos *et al.,* 1963). Similar treatment of the isolated rat heart yielded the so-called "microsomal pellet" which is identical with the above "particulate" fraction (Potter and Axelrod, 1963c). Potter and Axelrod found that tyramine in a concentration of 10^{-3} *M* released 17% of noradrenaline when allowed to act for one hour at 23°C. They claim that many factors within the tissues modify drug actions as observed on subcellular fractions, and that this would explain the relatively high concentration of drugs (tyramine, reserpine, and others) necessary to demonstrate the release of noradrenaline from the isolated storage granules.

Although there is much evidence that catecholamine stores are necessary for the action of tyramine, and that depletion of these stores by denervation or pretreatment with reserpine results in abolition of inotropic responses to tyramine which may be partly restored by infusions of noradrenaline (except in the case of denervation), it must be remembered that (*a*) tyramine is not a very effective liberator of noradrenaline and (*b*) that relatively high doses of tyramine must be employed to demonstrate depletion either in whole animals, isolated heart preparations, or subcellular fractions of heart homogenates. The claim that the mode of action of tyramine is solely by liberation of noradrenaline remains to be proved, for there are experimental results which do not fit in with this simple hypothesis, and there may be other tenable interpretations of the actions of this drug. For example, Lindmar and Muscholl (1961) found that tyramine in doses between 9 and 60 μg per milliliter administered to perfused rabbit hearts caused positive chronotropic and inotropic effects in addition to increasing the output of noradrenaline, while DMPP (1,1-dimethyl-4-phenyl-piperazinium iodide) in equipotent chronotropic doses liberated nearly seven times the quantity of noradrenaline from the heart. This suggested that tyramine could both liberate and increase the action of noradrenaline. This experiment could also mean that tyramine had a direct action in addition to the liberation of noradrenaline. A recent paper has suggested that the pressor responses to tyramine in the spinal cat may bear no relation to the total catecholamine stores and that release of noradrenaline by tyramine is associated with increased synthesis of the catecholamine and its entry into the store upon which tyramine acts (Bhagat *et al.*, 1965).

3. Guanethidine

Guanethidine is a derivative of guanidine which has at least two important actions: it blocks the effects of adrenergic nerve stimulation although it does not affect the responses of tissues to exogenous catecholamines, and it will bring about release of stored noradrenaline from tissues. These effects are usually exerted upon sympathetic nerves, for attempts to demonstrate depletion of adrenal catecholamines by guanethidine have given negative results, except when extraordinarily high doses of guanethidine have been used (Kuntzman *et al.,* 1962). These two actions have different time courses and whether they are independent of one another or are two manifestations of a common mechanism of action is as yet unresolved.

Blockade of responses to nervous stimulation occurred within a few minutes after intravenous administration of guanethidine and was complete before any measurable depletion of noradrenaline from the nerve endings in dog cardiac muscle had occurred (Gaffney *et al.,* 1963). This effect is in marked contrast to reserpine, for diminution of responses to nervous stimulation did not occur until noradrenaline content was reduced to levels about 0.3 μg per gram. Using rabbit hearts with the nervous supply from the right stellate ganglion intact and estimating catecholamines recovered from the perfusion fluid, it was shown that during nervous stimulation the release of catecholamines was increased 32 times over the resting output. However, when guanethidine was present, the effects of nervous stimulation were blocked and the output of noradrenaline was reduced by 77% (Huković and Muscholl, 1962). These results suggest that guanethidine interferes with the release of noradrenaline and that this may be so is supported by studies of the effects of guanethidine on isolated atria. Kroneberg and Schümann (1962) showed that guanethidine inhibited tyramine-induced liberation of catecholamines from isolated guinea pig atria without itself producing any catecholamine depletion. This effect appeared to be direct for the response to tyramine was restored simply by washing out the dose of guanethidine. These results were extended on isolated rat atria which failed to respond to tyramine or amphetamine in the presence of guanethidine, irrespective of whether or not the atrial noradrenaline content had been depleted by guanethidine (Bhagat and Shideman, 1963a). The responses to tyramine and amphetamine could be restored by incubating the atria with noradrenaline, and the authors concluded that guanethidine possessed a dual action—an acute effect which inhibited release of noradrenaline from stores by sympathomimetic amines, and a delayed effect which resulted in depletion of these stores. Thus there is evidence that guanethidine can interfere with the release of noradrenaline from cardiac nervous tissue whether this is effected by sympathetic nervous stimulation or by sympathomimetic agents in dose levels known to cause noradrenaline release.

The action of guanethidine which results in release of catecholamines from storage sites is an effect which is delayed in onset and which requires large doses of guanethidine (Zaimis, 1964, Table IV). Kroneberg and Schümann showed that doses of 2–5 mg per kilogram in rats lowered the cardiac catecholamines by 50% in one hour. The same authors demonstrated that in isolated guinea pig atria guanethidine had a sympathomimetic effect which they described as tyramine-like for it was abolished by cocaine and by prior treatment of the animals with 2 mg per kilogram reserpine. Apart from the direct inhibition of tyramine which was abolished by washing (see above) the authors showed that treatment of guinea pigs with large doses of guanethidine (30 mg per kilogram) 24 hours previously lowered the atrial noradrenaline content to 20% of normal, and also that this procedure inhibited the responses to tyramine. That the inotropic response to guanethidine involves catecholamines was supported by experiments on isolated rat atria, for the responses were prevented when the β-adrenergic blocking drug, DCI (dichloroisoprenaline), was present, or were inhibited by reserpine pretreatment and were restored by incubation of the atria with noradrenaline (Bhagat and Shideman, 1963b).

Guanethidine antagonizes the pharmacological responses to tyramine acutely by preventing tyramine-induced liberation of noradrenaline, and in a delayed manner by itself depleting tissue stores of the catecholamine and leaving no available noradrenaline for tyramine release. However, reserpine-induced depletion of catecholamines is not completely antagonized by the presence of guanethidine (Hertting *et al.,* 1962), which suggests that these drugs do not have the same mode of action in releasing noradrenaline. This finding was supported by studies in dogs with estimations of the concentrations of noradrenaline appearing in the coronary sinus blood at intervals, together with the degree of depletion of the atrial appendages (Harrison *et al.,* 1963c). Guanethidine, 15 mg per kilogram, released noradrenaline into the sinus blood for 2–3 hours, and the levels in the atrial appendage were depleted by 24%. After 24 hours the atrial content was depleted to very low levels although not measurable in the sinus blood. Reserpine, 3 mg per kilogram, released noradrenaline and after 4 hours the atrial appendage was depleted by 65%, although the quantities appearing in sinus blood were barely detectable. Thus the authors concluded that probably the two drugs produced noradrenaline release by different mechanisms. Studies on the effects of these two drugs at the subcellular level also revealed differences in action (Bhagat, 1964). Whereas reserpine depletes catecholamines in the bound or particulate fraction rich in microsomes (Campos and Shideman, 1962), guanethidine was found to exert its effect on the concentration of noradrenaline in the soluble fraction prepared from homogenized rat ventricles. To explain this discrepancy Bhagat postulated the existence of two storage sites of noradrenaline (see below). Not only does guanethidine interfere initially with release of noradrenaline from cardiac stores, but it also has been shown to inhibit uptake of circulating noradrenaline (Hertting *et al.,* 1962; Bhagat and Shideman, 1963b).

When guanethidine was first studied, its most striking property was the ability to block the effects of sympathetic nervous stimulation before there was any detectable depletion of catecholamines from the heart. Thus guanethidine produced immediate blockade of sympathetic activity, whereas depletion of catecholamines was not found for one hour or more, and took between 6 and 18 hours to reach a maximum of 80–90% and slowly recovered, although not completely, after 48 hours (Cass and Spriggs, 1961). Thus, there was no parallelism between the rates of onset of sympathetic blockade and of noradrenaline depletion, which was confirmed by Gaffney *et al.* (1963). Further, the recovery of sympathetic function appears long before the catecholamine levels in the tissues are restored to normal values (Chang *et al.,* 1965). These observations suggest that the two actions of guanethidine are distinct and that two modes of action may be necessary to explain the two types of effect. However, as all the actions of guanethidine appear to be intimately related to the functional noradrenaline in the heart, it must be borne in mind that although these two effects have different time relationships, they could quite conceivably be two separate manifestations of a single mechanism of action.

It has been shown that the action of guanethidine is associated with uptake of the drug into neuronal structures within tissues. Following administration of 15 mg per kilogram to rats, the hearts were extracted at various times and the tissue concentrations of guanethidine determined spectrophotometrically by coupling with ninhydrin in alkaline solution after extraction and part-purification. Initial uptake was high—9 μg per gram 15 minutes after injection—and slowly declined to 6.2 μg per gram after one hour and 5.7 μg per gram after 3 hours. The content of noradrenaline was also determined and was depleted by 56% in 3 hours and 93% in 14 hours. Thus guanethidine was shown to be concentrated and firmly bound in the heart during the period when noradrenaline was depleted (Bisson and Muscholl, 1962).

A recent study of the interaction of guanethidine with adrenergic neurones in rat tissues has shown that guanethidine can be taken up into two binding sites, one of which is nonspecific adsorption onto tissue components up to a concentration of 15 μg per gram and the other which is specific uptake into noradrenaline storage compartments. The two types of binding can be differentiated by the use of amphetamine which selectively displaces guanethidine from the specific binding sites (Chang et al., 1965). Uptake of guanethidine is antagonized by reserpine in such tissues as heart and spleen which contain relatively high concentrations of noradrenaline, and stored radioactive guanethidine is released from the heart by reserpine. The specific sites of binding are saturable, and take up about 3 molecules of guanethidine per molecule of endogenous noradrenaline. Support for these findings has been provided with studies on heart slices, confirming that there are two mechanisms of binding of guanethidine. The specific binding appeared to be an active process which is suppressed by amphetamine or by an atmosphere of nitrogen, although introduction of oxygen to the system will prevent the latter type of inhibition (Schanker and Morrison, 1965).

Chang et al. have provided evidence that adrenergic blockade is related to the quantity of guanethidine accumulated in the specific binding sites. Amphetamine displaced guanethidine from these sites and also reversed the sympathetic blockade, and if administered prior to guanethidine, inhibited the uptake and prevented sympathetic block. The duration of blockade after a single dose of guanethidine (8 mg per kilogram) is in the vicinity of 12 hours. At that time the amount of guanethidine remaining in the specific sites in the heart is equivalent to the amount taken up by these sites when given in minimal effective doses and this is of the order of 1.4 μg per gram (Costa, unpublished, cited by Chang *et al.,* 1965).

Similarly, the degree of noradrenaline depletion from the heart following guanethidine was also related to the degree of specific uptake of guanethidine by the tissue. Thus both actions of guanethidine could be correlated with the quantitative uptake of the drug into the specific storage sites, and this suggests that both effects may be consequences — possibly unrelated — of the same action of the drug. This view is plausible and further evidence is awaited with interest.

The mode of action of guanethidine is still not clear. The drug was shown to have weak local anesthetic properties, but this was never seriously considered to be the mode of action in producing sympathetic nervous blockade although this mechanism was considered possible for the pharmacologically related drug bretylium. The up-to-date view of the mode of action of guanethidine is to be found in the paper by Chang *et al.* (1965). They present a hypothesis which explains both adrenergic blockade and noradrenaline depletion in terms of one primary action.

When a nerve impulse involves a presynaptic terminal it produces depolarization which results in an accelerated loss of the transmitter substance (Eccles, 1964). During repolarization of the membrane, much of the neurotransmitter is thought to be recaptured into its storage sites within the nerve terminal via the uptake mechanisms to prevent strain on the limited rate of synthesis of transmitter at the nerve ending. Chang *et al.* suggest that if guanethidine were to produce a persistent depolarization of presynaptic terminals, noradrenaline could not be returned to the storage sites and there would consequently be loss of the catecholamine, and also the effects of nervous stimulation would be blocked. This postulate is ingenious and simple and allows explanation of all the actions of guanethidine discussed above. Depolarization would prevent the effects of nervous stimulation before loss of noradrenaline became appreciable, and prolonged depolarization would allow loss of noradrenaline at a rate faster than it could be synthesized. High doses of guanethidine could allow sufficient loss of noradrenaline to receptor sites to provide initial sympathomimetic responses but the level of noradrenaline would continue to decline until the rate of synthesis just balanced the rate of loss. Reversal of the effects of guanethidine by amphetamine would result in removal of guanethidine from the specific storage sites thus allowing repolarization of the presynaptic membrane and restoration of adrenergic function.

4. Bretylium

$$\langle\!\!\!\bigcirc\!\!\!\rangle\!\!-\!CH_2\!-\!\overset{CH_3}{\underset{CH_3}{\overset{|}{N}}}\!\!\overset{+}{\!-}\!CH_2\!-\!CH_3$$

Bretylium is a benzyl quaternary ammonium compound which, like guanethidine, blocks postganglionic adrenergic nerve endings, but the innervated structures retain their sensitivity to released or injected catecholamines (Boura and Green, 1959). Unlike reserpine, bretylium does not interfere with the release of pressor amines from the adrenal medulla and does not block sympathetic stimulation where the postganglionic pathway is cholinergic, e.g., sweat gland secretion. The blocking action is slow in onset, taking about 20 minutes to reach a maximum after the subcutaneous administration of 10 mg per kilogram in cats, and is accompanied by accumulation of the drug in the postganglionic nerve endings.

The effects of bretylium resemble those following denervation of a tissue. Continued administration causes gradual depletion of stored noradrenaline, and the tissue exhibits increasing sensitivity to injected catecholamines but a decreased sensitivity to tyramine. However, postganglionic nervous blockade precedes measurable depletion, in contrast to reserpine, and thus depletion of catecholamines is not the cause of the blockade but may be regarded as a consequence of the blockade as after nerve section (Green, 1960).

Large doses of bretylium exhibit a transient sympathomimetic action prior to block (Gaffney, 1961; Bhagat and Shideman, 1963b), but the inotropic effect of bretylium is prevented by pretreatment of rat atria with DCI or when atria from a reserpinized animal are used.

Bhagat and Shideman (1963b) showed that bretylium did not inhibit uptake of noradrenaline by rat atria, although the reverse has been demonstrated by others (Hertting *et al.,* 1962).

Although the actions of bretylium and guanethidine are superficially similar, recent evidence suggests that the two drugs differ in their properties and modes of action on adrenergic neurones (Brodie *et al.,* 1965). Chang *et al* (1965) have suggested that guanethidine is taken up into neurones by the mechanism responsible for uptake of noradrenaline into the storage sites. Reserpine was found to inhibit uptake of guanethidine in rat heart but had no effect on the uptake of bretylium. Reserpine also released guanethidine from heart muscle. Further, pharmacological doses of unlabeled guanethidine administered 30 minutes earlier inhibited heart uptake of tracer doses of H^3-guanethidine, but similar experiments with bretylium did not prevent uptake of C^{14}-labeled bretylium. Moreover, prior doses of catecholamines were found to block the uptake of H^3-guanethidine but not C^{14}-bretylium by the rat heart when the radioactive drugs were administered 30 minutes later. Finally, bretylium has been shown to inhibit the uptake of guanethidine in tracer doses although not when given in full pharmacological doses. Since bretylium antagonizes release of noradrenaline from tissues induced by guanethidine, Brodie and his co-workers have suggested that bretylium interacts with and antagonizes guanethidine within the nerve ending rather than by displacing guanethidine from its binding sites. This evidence does suggest that the two drugs interact with adrenergic neurones in different ways to produce block of nervous conduction, for their mechanisms of accumulation differ, and they are probably bound to different sites within the nerve ending.

B. Metabolism of Catecholamines in the Heart

There are two major routes of metabolism of catecholamines in the tissues (in addition to tissue binding) which operate as the means of inactivation of noradrenaline and adrenaline. One route depends on the enzyme amine oxidase which is present in practically all tissues (Blaschko, 1952). Although this enzyme oxidizes the side chain of the catecholamines *in vitro,* the administration of monoamine oxidase inhibitors does not result in potentiation of the effects of catecholamines administered *in vivo* (Griesemer *et al.,* 1953; Corne and Graham, 1957; Vane, 1959). Thus the importance of the enzyme for physiological inactivation of catecholamines is doubtful. Derivatives of adrenaline and noradrenaline methylated in the 3-hydroxy position of the phenol ring were discovered in the urine of patients with pheochromocytoma by Armstrong *et al.* (1957) and were confirmed to be present in rat urine (Axelrod, 1957). It was shown subsequently that another enzyme, catechol-*O*-methyl transferase, was present in tissues and that this enzyme was responsible for the major inactivation of the catecholamines. Moreover, many substances, including pyrogallol, which were known to potentiate the effects of catecholamines (Bacq, 1936) were found to be competitive inhibitors of catechol-*O*-methyl transferase both *in vitro* (Bacq *et al.,* 1959) and *in vivo* (Axelrod and Laroche, 1959). The properties of catechol-*O*-methyl transferase and its necessary cofactors have been summarized recently (Axelrod, 1965).

The importance of catechol-*O*-methyl transferase in the inactivation of catecholamines is largely associated with circulating catecholamines outside the boundary of the sympathetic neurone or catecholamines which are easily released from storage sites. The enzyme is found in all tissues and is located in the cytoplasm. Monoamine oxidase is also widely distributed but is found in the mitochondrial fractions of cell homogenates and its importance is thought to be associated with the inaction of catecholamines which are firmly bound or slowly released from stores within the nerve cells. However, the relative importance of the two processes of metabolic inactivation depend on many factors such as the type of tissue studied and the species under study, as well as whether the catecholamines are bound or circulating. Nevertheless, information derived from metabolic studies taken in conjunction with data from the kinetics of uptake of noradrenaline and the interactions of drugs with noradrenaline are currently being used to explain the nature of the noradrenaline storage mechanism in the heart and other tissues.

C. Multicompartment Storage of Noradrenaline in the Heart

When H^3-noradrenaline is administered intravenously, it is rapidly taken up by tissues and is retained by them for a considerable time.

It was shown that after such an injection the amount of radioactive noradrenaline in the heart was the same after 2 hours as it was after 2 minutes (Whitby *et al.,* 1961). This experiment demonstrates that the noradrenaline is taken up by the tissue and suggests that it is bound to some cellular constituent in a manner which protects it from enzymatic destruction by monoamine oxidase or catechol-*O*-methyl transferase. Presumably the binding prevents the noradrenaline from being physiologically active but preserves it in a potentially active state. The studies on the kinetics of uptake of H^3-noradrenaline in small doses (less than 1 μg per milliliter) by the perfused rat heart showed that noradrenaline entered the heart, increased the tissue content, and that it exchanged with endogenous noradrenaline (Iversen, 1963), although a large proportion of the total content, about 75%, exchanged very slowly if at all. It was shown that noradrenaline entered at least two intracellular pools at different rates. Similarly, by studying the kinetics of disappearance of H^3-noradrenaline it was shown that in the hearts of intact animals, labeled amine was taken up into a readily miscible pool and slowly diffused into a second pool (Montanari *et al.,* 1963).

These results support a suggestion made earlier (Trendelenburg, 1961) that noradrenaline is present in nerve endings in a labile available pool which exchanges slowly with a stable pool of bound noradrenaline. Direct evidence for this suggestion became available when it was shown that the noradrenaline of the heart was present in two stores, from one of which it was easily released by tyramine but not from the other (Potter *et al.,* 1962). The concept of two stores was supported by Potter and Axelrod (1963c) who showed that the rat heart had a small store which rapidly took up H^3-noradrenaline with a half life of several hours and which was acted upon by tyramine. However there was also a second store which was gradually filled with radioactive noradrenaline from the smaller store and which had a half life for noradrenaline of about one day. This second store was tyramine resistant, but it was shown that reserpine acted on both stores to release noradrenaline.

Radioactive noradrenaline is rapidly released from the small store by tyramine, and identification of the metabolic products showed that it was inactivated by catechol-*O*-methyl transferase. In contrast, reserpine released H^3-noradrenaline slowly and it was metabolized by monoamine oxidase. As the physiological activity of reserpine-released noradrenaline is very slight, it was concluded that deamination proceeded intraneuronally, whereas O-methylation occurred outside the nerve cell after the released transmitter had acted upon the adrenergic receptors (Kopin and Gordon, 1962).

It is generally agreed that the noradrenaline released by nervous stimulation and the noradrenaline released by tyramine originate from separate stores; however, quantitative studies do not always agree. Chidsey *et al.* (1962) showed that only a slight depletion of the cardiac noradrenaline stores was necessary to abolish responses to tyramine, but responses to nervous stimulation were still obtained. Tyramine infusions caused tachyphylaxis to injections of large doses of tyramine, but stimulation of the cardiac nerves still caused effects (Harrison *et al.,* 1963b). When catecholamines were depleted from dog hearts by prior treatment with reserpine, the responses to tyramine and nerve stimulation were abolished. Infusions of noradrenaline restored responses to tyramine but not to sympathetic nervous stimulation (Gaffney *et al.,* 1963; Trendelenburg, 1965). These results may be interpreted in terms of two stores of noradrenaline, one of which was readily acted upon by nervous stimulation and the other was postulated to be located near nerve endings and contained noradrenaline easily released by tyramine (Bhagat, 1964).

At present, it is usually accepted that noradrenaline is stored in sympathetic nerve endings in tissues in at least a two-compartment system, and many workers have attempted to avoid the complication of postulating a greater number of storage compartments. It is unfortunate that the various two-compartment models postulated by different authors are not always mutually consistent, and although a particular model may explain the limited data found in one laboratory, it is not always adequate to include the results of other workers. This field is necessarily complex and only by consideration of all experimental findings will the best model be described.

A tentative model in which a number of experimental results are coordinated is given in Fig. 6.3. In this model it is assumed that there are two storage compartments for noradrenaline, one of which, store 1, releases noradrenaline upon the arrival of nervous impulses, and another, store 2, contains easily mobilized noradrenaline which is liberated by such agents as tyramine. It is assumed that the release of noradrenaline from each of these stores is sufficiently rapid to enable the amine to escape from the nerve ending before it can be deaminated and rendered inert by monoamine oxidase contained in the intracellular mitochondria. According to Kopin and Gordon (1962), the free noradrenaline, therefore, can diffuse across to the receptor sites and bring about its inotropic action before being inactivated by O-methylation.

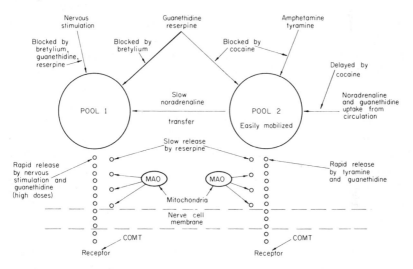

Fig. 6.3. A diagrammatic summary of some contemporary notions of the interactions of various drugs on the cardiac noradrenaline storage mechanism in terms of the two-pool storage concept. COMT = catechol-*O*-methyl transferase; MAO = monoamine oxidase. For further discussion see text.

Reserpine is thought to liberate noradrenaline from both stores but although the extent of liberation may approach complete depletion, the rate of liberation is thought to be slow, so that the mitochondrial monoamino oxidase inactivates the released amine before it can escape from the confines of the cell, and only deaminated metabolic products are found in the circulation. After reserpine-induced depletion of the stores, infusions of noradrenaline will partially replenish store 2 (Crout *et al.,* 1962) although uptake of noradrenaline is delayed by the presence of cocaine (Farrant, 1963). Store 1, on the other hand, is not easily replenished by infusions of noradrenaline (Gaffney *et al.,*

1963; Trendelenburg, 1965) for even after infusions, nervous stimulation remains ineffective after depletion of the stores has been induced originally by reserpine. Failure of nervous stimulation after reserpine depletion and subsequent noradrenaline infusion may simply be the consequence of slow uptake into store 1, but it is more likely that reserpine may inhibit the process by which noradrenaline is taken up into this compartment.

Bretylium is thought to block the effects of nervous stimulation by preventing noradrenaline release from store 1. This drug will also diminish the release of noradrenaline as a result of exposure to reserpine and guanethidine, which suggests that guanethidine will also act on both stores to liberate the amine. Bhagat (1964) suggested that guanethidine acted preferentially on store 1 to release noradrenaline, but could also act upon store 2 similarly to tyramine, and that this latter action was not antagonized by bretylium.

Cocaine acts on store 2 to prevent noradrenaline release by tyramine but apparently does not abolish release after nerve stimulation (Trendelenburg, 1959). Cocaine also diminishes the release of noradrenaline by reserpine and guanethidine. This is further evidence that reserpine and guanethidine act upon both storage sites. An interesting test of this model would be to see whether cocaine and bretylium together would block completely the release of noradrenaline by reserpine or guanethidine. It was suggested that reserpine and guanethidine together caused greater release of noradrenaline than either substance alone (Fawaz and Simaan, 1963). These authors thought, however, that each substance would deplete both storage sites if given time and thus their results are not beyond the scope of this model, for they may be the result of different rates of release from each of the two stores.

We do not know whether guanethidine is taken up into both stores in the specific manner described by Chang *et al.* (1965). If this is so, then amphetamine which prevents guanethidine uptake into specific sites associated with noradrenaline stores, or displaces guanethidine from these sites and thus reverses its action, must be capable of acting on both stores, although amphetamine is not antagonized by bretylium. Neither do we know whether the rates of release of noradrenaline by guanethidine from both stores are identical, or whether there is rapid release from store 2 and only slow release from store 1.

Some authors have found a two-compartment storage system inadequate and have postulated a three-compartment system. Fawaz and Simaan (1963) suggested that there was a third store which took up noradrenaline infused into the cardiac tissue prior to administration of reserpine in addition to the easily mobilized noradrenaline, described as store 2 above. Such an infusion did not increase the amount of noradrenaline released by reserpine plus guanethidine. It is doubtful whether such an uptake can be regarded as a physiological store and it may well represent binding of noradrenaline to nonspecific sites not associated with normal function. Evidence for a true third storage compartment does not appear convincing at present, and unless a two-compartment system eventually proves inadequate to explain storage of noradrenaline, there appears to be no virtue in postulating a third store.

There is little morphological evidence available to differentiate the storage compartments. As reserpine depletes both stores and also results in the disappearance of granules from nerve endings in tissues, there may be two types of granules which are acted upon by different agents. Alternatively, the easily mobilized noradrenaline may be located closer to the boundary of the cell, and the remainder may be deep in the neurone as postulated by Potter and Axelrod (1963a). A third explanation of the different storage sites and mechanisms of release may depend on the type of binding of noradrenaline within the storage particles.

At present it is impossible to postulate a model which gives a complete picture of the noradrenaline storage process, and a complete picture of the interactions of many different drugs with one another and the storage sites. For this reason, although the model presented in Fig. 6.3 coordinates a lot of data, it falls far short of the ideal. However it may provide a useful conceptual framework for further study of this problem. An objection to this or other models involving the sympathetic nerve ending is that no account has been taken of effector cells (Zaimis, 1964). Bretylium, for instance, was shown to have a positive inotropic effect in cardiac denervated dogs, whereas guanethidine had a direct negative inotropic effect in doses from 1 to 10 mg per kilogram (Gaffney *et al.*, 1962a).

V. Pharmacological Actions of Sympathomimetic Amines

A. Physiological Importance of Catecholamines

Early in the embryological development of the heart, all primitive cardiac cells exhibit the properties of automaticity, conduction, and contractility. These properties are later taken over by specialized tissues within the whole organ—the pacemaker, the bundle of His, and the muscular tissue, respectively. However, these three properties appear long before the heart receives sympathetic innervation, and therefore presumably before it contains any catecholamines. It is well known that the heart can function in the absence of catecholamines, for depletion of these substances down to very low levels by pharmacological agents or following acute denervation is not followed by cessation of the heart. It is reasonable to suppose that depletion of cardiac catecholamines would reduce the ability of the animal to cope with sympathetically mediated adjustments to imposed stresses, but whether or not the only function of catecholamines is to participate in reflex adjustments is, as yet, an unsolved question.

Papillary muscles removed from cats after catecholamine depletion induced by reserpine, or following bilateral cardiac sympathectomy, exhibited a marked reduction in contractility when compared with those removed from control animals. In each treated group, the catecholamine depletion was not complete, and although reserpine-treated animals contained less catecholamines than denervated animals the reduction in contractility was approximately the same, suggesting that a separate direct toxic action of reserpine upon the heart was not involved (Lee and Shideman, 1959). Using isolated rabbits hearts and recording the isometric tension developed in response to increments of stretch, it was shown that reserpine in doses which produced 94% depletion of cardiac catecholamines had very slight effects upon the active tension developed at all degrees of stretch, and that guanethidine-treated hearts with about 70% depletion showed only moderate reduction in developed tension (Maxwell *et al.,* 1964). Lee and Shideman concluded that catecholamines were essential for contractility, whereas Maxwell *et al.* concluded that the heart maintained essentially normal contractility even when almost completely depleted of catecholamines. There appears to be no disagreement that depletion of catecholamines reduces the spontaneous cardiac rate either in isolated preparations (Maxwell *et al.,* 1964) or in whole animals (Roberts and Modell, 1961), where it was shown that effects of reserpine on cardiac rate paralleled the degree of depletion.

It has been suggested that depletion of catecholamines may have some importance in heart failure. For instance, it was found that in human hearts from patients with congestive heart failure or fresh myocardial infarction, adrenaline formed a much greater proportion of the total catecholamines than in normal hearts (Raab and Gigee, 1955), thus implying a degree of depletion of noradrenaline. Small portions of atrial appendage were removed from human patients undergoing open-thorax surgery, and in 29 patients without failure the mean noradrenaline content was 1.82 ± 0.77 μg per gram, but in 17 patients with congestive heart failure the noradrenaline content was only 0.53 ± 0.47 μg per gram (Chidsey *et al.,* 1963a). Similar results were obtained in guinea pigs where a condition of experimental heart failure was induced by partial constriction of the ascending aorta. Marked reduction of the ventricular catecholamine content was observed which could not be explained simply by a "dilution" of sympathetic nerve endings in the hypertrophied cardiac muscle mass (Spann *et al.,* 1964). Indeed it has been suggested that "the use of sympathomimetic amines in the treatment of congestive heart failure is a field worthy of exploration" (Fawaz, 1963).

With the aid of a new type of whole animal preparation it may be possible to answer the question of whether catecholamines have a fundamental role in maintaining normal cardiac function. It has been shown that there are nerve growth factors of a protein nature, to which it is possible to develop an antiserum (Levi-Montalcini, 1964). Following administration of the antiserum for the first 5 days after birth, there was a marked diminution in the number of cells in sympathetic ganglia of mice, rats, kittens, and rabbits, and in the peripheral organs of these species the levels of catecholamines were greatly reduced although the brain and the suprarenal glands appeared to be unaffected. Such animals are described as "immuno-sympathectomized" by Levi-Montalcini and her co-workers, and this term has found favor with others. The value of the immuno-sympathectomized rat for cardiac investigators is that cardiac catecholamines are permanently depleted to virtually zero levels (Klingman, 1965; Berk *et al.,*

1965). The promise of this experimental research tool has recently been demonstrated by Zaimis (1965), who showed that immuno-sympathectomized rats, after adrenalectomy, responded to tyramine with pressor responses similar to those observed in control animals, and with greater positive chronotropic responses than those induced by adrenaline or noradrenaline. This suggests very strongly that tyramine also possesses a direct action on cardiac tissue, unrelated to any action mediated by the release of noradrenaline. In the near future, we may expect to obtain a clearer and more complete understanding of the physiological importance of the catecholamines in the heart, and with the aid of this preparation we have the means for a new approach in the investigation of the actions of drugs upon the heart.

B. Pharmacological Actions of Catecholamines

The three fundamental properties of cardiac cells, automaticity, conduction, and contractility, are all enhanced by the catecholamines, although the effects upon conduction are not as striking as those upon the other two properties. In addition the catecholamines have important actions on coronary vessels and the oxygen consumption of cardiac tissue. Considerable confusion exists in earlier literature concerning the actions of these substances upon the coronary vascular bed, and some observations have been summarized (von Euler, 1956). In our laboratories, the perfused kitten heart responded to noradrenaline with coronary vasoconstriction and to adrenaline with transient constriction of small magnitude followed by secondary vasodilatation (Cobbin, 1959). When administered directly into the coronary circulation, both adrenaline and noradrenaline acted primarily as vasoconstrictors; subsequent vasodilatation was considered to be secondary to the increased rate of metabolism induced by these drugs with consequent liberation of vasodilator metabolites (Berne, 1958). It is now thought that increases in coronary flow are the result of the effects of catecholamines upon oxygen consumption of cardiac muscle, even though the primary direct action of these substances upon the coronary vessels is vasocontrictor (Marchetti *et al.,* 1963; Winbury, 1964; Marks, 1964).

The catecholamines have a profound effect upon oxygen consumption of cardiac tissue, bringing about such an increase that it is agreed that these drugs induce an oxygen-wasting or calorigenic effect. The calorigenic effect represents the increase in oxygen consumption which cannot be accounted for by the increase in heart rate taken in conjunction with the increase in work output. In human hearts, the increase in oxygen consumption following adrenaline was 4–10 times greater than that due to noradrenaline. The efficiency of the heart was lowered by adrenaline, and the organ ultimately became hypoxic due to the magnitude of the oxygen-wasting effect (Raab and Gigee, 1955). In the dog heart-lung preparation, noradrenaline was shown to have chronotropic, inotropic, and coronary dilator potencies equal to those of adrenaline, but it had an even greater calorigenic effect than did adrenaline (Fawaz and Tutunji, 1960). Because of the oxygen-wasting effects of the catecholamines, an increase in work output is frequently accompanied by a decrease in efficiency of the heart. For this reason the use of catecholamines as therapeutic agents in various clinical conditions of cardiac origin has been limited, for benefits arising from coronary dilator or inotropic actions of the drugs might well be outweighed by diminished metabolic efficiency. However, the clinical use of the inotropic actions of these drugs is a field which should be studied, for small doses of adrenaline result in inotropic actions on the dog heart-lung preparation without a measurable increase in oxygen consumption (Fawaz and Tutunji, 1960).

The actions of catecholamines upon conduction velocity in the heart are not very striking. When measured with close bipolar electrodes, the conduction velocity in dog heart-lung preparations was slightly increased by adrenaline, and, simultaneously, the QRS complex of the electrocardiogram was shortened (Brendel *et al.*, 1951). Increased velocity of conduction was observed in exposed dog hearts in both auricular and ventricular myocardium (Gilbert *et al.*, 1958). Noradrenaline was shown to have slightly less effect on conduction velocity than adrenaline when the two catecholamines were compared in equimolar doses administered by infusion at a rate of about 7 μg per kilogram per minute (Siebens *et al.*, 1953). The effects of catecholamines upon the velocity of conduction of the cardiac impulse depend on the state of the cardiac muscle, being much more pronounced in a deteriorated preparation. Under the influence of adrenaline, the impulse may even be conducted into areas which are partially or completely blocked (Trautwein and Schmidt, 1960).

Perhaps the most striking action of the catecholamines is that upon contractility of the heart. This action is apparent qualitatively in the embryonic chick heart observed microscopically after 48 hours' incubation (Emmett, 1965) before the heart is innervated, which does not begin until the end of the third day of incubation (Romanoff, 1960). Measurement of contractile force of the heart can be made after 4 days (McCarty *et al.,* 1960), and the force of contraction of atria isolated from 8-day embryos has been recorded by Emmett. In each of these preparations the catecholamines stimulated the cardiac tissue to beat more forcefully. At the 8-day stage the heart is not fully innervated and it is doubtful if the sympathetic nerves contain functional noradrenaline. Emmett has shown that tyramine will not stimulate the isolated embryonic atria until 13 days and then not in all preparations. However at 15 days, a steep log dose-response curve is found for tyramine, which suggests that at this stage of development tyramine produces its inotropic effects by liberation of noradrenaline. To support this view it was also shown that pretreatment of the embryos by injection of 125 μg reserpine into the yolk sac — 24 hours prior to experimentation — abolished the stimulant action of tyramine on the atria, and, indeed, this substance then depressed the force of contraction. After reserpine pretreatment, the atria were still very sensitive to noradrenaline, but no experiments were performed to find out whether supersensitivity existed.

The relative potencies of noradrenaline and adrenaline as inotropic agents have been studied by many workers using varied preparations from a wide range of species. It has been reported that adrenaline has greater inotropic potency on isolated amphibian heart preparations, e.g., the perfused frog heart and sinoauricular preparation from the tortoise. On isolated rabbit auricles and perfused rabbit hearts, noradrenaline was found to have double the potency of adrenaline, whereas isoprenaline was the most potent on all the above preparations (Lands and Howard, 1952).

In the majority of experiments it is usually agreed that adrenaline and noradrenaline exhibit approximately equal potency. No significant difference between the two compounds was shown in dogs when the cardiac cycle duration, systolic and diastolic pressures, calculated Stroke Index, and carotid and femoral flows were compared (Zanetti and Opdyke, 1953). More refined studies using direct measurement of cardiac contractile force have provided supporting evidence. In open-thorax dogs with modified Cushny levers attached to the right ventricle, it was shown that in equipressor doses, adrenaline and noradrenaline caused effects on the contractile force of equal magnitude with an approximate duration of 2 minutes (Goldberg *et al.*, 1953). When strain gauges were used in anesthetized or conscious dogs it was found that over a wide range of concentrations (0.05–5 μg per kilogram), the positive inotropic effects produced by both catecholamines were similar and essentially equal at each dose level. Further, there was a linear relationship between the inotropic effect and the increase in systolic pressure, and the separate curves obtained for each drug were practically identical as shown in Fig. 6.4 (Cotten and Pincus, 1955).

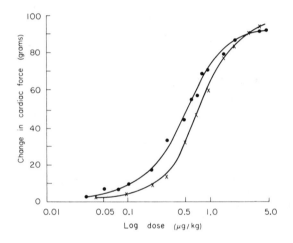

Fig. 6.4. Log dose-response curves prepared from strain gauge measurements of ventricular contractile force in the anesthetized dog after adrenaline (●) and noradrenaline (X) administration (Cotten and Pincus, 1955).

West and Rushmer (1957) prepared dogs surgically to provide continuous measurement of left ventricular pressure, diameter, and rate. They compared the effects of adrenaline and noradrenaline at three equimolar concentrations in both conscious and anesthetized animals. There was no suggestion of major differences on ventricular contractility, and stroke work was increased equally by each drug, although greater effects were recorded in anesthetized animals. Somewhat greater effects on left ventricular pressure were observed in all cases following noradrenaline, but in all likelihood, this is merely a reflection of a greater pressor effect as evidenced by a concomitant slowing of the pulse rate. In conscious animals, both drugs caused increased left ventricular stroke changes and also decreased pulse rate, whereas in anesthetized animals a greater left ventricular stroke change was found following doses of adrenaline, which might be due to the increased pulse rate observed with this drug as opposed to the slowing found with noradrenaline.

In human patients undergoing surgery, strain gauges were sutured to the right ventricles with the piece of muscle between the two arms stretched by 50% of its diastolic length to prevent significant changes in cardiac contractility arising from extracardiac effects of drugs, for example, variations in peripheral resistance which might modify diastolic length and thus increase the contractile force. It was found that adrenaline and noradrenaline were equipotent in their effects upon contractile force, although the effects had a short duration (Goldberg *et al.,* 1960). However, adrenaline increased, and noradrenaline decreased cardiac output in these observations. The variation in cardiac output responses was interpreted to be a result of the different actions on peripheral vascular beds, which activate baroreceptors resulting in a reflex bradycardia in the case of noradrenaline. When reflex bradycardia is blocked by atropine or tetraethylammonium (TEA), noradrenaline produced elevation of the cardiac output (Wilber and Brust, 1958).

Dopamine also increases the force of contraction of cardiac muscle. On isolated cat papillary muscles dopamine causes inotropic responses, but the onset of the effect is slower and persists for longer than noradrenaline in equiactive doses. In dog heart-lung preparations stimulated electrically at a constant rate, dopamine in doses of 0.5–1.0 mg in the venous inflow resulted in inotropic effects with an average increase in the cardiac output of 32% (Holmes and Fowler, 1962). The course of this action was slower in onset and more persistent than that of noradrenaline, and required doses 25–100 times as great as noradrenaline to produce comparable effects.

In anesthetized dogs with strain gauges sutured to the right ventricle, threshold doses of dopamine were about 4 μg per kilogram and responses to logarithmically graded doses were linear (McDonald and Goldberg, 1963). Infusions of dopamine at a rate of 50 μg per kilogram per minute increased cardiac output, stroke volume, and the work of both right and left ventricles (Maxwell *et al.,* 1960). However, the cardiac efficiency decreased and in contrast to noradrenaline, there was no change in calculated peripheral resitance. In man, infusions of 5–11 μg per kilogram per minute were shown to increase cardiac output by about 33%, principally as a result of increased stroke volume, for effects on the heart rate were small and variable (Horwitz *et al.,* 1960). These authors also reported a decrease in systemic vascular resistance.

Although dopamine is usually regarded as a precursor of noradrenaline, the possibility remains that this amine exerts its actions directly on the heart and that few, if any, of the responses observed result from biotransformation to noradrenaline, for dopamine either has no effect or diminishes the peripheral resistance in doses which cause marked cardiac effects. The distribution of dopamine in the heart does not parallel that of noradrenaline (see Section II), and it is found in high concentrations in the sinus node. Whether this means simply that this region of the heart has a greater utilization of noradrenaline, or whether dopamine has a separate functional role has not been determined. Evidence from current research on the catecholamines in brain suggests that dopamine may have its own functional role in the caudate nucleus, unrelated to its function as a noradrenaline precursor.

In an endeavor to provide a more complete and ultimately more quantitative description of the inotropic effects of catecholamines and other drugs, a current trend in cardiac research is the examination of the effects of drugs upon biophysical parameters, such as the "Force-Velocity" relation and the active state, which were originally described in skeletal muscle by A. V. Hill and his various collaborators. Study of these properties in cardiac muscle is comparatively recent, for contraction of heart muscle is more complicated than that of skeletal muscle owing to the complexity of the tissue structure and to certain functional properties of cardiac muscle which are not found in skeletal muscle. The basic properties of cardiac muscle and the effects of drugs thereon have been reviewed recently (Blinks and Koch-Weser, 1963; Koch-Weser and Blinks, 1963; Edman, 1965) in far greater detail than is possible here, and the interested reader should consult these sources.

Koch-Weser and Blinks have concluded that the inotropic actions

of catecholamines result from marked increases in the rate of shortening of the muscle (or rate of rise of tension) and slight decreases in the
time required to reach peak tension. This is clearly shown in Fig. 6.5
where the effects of adrenaline upon isometric contractions of guinea

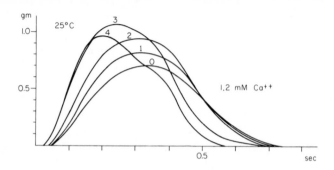

Fig. 6.5. The action of adrenaline upon the isometric contraction curve (0) recorded
from guinea pig papillary muscles stimulated at 60 per minute. The superimposed
curves were recorded between 3 and 7 minutes following additions of adrenaline to
provide the following final concentrations. Curve 1, $9.5 \times 10^{-9} M$; curve 2, $3.8 \times 10^{-8} M$;
curve 3, $1.5 \times 10^{-7} M$; curve 4, $6.0 \times 10^{-7} M$. (Reiter and Schöber, 1965.)

pig papillary muscles are recorded (Reiter and Schöber, 1965). It will
be seen that quite small concentrations of adrenaline in the organ bath
caused an increase in the isometric tension developed by the muscle,
together with a decrease in the amount of time needed to reach the
maximum tension. As the concentration of adrenaline was increased
up to about $10^{-7} M$, the amplitude of the response increased and the
time to maximum tension diminished. As the concentration was increased further, the maximum isometric tension became smaller although the time taken to develop this tension continued to decrease.
It is apparent from this figure that the inotropic actions of adrenaline
result from marked increase in the velocity of shortening of the muscle,
and in the time required to reach peak tension. Thus, adrenaline and
other catecholamines increase the force of contraction of cardiac
muscle by increasing the degree of activation of the contractile
elements.

Koch-Weser and Blinks have postulated that the amplitude of an
isometric cardiac contraction is the algebraic sum of the separate

influences of *(a)* the rested-state contraction, *(b)* the negative inotropic effect of inactivation (NIEA), and *(c)* the positive inotropic effect of activation (PIEA). The two factors NIEA and PIEA are the accumulated negative and positive inotropic consequences of preceding beats, respectively, and it is claimed that the main effect of the sympathomimetic amines is to increase the amount of PIEA produced by each beat and therefore to increase its cumulation (Koch-Weser, 1963). However, these concepts remain purely descriptive and, as yet, cannot be equated with measurable parameters such as the force-velocity relation or the active state of cardiac muscle, although they may represent changes in both the intensity and the duration of the active state.

Inotropic effects of catecholamines upon dog hearts have been described where the end diastolic volume and mean aortic pressure were kept constant (Wallace *et al.,* 1963). In these preparations, the effect of noradrenaline was to reduce the duration of both the iso-volumic phase and the ejection time, thus shortening the total systolic period. These more complex studies may be explained as the results of increased intensity of the active state, and of increased velocity of shortening together with reduced duration of activity.

The work output of cardiac tissue is increased by noradrenaline. In addition to increasing the velocity of shortening of isolated cat papillary muscles, noradrenaline also increased the extent of shortening at all initial loads and thus the work performed by the muscle. Before addition of noradrenaline, the maximum work was achieved when the initial load was about 40% of the isometric tension, and after the drug, the initial tension at which maximum work was performed was increased (Sonnenblick, 1962). The isolated cat heart showed similar responses when infused with noradrenaline at a rate of 5 μg per minute. The catecholamine enhanced ventricular performance at a given arterial pressure by augmenting the stroke volume (Sonnenblick and Downing, 1963).

C. The Mode of Action of Catecholamines as Inotropic Agents

The difficulty in describing the mode of action of catecholamines as inotropic agents is in ascertaining the level in the excitation-contraction process at which the drugs act, and to date this has not been determined. Initially some type of stimulus acts upon the cardiac muscle cell and after a series of unknown reactions, a contractile response is observed. The problem has been studied by electrophysiologists in terms of electrical events at the cell membrane but with disappointing results, for although there is substantial agreement that the mechanisms of the action potentials of nerve cells and cardiac muscle cells are qualitatively similar (Edman, 1965), the effects of catecholamines upon the amplitude of the action potential are slight and do not parallel the dramatic increases observed in contractile force. Although the fluxes of Na^+ and K^+ across the cell membrane of the frog heart are increased by catecholamines, there is very little change in the configuration of the action potential in terms of its amplitude and duration (Glitsch *et al.*, 1965). In view of the lack of correlation between observed electrical and mechanical events it is difficult to form a hypothesis to link the duration of the action potential with the duration of the active state in cardiac muscle.

The link between the excitation of cardiac muscle cells and the contractile response remains obscure as in other contractile tissues, although it is generally agreed that depolarization of the cell allows increased influx of Ca^{++}, which in some way activates the contractile mechanism. The relation of Ca^{++} to electromechanical coupling has been reviewed recently (Edman, 1965) and will not be repeated here. The importance of Ca^{++} in the initiation of the contractile process is not well understood, although Ca^{++} is known to activate myosin adenosinetriphosphatase (ATPase) *in vitro*. However, there is little evidence available to associate the inotropic effects of the catecholamines with direct effects on Ca^{++} permeability or other processes.

An interesting approach to explain the mode of inotropic action of these substances concerns catecholamine-induced changes in the energy metabolism of cardiac muscle glycogen. Although this approach may explain how energy is made available for increased cardiac contraction, it fails to explain how greater activation of the contractile elements is achieved, and it must be borne in mind that there is not necessarily a causal relationship between the two phenomena.

The effects of the catecholamines are exerted upon a complex system sometimes referred to as the cyclic adenosine monophosphate (AMP)-phosphorylase system, and which is a target for the action of several drugs (Haugaard and Hess, 1965). Glycogen phosphorylase catalyzes the formation of glucose-1-phosphate from glycogen in many tissues including the heart. Three peaks of phosphorylase activity can be separated on a cellulose column run with extracts of rabbit heart muscle, one of which is indistinguishable from skeletal muscle phosphorylase b, and the other two are probably isozymes of this enzyme (Yunis *et al.*, 1962). Phosphorylase exists in two forms: phosphorylase b which is enzymatically inactive but serves as a precursor to phosphorylase a, the active form, when the b form is in the presence of adenosine monophosphate. The reaction is a process of dimerization

$$2 \text{ Phosphorylase b} + 4 \text{ ATP} \xrightarrow[\text{kinase}]{\text{phosphorylase b}} \text{phosphorylase a} + 4 \text{ ADP}$$

and is catalyzed by an enzyme, phosphorylase b kinase, whose properties are extremely complicated, but which is activated by $3', 5'$-cyclic-AMP and by Ca^{++} (Krebs *et al.*, 1959). Using histochemical methods, the presence of phosphorylase enzymes has been demonstrated in the heart and other tissues, and although the methods will not distinguish between the two forms of the enzyme (Takeuchi and Kuriaki, 1955), it was shown that phosphorylase is located in the cellular cytoplasm but not in the nuclei. Recently, the distribution of phosphorylase in cardiac muscle has been found to parallel the distribution of glycogen (Jedeikin, 1964).

$3', 5'$-Cyclic AMP has an important role in the system for it aids the conversion of phosphorylase b to active phosphorylase a by activating phosphorylase b kinase in the presence of ATP and Mg^{++} (Krebs *et al.*, 1959). In preparations from the bovine adrenal cortex, it has been shown to inhibit the destruction of activated enzyme (Riley and Haynes, 1963). Another important action of $3', 5'$-cyclic AMP in cardiac metabolism is to increase the activity of cardiac phosphofructokinase which is a rate-limiting enzyme in glycolysis (Mansour, 1963). The quantity of $3', 5'$-cyclic AMP in intact cells is very small, and after procedures which increase its production, such as exposure to adrenaline, the intracellular concentration is less than $10^{-6} M$ in the working rat heart (Sutherland *et al.*, 1965). The formation of $3', 5'$-cyclic AMP is controlled by a system of unidentified enzymes roughly grouped together and described collectively as the adenyl-cyclase system. This system is associated with the cell membrane, but not the nucleus or the mitochondria when prepared from rat liver cells or avian erythrocytes (Sutherland *et al.*, 1965). Adenyl-cyclase is distributed widely throughout the tissues and relatively high levels are found in the heart (Sutherland *et al.*, 1962).

The whole complicated system is now thought to play an important role in effecting many hormonal responses, and 3′, 5′-cyclic AMP has been described as a "second messenger" for the mediation of certain hormonal controlling mechanisms (Sutherland *et al.*, 1965). The following discussion will be limited to a brief description of the interactions of the catecholamines with the cyclic AMP-phosphorylase sytem, and a diagram showing some of the interrelationships is given in Fig. 6.6.

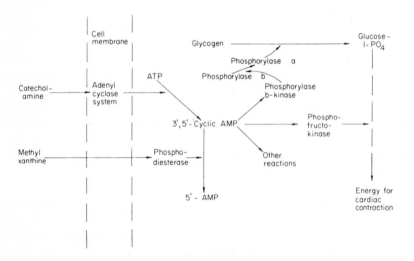

Fig. 6.6 A diagrammatic summary of some possible interrelations between catecholamines and the adenyl-cyclase, 3′, 5′-cyclic AMP, and phosphorylase systems in the heart. For further discussion see text.

The isolated perfused rat heart responded to infusions of noradrenaline with inotropic effects and increased phosphorylase a levels (Hess and Haugaard, 1958), and later it was demonstrated that the increases in both parameters were dose-dependent and that linear log dose-response lines could be constructed (Kukovetz *et al.*, 1959). Moreover, noradrenaline had approximately twice the potency of adrenaline in increasing force of contraction and enzyme activity, and isoprenaline was about five times as active. These results were confirmed in the open-thorax dog hearts, although isoprenaline was found to be approximately ten times as potent as noradrenaline or adrenaline (Mayer and Moran, 1960).

Hess *et al.* (1962) found no dissociation between the inotropic responses and phosphorylase activation in the rat heart even when small doses of adrenaline between 0.05 and 1.0 μg were added to the perfusion fluid. Similarly it has been reported that adrenaline caused rapid and simultaneous increase in the heart rate, systolic pressure, cyclic AMP and phosphorylase a levels in recirculated perfusion experiments (Øye *et al.,* 1964). However, other workers do not agree, and they claim that the inotropic response to catecholamines can be dissociated from phosphorylase activation by the use of very small doses of these substances. In the open-thorax dog heart, significant inotropic effects could be obtained following doses of noradrenaline which produced no measurable change in phosphorylase a activity (Mayer *et al.,* 1963). More recently, it has been suggested that the inotropic effects of adrenaline precede the glycogenolytic effects in perfused rat hearts, with the activation of phosphorylase a following the onset of the inotropic action after a delay of several seconds, and reaching a maximum in 15–20 seconds with about 75% of the total phosphorylase in the "a" form. It is not yet resolved whether the two actions of the catecholamines can be dissociated temporally by the use of small doses of catecholamines. The reason for the conflicting reports may well lie in the errors of estimating phosphorylase a activity. Small changes in concentration of this enzyme are difficult to measure accurately, and it is far from certain whether the processes of freezing and thawing of tissue samples allows an accurate determination of the state of the enzyme at a given time. Where tissue samples are employed in a determination, there is the added difficulty of sampling error as the distribution of phosphorylase enzymes in cardiac tissue is nonuniform (Jedeikin, 1964).

Although disagreement exists concerning the significance of the action of catecholamines on phosphorylase activation, there is agreement that these substances may exert their actions via 3', 5'-cyclic AMP. The cyclic nucleotide is accumulated in cell-free adenyl-cyclase systems prepared from dog hearts in the presence of catecholamines, and the relative potencies of isoprenaline, noradrenaline, and adrenaline are similar to those described for phosphorylase activation described above (Murad *et al.*, 1962). Mayer *et al.* (1963) and Williamson and Jamieson (1965), while disagreeing with phosphorylase activation as the mode of action of catecholamines, have each pointed to the significance of 3′, 5′-cyclic AMP as the possible mediator of the effects of catecholamines. With a rapid freezing technique to produce speedy arrest of biochemical changes occurring in the isolated perfused rat heart at selected time intervals after exposure to adrenaline in small doses (0.04 μg per milliliter), it has been shown that within 6 seconds the levels of 3′, 5′-cyclic AMP and the percentage of phosphorylase in the "a" form were increased almost fivefold. Further preliminary results have shown that the 3′, 5′-cyclic AMP response is maximal in 2–4 seconds, apparently preceding the observed inotropic effect, whereas phosphorylase activation may require 45 seconds to be maximal (Sutherland *et al.*, 1965). Since phosphorylase b kinase is activated by 3′, 5′-cyclic AMP, it is not surprising to find this degree of dissociation in peak effects; this may well explain the temporal separation of inotropy and phosphorylase activation reported by Williamson and Jamieson.

Whether the action of catecholamines upon the cyclic AMP-phosphorylase system results in inotropic responses is still not determined. There may be other links between 3′, 5′-cyclic AMP accumulation and the inotropic response which are not yet known. It has been suggested that cyclic AMP might directly affect cardiac β-receptors and thus mediate the positive inotropic response (Rall and Sutherland, 1961; Mayer *et al.*, 1963). It is conceivable that activation of phosphorylase and phosphofructokinase by 3′, 5′-cyclic AMP are responses which accompany but do not cause the inotropic response, but provide the energy necessary for the increased contractility and rate of cardiac muscle stimulated by the catecholamines.

In a recent publication, Waugh (1964) discussed the mode of action of catecholamines on the excitation-contraction coupling in arterial smooth muscle. It was concluded that adrenergic agents activated contractions by increasing the influx of Ca^{++} bound in a labile manner to the cell wall, and that this extra Ca^{++} then initiates contraction by an action on the actomyosin-ATP-ATPase system. However such studies do not appear to have been performed on cardiac muscle, and the nature of the excitation-contraction coupling remains speculative in this tissue (a fuller discussion may be found in Chapter 4).

D. The Actions of Other Sympathomimetic Amines

Sympathomimetic amines have been divided into three different groups according to whether their actions upon the tissues were potentiated, inhibited, or unchanged by administration of cocaine or by chronic denervation (Fleckenstein and Bass, 1953; Fleckenstein and Burn, 1953; Fleckenstein and Stöckle, 1955). In this classification there are direct-acting catecholamines which act upon receptor sites in the innervated tissues, and which have been considered already. Indirect-acting amines which possess no more than one hydroxyl group on the aromatic ring and which have no hydroxyl group in the β-position of the side chain include substances such as tyramine and amphetamine. These sympathomimetic amines have been shown to release stored noradrenaline, and if the stores are depleted by previous treatment with other agents, e.g., reserpine, then the indirect-acting non-catecholamines have no action (Kuschinsky *et al.,* 1960; Moore and Moran, 1962). Inotropic actions can be restored by the addition of small quantities of adrenaline or particularly of noradrenaline, but not by dopamine or isoprenaline. Kuschinsky's group concluded that the presence of small concentrations of biologically active noradrenaline is essential for the cardiac stimulant effects of these non-catecholamines, and the view has been suggested and discussed with supporting evidence that the catecholamines act as catalysts for their action (Fawaz, 1963).

The final group of amines in the Fleckenstein classification includes those with no more than one hydroxyl group in the aromatic ring structure, but with an alcoholic hydroxyl group in the β-position of the side chain. These substances were found to possess mixed actions — partially involving noradrenaline release and partly acting directly on receptor sites, e.g., ephedrine. The stimulant action of ephedrine measured in open-thorax dogs was shown to be unaffected by prior treatment with reserpine, and it was concluded that intact stores of noradrenaline were not essential for the action of ephedrine (Moore and Moran, 1962). However, with isolated papillary muscles, diminution but not abolition of the inotropic action of ephedrine was reported after treatment with reserpine (Cairoli *et al.,* 1962), which suggested a mixed action. Recently, study of the four possible stereoisomers of ephedrine has indicated that D-configuration of the β-carbon favors direct action, while the L-configuration favors indirect action (Patil *et al.,* 1965).

It is difficult to discuss the inotropic actions of these other sympathomimetic amines and to decide whether or not they fall neatly into Fleckenstein's classification, or to speculate upon their possible modes of action for surprisingly little work has been reported. Most studies of these drugs have been concerned with effects upon cardiac rate, pressor effects, or actions on sympathetically innervated organs other than the heart. There is an urgent need for proper evaluation of the sympathomimetic amines as inotropic agents and for an appreciation of their modes of action, whether direct, indirect, or mixed, so that their well-documented circulatory actions can be combined to make an assessment of their potential value in circulatory disturbances.

References

Angelakos, E. T. (1959). *Circulation Res.* **16,** 39.
Angelakos, E. T. (1965) *Circulation Res.* **16,** 39.
Angelakos, E. T., and Torchiana, M. L. (1963). *Federation Proc.* **22,** 447.
Anton, A. H., and Sayre, D. F. (1964). *J. Pharmacol.* **45,** 326.
Armstrong, M. D., McMillan, A., and Shaw, K. N. F. (1957). *Biochim. Biophys. Acta* **25,** 422.
Axelrod, J. (1957). *Science* **126,** 400.
Axelrod, J. (1965). *Recent Progr. Hormone Res.* **21,** 597.
Axelrod, J., and Laroche, M. J. (1959). *Science* **130,** 800.
Axelrod, J., Kopin, I. J., and Mann, J. D. (1959). *Biochim. Biophys. Acta* **36,** 576.
Bacq, Z. M. (1936). *Arch. Intern. Physiol.* **42,** 340.
Bacq, Z. M., Gosselin, L., Dresse, A., and Renson, J. (1959) *Science* **130,** 453.
Berk, L., Filipe, I., and Zaimis, E. (1965). *J. Physiol. (London)* **177,** 1P.
Berne, R. M. (1958). *Circulation Res.* **6,** 644.
Bertler, A., Carlsson, A., and Rosengren, E. (1956). *Naturwissenschaften* **43,** 521.
Bhagat, B. (1964). *Brit. J. Pharmacol.* **22,** 238.
Bhagat, B., and Shideman, F. E. (1963a), *J. Pharmacol.* **140,** 317.
Bhagat, B., and Shideman, F. E. (1963b). *Brit. J. Pharmacol.* **20,** 56.
Bhagat, B., Gordon, E. K., and Kopin, I. J. (1965). *J. Pharmacol.* **147,** 319.
Bisson, G. M., and Muscholl, E. (1962). *Arch. Exptl. Pathol. Pharmakol.* **244,** 185.
Blaschko, H. (1939). *J. Physiol. (London)* **96,** 50P.
Blaschko, H. (1952). *Pharmacol. Rev.* **4,** 415.
Blinks, J. R., and Koch-Weser, J. (1963). *Pharmacol. Rev.* **15,** 531.
Boura, A. L. A., and Green, A. F. (1959). *Brit. J. Pharmacol.* **14,** 536.
Brendel, W., Gladewitz, H., Hildebrandt, F., and Trautwein, W. (1951). *Cardiologia* **18,** 345.

Brodie, B. B., Chang, C. C., and Costa, E. (1965). *Brit. J. Pharmacol.* **25**, 171.
Burgen, A. S. V., and Iversen, L. L. (1965). *Brit. J. Pharmacol.* **25**, 34.
Burn, J. H., and Rand, M. J. (1958). *J. Physiol. (London)* **144**, 314.
Cairoli, V. J., Reilly, J. F., and Roberts, J. (1962). *Brit. J. Pharmacol.* **18**, 588.
Callingham, B. A., and Cass, R. (1962). *J. Pharm. Pharmacol.* **14**, 385.
Campos, H. A., and Shideman, F. E. (1962). *Intern. J. Neuropharmacol.* **1**, 13.
Campos, H. A., Stitzel, R. E., and Shideman, F. E. (1963). *J. Pharmacol.* **141**, 290.
Cass, R., and Spriggs, T. L. B. (1961). *Brit. J. Pharmacol.* **17**, 442.
Chang, C. C., Costa, E., and Brodie, B. B. (1965). *J. Pharmacol.* **147**, 303.
Chidsey, C. A., Harrison, D. C., and Braunwald, E. (1962). *Proc. Soc. Exptl. Biol. Med.* **109**, 488.
Chidsey, C. A., Braunwald, E., Morrow, A. G., and Mason, D. T. (1963a). *New Engl. J. Med.* **269**, 653.
Chidsey, C. A., Kahler, R. L., Kelminson, L. L., and Braunwald, E. (1963b). *Circulation Res.* **12**, 220.
Chidsey, C. A., Kaiser, G. A., and Braunwald, E. (1963c). *Science* **139**, 828.
Clementi, F., and Garbagnati, E. (1964). *In* "Electron Microscopy" (M. Titlbach, ed.), 3rd European Regional Conf. Electron Microscopy, pp. 305–306. Czechoslovak Acad. Sci., Prague.
Cobbin, L. B. (1959). Ph.D. Thesis, University of Sydney.
Corne, S. J., and Graham, J. D. P. (1957). *J. Physiol. (London)* **135**, 339.
Cotten, M. de V., and Pincus, S. (1955). *J. Pharmacol.* **114**, 110.
Creveling, C. R., Levitt, M., and Udenfriend, S. (1962). *Life Sci.* **10**, 523.
Crout, J. R., Muskus, A. J., and Trendelenburg, U. (1962). *Brit. J. Pharmacol.* **18**, 600.
Davey, M. J., and Farmer, J. B. (1963). *J. Pharm. Pharmacol.* **15**, 178.
Demis, D. J., Blaschko, H., and Welch, A. D. (1956). *J. Pharmacol.* **117**, 208.
Eccles, J. C. (1964). "The Physiology of Synapses." Academic Press, New York.
Edman, K. A. P. (1965). *Ann. Rev. Pharmacol.* **5**, 99.
Emmett, F. A. (1965). M.Sc. Thesis, University of Sydney.
Falck, B. (1962). *Acta Physiol. Scand.* **56**, Suppl. 197, 18.
Farrant, J. (1963). *Brit. J. Pharmacol.* **20**, 540.
Fawaz, G. (1963). *Ann. Rev. Pharmacol.* **3**, 57.
Fawaz, G., and Simaan, J. (1963). *Brit. J. Pharmacol.* **20**, 569.
Fawaz, G., and Tutunji, B. (1960). *Brit. J. Pharmacol.* **18**, 389.
Fleckenstein, H., and Bass, H. (1953). *Arch. Exptl. Pathol. Pharmakol.* **220**, 143.
Fleckenstein, H., and Burn, J. H. (1953). *Brit. J. Pharmacol.* **8**, 69.
Fleckenstein, H., and Stöckle, D. (1955). *Arch. Exptl. Pathol. Pharmakol.* **224**, 401.
Gaffney, T. E. (1961). *Circulation Res.* **9**, 83.
Gaffney, T. E., Braunwald, E., and Cooper, T. (1962a). *Circulation Res.* **10**, 83.
Gaffney, T. E., Morrow, D. H., and Chidsey, C. A. (1962b). *J. Pharmacol.* **137**, 301.
Gaffney, T. E., Chidsey, C. A., and Braunwald, E. (1963). *Circulation Res.* **12**, 264.
Gilbert, J. L., Lange, G., Polevoy, I., and Brooks, C. McC. (1958). *J. Pharmacol.* **123**, 9.
Glitsch, H. G., Haas, H. G., and Trautwein, W. (1965). *Arch. Exptl. Pathol. Pharmakol.* **250**, 59.

Goldberg, L. I., Cotten, M. de V., Darby, T. D., and Howell, E. V. (1953). *J. Pharmacol.* **108,** 177.

Goldberg, L. I., Bloodwell, R. D., Braunwald, E., and Morrow, A. G. (1960). *Circulation* **22,** 1125.

Goodall, McC. (1951). *Acta Physiol. Scand.* **24,** Suppl., 85.

Goodall, McC., and Kirshner, N. (1958). *Circulation* **17,** 366.

Green, A. F. (1960). *In* "Adrenergic Mechanisms" (G. E. W. Wolstenholme and M. O'Connor, eds.), pp. 148–157. Churchill, London.

Griesemer, E. C., Barksy, J., Dragstedt, C. A., Wells, J. A., and Zeller, E. A. (1953). *Proc. Soc. Exptl. Biol. Med.* **84,** 699.

Hagen, P. (1959). *Pharmacol. Rev.* **11,** 361.

Hagen, P., and Welsh, A. D. (1956). *Recent Progr. Hormone Res.* **12,** 27.

Harrison, D. C., Chidsey, C. A., and Braunwald, E. (1963a). *J. Pharmacol.* **141,** 22.

Harrison, D. C., Chidsey, C. A., and Braunwald, E. (1963b). *Proc. Soc. Exptl. Biol. Med.* **112,** 37.

Harrison, D. C., Chidsey, C. A., Goldman, R., and Braunwald, E. (1963c). *Circulation Res.* **12,** 256.

Haugaard, N., and Hess, M. E. (1965). *Pharmacol. Rev.* **17,** 27.

Hertting, G., Axelrod, J., and Patrick, R. W. (1962). *Brit. J. Pharmacol.* **18,** 161.

Hess, M. E., and Haugaard, N. (1958). *J. Pharmacol.* **122,** 169.

Hess, M. E., Shanfeld, J., and Haugaard, N. (1962). *Biochem. Pharmacol.* **11,** 1031.

Hirsch, E. F., William, V. L., Jellinek, M., and Cooper, T. (1963). *Arch. Pathol.* **76,** 677.

Hökfelt, B. (1951). *Acta Physiol. Scand.* **25,** Suppl. 92.

Holmes, J. C., and Fowler, N. O. (1962). *Circulation Res.* **10,** 68.

Holtz, P. (1939). *Naturwissenschaften* **27,** 724.

Holtz, P., Kroneberg, G., and Schümann, H. J. (1951). *Arch. Exptl. Pathol. Pharmakol.* **212,** 551.

Horwitz, D., Fox, S. M., and Goldberg, L. I. (1960). *Clin. Res.* **8,** 184.

Hukovič, S., and Muscholl, E. (1962). *Arch. Exptl. Pathol. Pharmakol.* **244,** 81.

Innes, I. R., and Krayer, O. (1958). *J. Pharmacol.* **124,** 245.

Iversen, L. L. (1963). *Brit. J. Pharmacol.* **21,** 523.

Iversen, L. L. (1965a). *Brit. J. Pharmacol.* **24,** 387.

Iversen, L. L. (1965b). *Brit. J. Pharmacol.* **25,** 18.

Iversen, L. L., and Whitby, L. G. (1962). *Brit. J. Pharmacol.* **19,** 355.

Jedeikin, L. A. (1964). *Circulation Res.* **14,** 202.

Kimata, S. (1965). *Japan. Circulation J.* **29,** 11.

Kirshner, N. (1959). *Pharmacol. Rev.* **11,** 350.

Kirshner, N., and Goodall, McC. (1957). *Federation Proc.* **16,** 73.

Klingman, G. I. (1965). *J. Pharmacol.* **148,** 14.

Klouda, M. A. (1963). *Proc. Soc. Exptl. Biol. Med.* **112,** 728.

Koch-Weser, J. (1963). *Biochem. Pharmacol.* **12,** Suppl., p. 190.

Koch-Weser, J., and Blinks, J. R. (1963). *Pharmacol. Rev.* **15,** 601.

Kopin, I. J., and Gordon, E. K. (1962). *J. Pharmacol.* **138,** 351.

Kopin, I. J., and Gordon, E. K. (1963). *Nature* **199,** 1289.

Krebs, E. G., Graves, D. J., and Fischer, E. H. (1959). *J. Biol. Chem.* **234**, 2867.

Kroneberg, G., and Schümann, H. J. (1962). *Arch. Exptl. Pathol. Pharmakol.* **243**, 16.

Kukovetz, W. R., Hess, M. E., Shanefeld, J., and Haugaard, N. (1959). *J. Pharmacol.* **127**, 122.

Kuntzman, R., Costa, E., Gessa, G. L., and Brodie, B. B. (1962). *Life Sci.* **1**, 65.

Kuschinsky, G., Lindmar, R., Lüllmann, H., and Muscholl, E. (1960). *Arch. Exptl. Pathol. Pharmakol.* **240**, 242.

Lands, A. M., and Howard, J. W. (1952). *J. Pharmacol.* **106**, 65.

Lee, W. C., and Shideman, F. E. (1959). *Science* **129**, 967.

Levi-Montalcini, R. (1964). *Science* **143**, 105.

Levitt, M., Spector, S., Sjoerdsma, A., and Udenfriend, S. (1965). *J. Pharmacol.* **148**, 1.

Lindmar, R., and Muscholl, E. (1961). *Arch. Exptl. Pathol. Pharmakol.* **242**, 214.

McCarty, L. P., Lee, W. C., and Shideman, F. E. (1960). *J. Pharmacol.* **129**, 315.

McDonald, R. H., and Goldberg, L. I. (1963). *J. Pharmacol.* **140**, 60.

Mansour, T. E. (1963). *J. Biol. Chem.* **238**, 2285.

Marchetti, P. G., Maccari, M., and Merlo, L. (1963). *Cardiologia* **42**, 1.

Marks, B. H. (1964). *Ann. Rev. Pharmacol.* **4**, 155.

Marks, B. H., Samorajski, T., and Webster, E. J. (1962). *J. Pharmacol.* **138**, 376.

Matsuo, T., and Tachi, S. (1962). *Japan. J. Pharmacol.* **12**, 191.

Maxwell, G. M., Rowe, G. G., Castillo, C. A., Clifford, J. E., Afonso, S., and Crumpton, C. W. (1960). *Arch. Intern. Pharmacodynamie* **129**, 62.

Maxwell, R., Kelley, J. J., and Eckhardt, E. T. (1964). *Proc. Soc. Exptl. Biol. Med.* **116**, 672.

Mayer, S. E., and Moran, N. C. (1960). *J. Pharmacol.* **129**, 271.

Mayer, S. E., Cotten, M. de V., and Moran, N. C. (1963). *J. Pharmacol.* **139**, 275.

Montagu, K. A. (1956). *Biochem. J.* **63**, 559.

Montanari, R., Costa, E., Beaven, M. A., and Brodie, B. B. (1963). *Life Sci.* **4**, 232.

Moore, J. I., and Moran, N. C. (1962). *J. Pharmacol.* **136**, 89.

Murad, F., Chi, Y. M., Rall, T. W., and Sutherland, E. W. (1962). *J. Biol. Chem.* **237**, 1233.

Muscholl, E. (1959). *Arch. Exptl. Pathol. Pharmakol.* **237**, 350.

Nayler, W. G. (1963). *J. Phamacol.* **139**, 222.

Øye, I., Butcher, R. W., Morgan, H. E., and Sutherland, E. W. (1964). *Federation Proc.* **23**, 562.

Patil, P. N., Tye, A., and La Pidus, J. B. (1965). *J. Pharmacol.* **148**, 158.

Porter, C. C., Totaro, J. A., and Stone, J. A. (1963). *J. Pharmacol.* **140**, 308.

Potter, L. T., and Axelrod, J. (1962). *Nature* **194**, 581.

Potter, L. T., and Axelrod, J. (1963a). *J. Pharmacol.* **140**, 199.

Potter, L. T., and Axelrod, J. (1963b). *J. Pharmacol.* **142**, 291.

Potter, L. T., and Axelrod, J. (1963c). *J. Pharmacol.* **142**, 299.

Potter, L. T., Axelrod, J., and Kopin, I. J. (1962). *Federation Proc.* **21**, 177.

Potter, L. T., Cooper, T., William V. L., and Wolfe, D. E. (1965). *Circulation Res.* **16**, 468.

Raab, W., and Gigee, W. (1955). *Circulation* **11**, 593.

Rall, T. W., and Sutherland, E. W. (1961). *Cold Spring Harbor Symp. Quant. Biol.* **36,** 347.

Reiter, M., and Schöber, H. G. (1965). *Arch. Exptl. Pathol. Pharmakol.* **250,** 9.

Riley, G. A., and Haynes, R. C. (1963). *J. Biol. Chem.* **238,** 1563.

Roberts, J., and Modell, W. (1961). *Circulation Res.* **9,** 171.

Romanoff, A. L. (1960). "The Avian Embryo." Macmillan, New York.

Schanker, L. S., and Morrison, A. (1965). *Intern. J. Neurophysiol.* **4,** 27.

Schümann, H. J. (1958). *Arch. Exptl. Pathol. Pharmakol.* **234,** 17.

Shore, P. A. (1962). *Pharmacol. Rev.* **14,** 531.

Shore, P. A., Cohn, V. H., Highman, B., and Maling, H. M. (1958). *Nature* **181,** 848.

Siebens, A. A., Hoffman, B. F., Ensor, Y., Farrell, J. E., and Brooks, C. McC. (1953). *Am. J. Physiol.* **175,** 1.

Sonnenblick, E. H. (1962). *Am. J. Physiol.* **202,** 931.

Sonnenblick, E. H., and Downing, S. E. (1963). *Am. J. Physiol.* **204,** 604.

Spann, J. F., Chidsey, C. A., and Braunwald, E. (1964). *Science* **145,** 1439.

Spector, S., Melman, K., Lovenberg, W., and Sjoerdsma, A. (1963a). *J. Pharmacol.* **140,** 229.

Spector, S., Sjoerdsma, A., Zaltzman-Nirenberg, P., Levitt, M., and Udenfriend, S. (1963b). *Science* **139,** 1299.

Stromblad, B. C. R., and Nickerson, M. (1961). *J. Pharmacol.* **134,** 154.

Sutherland, E. W., Rall, T. W., and Menon, T. (1962). *J. Biol. Chem.* **237,** 1220.

Sutherland, E. W., Øye, I., and Butcher, R. W. (1965). *Recent Progr. Hormone Res.* **21,** 623.

Takeuchi, T., and Kuriaki, H. (1955). *J. Histochem. Cytochem.* **3,** 153.

Trautwein, W., and Schmidt, R. F. (1960). *Arch. Ges. Physiol.* **271,** 715.

Trendelenburg, U. (1959). *J. Pharmacol.* **125,** 55.

Trendelenburg, U. (1961). *J. Pharmacol.* **134,** 8.

Trendelenburg, U. (1965). *J. Pharmacol.* **147,** 313.

Udenfriend, S., and Wyngaarden, I. B. (1956). *Biochim. Biophys. Acta* **20,** 48.

Vane, J. R. (1959). *Brit. J. Pharmacol.* **14,** 87.

von Euler, U. S. (1954). *Pharmacol. Rev.* **6,** 15.

von Euler, U. S. (1956). "Noradrenaline." Thomas, Springfield, Illinois.

von Euler, U. S. (1958). *Acta Physiol. Scand.* **43,** 155.

von Euler, U. S. and Hellner-Björckman, S. (1955). *Acta Physiol. Scand.* **33,** Suppl. 118, 17.

Wallace, A. G., Mitchell, J. H., Skinner, N. S., and Sarnoff, S. J. (1963). *Circulation Res.* **12,** 611.

Waud, D. R., Kottegoda, S. R., and Krayer, O. (1958). *J. Pharmacol.* **124,** 340.

Waugh, W. H. (1964). *In* "Muscle," Proc. Symp. Univ. of Alberta, Edmonton, Alberta, pp. 253–266. Pergamon Press, Oxford.

West, T. C., and Rushmer, R. F. (1957). *J. Pharmacol.* **120,** 361.

Whitby, L. G., Axelrod, J., and Weil-Malherbe, H. (1961). *J. Pharmacol.* **132,** 193.

Wilber, J. A., and Brust, A. A. (1958). *J. Clin. Invest.* **37,** 476.

Williamson, J. R., and Jamieson, D. (1965). *Nature* **206,** 364.

Winbury, M. M. (1964). *Advan. Pharmacol.* **3,** 1.

Withrington, P., and Zaimis, E. (1961). *Brit. J. Pharmacol.* **17,** 380.
Yunis, A. A., Fischer, E. H., and Krebs, E. G. (1962). *J. Biol. Chem.* **237,** 2809.
Zaimis, E. (1964). *Ann. Rev. Pharmacol.* **4,** 365.
Zaimis, E. (1965). *J. Physiol. (London)* **177,** 35P.
Zanetti, M. E., and Opdyke, D. F. (1953). *J. Pharmacol.* **109,** 107.

CHAPTER 7

NATURALLY OCCURRING CARDIOTONIC
SUBSTANCES OF ANIMAL ORIGIN

I. Historical Introduction: The Concept of a Cardiac Hormone

It is well known that substances which occur naturally in the body have direct effects upon the heart. The actions of the catecholamines have already been considered in Chapter 6. In this chapter, the actions upon the heart of naturally occurring chemical substances, whether completely characterized or not, will be considered.

It has been known since the early experiments of Sidney Ringer in 1885 that serum has a stimulant action upon the isolated heart. Confirmation of Ringer's findings was provided in 1913 by A. J. Clark who showed that prolonged perfusion of an isolated frog's heart with Ringer's solution led to the development of a hypodynamic state which could be reversed by the addition of serum from the frog or from other species, and which was accompanied by restoration of oxygen consumption to normal levels. The stimulant substance was found in alcoholic extracts of serum and was not destroyed by saponification, and Clark suggested that the active substance was a soap, which exerted its action by effects on the fixation of calcium on the surface of the heart muscle.

While discussing the biological importance of animal saponins and sapotoxins, Faust (1921) defined saponins, in terms of the available knowledge at this period, as nitrogen-free compounds of high molecular weight of which a solution in water foams as that of a soap. Some sapotoxins, such as bufotalin secreted by the toad have a digitalis-like action upon the heart, and Faust proposed that perhaps animals produce their own "digitalis" even under normal conditions. In his view, medical administration of digitalis would thus cause an increase in a normal physiological function by the addition of a preformed active substance. He also considered that there was a pharmacological and perhaps even a chemical link between the "physiological digitalis" and adrenaline. It is interesting to note in passing that the same speculation about a naturally occurring physiological "digitalis" has been made in more recent times by Szent-Györgyi in 1953 and about which more will be said later.

During the 1920's a considerable number of research investigations were performed on the activities of a variety of tissue extracts upon isolated test objects among which the isolated heart was widely used. The aim of these investigations was to discover pharmacologically active substances which would help to explain some fundamental physiological mechanisms. As many tissue extracts exerted effects upon isolated perfused hearts, it is not surprising that the notion of a specific cardiac hormone began to develop. The properties of such an hypothetical substance were never clearly defined, but as time proceeded it became clear that tissue extracts containing substances which produced coronary dilatation were acceptable as "cardiac hormones."

During the course of a comprehensive survey of the physiology of organs, Asher and his colleagues showed particular interest in the liver. It was observed that fluids perfused through the liver acquired an adrenaline-like property when tested subsequently upon the isolated hearts of frogs or turtles (Asher and Takahashi, 1924; Asher, 1925). It was shown that improvements in cardiac performance could not be explained in terms of pH (Asher and Richardet, 1925). Extracts of liver were prepared which were capable of increasing the cardiac output and blood pressure in mammals (Asher, 1926). Similar effects were observed following the administration of cholates, and this work was rounded off with the suggestion that the liver added cholates to the blood or perfusion fluid which then produced the observed improvements in cardiac function (Asher and Beyeler, 1926).

Extracts of the auricular tissue of dogs were found to stimulate the perfused rabbit heart (Demoor, 1922), and similar results were reported for extracts of auricle, AV node, and ventricle upon the frog heart (Haberlandt, 1925). Subsequently, Haberlandt (1929) prepared a "heart hormone" from beef heart, alleged to be a sterile solution free of protein, lipid, adrenaline, and histamine which was capable of arresting auricular fibrillation in the warm-blooded heart, and which augmented the rate and amplitude of the frog heart. Repetition of this work by Oppenheimer (1929) showed that extracts of cardiac tissue produced inconstant effects upon isolated perfused hearts and suggested that the substance responsible could be histamine. Oppenheimer also showed that the heart was not the only tissue from which cardiac stimulant extracts could be prepared, and that extracts of skeletal and smooth muscles, liver, and lung also possessed stimulant properties upon the perfused heart. She concluded that her results did not confirm the hypothesis of a specific cardiac hormone, but merely supported the view that there was a substance distributed throughout the tissues which in suitable concentrations caused augmentation of the heart beat.

Zuelzer was also interested in the concept of a cardiac hormone and prepared an extract of liver which was tested initially on frog hearts and heart-lung preparations before being administered to selected clinical cases (Salomon and Zuelzer, 1929). A standardized liver extract was made according to Zuelzer's process and was commercially available under the name of "Eutonon." Eventually this was disclosed as a 7.5% solution of a special extract of deproteinized liver processed with 2.5% dextrose and alleged to be free from hemopoietic factors, protein, α-amino acids, adrenaline-like materials, histamine, choline, and acetylcholine (Zuelzer, 1942). However, earlier examinations of Eutonon by other workers revealed the presence of choline and tyramine (Heinsen, 1934). Although it was claimed that Eutonon arrested failure in the dog heart-lung preparation (Zuelzer, 1930), no great effects on cardiac output, coronary flow, or heart rate were found in the same preparation by Krayer (1933) although the doses used in the latter experiments were rather small. Zuelzer proposed Eutonon as a specific cardiac hormone differing from digitalis in possessing a wide safety margin without toxic effects, no danger of accumulation, central nervous, or diuretic actions. Owing to its coronary dilator action, Eutonon was claimed to render frog and cat hearts resistant to the toxic action of digitalis. "Cortunon," an identical preparation to Eutonon, has been shown more recently to cause vasodilatation in isolated perfused hearts which cannot be explained by the presence of histamine (Melville, 1948) or parasympathomimetic substances (Lu, 1950).

At the end of the second decade of this century, extracts prepared from many tissues were commercially available for clinical treatment requiring coronary vasodilatation. It was found that many of these extracts exhibited essentially similar actions upon the circulations of the dog and the rabbit and therefore it was proposed that the extracts contained a similar substance (Hochrein and Keller, 1931). Shortly afterward, many commercial preparations were shown to contain adenyl compounds (Lindner and Rigler, 1931; Heinsen, 1933; Joos, 1933; Drury, 1936), histamine, or a closely allied substance (Heinsen and Wolf, 1934), and that some exhibited coenzyme properties and should therefore be regarded as coenzymes (Brügsch *et al.,* 1931). Drury (1936) suggested that cozymase might account for the depressor effects of tissue extracts. These various findings are summarized in Table 7.1 which has been adapted from Drury (1936).

It is interesting that the presence of adenyl compounds alone cannot explain the coronary dilator properties of all these commercial extracts. This fact was pointed out by Joos (1932) and can be seen from Table 7.1. The presence of histamine, shown by Heinsen and Wolf

Table 7.1

The Nature of Active Materials in Commercial Tissue Extracts
Used for Cardiac Treatment in the 1930's[a]

Preparation	Source	Adenyl compounds	Histamine	Coenzyme characteristics
Eutonon	Liver	Conflicting reports (2)	Absent (7)	Yes (1)
Campolon	Liver	Absent (2, 3)	Present (4)	—
Degewop	Liver	Occasionally present (2, 3)	Present (4)	—
Hepatrat	Liver	Absent (2, 3)	Present (4)	—
Hepatopson	Liver	Absent (2) Present (3)	Present (4)	—
Schwarzmann's extract	Muscle	Absent (2)	—	—
Lacarnol	Muscle	Present (2, 5, 6)	—	Yes (1)
Myoston	Muscle	Present (2, 5)	—	—
Angioxyl	Pancreas	Absent (2)	—	—
Padutin	Pancreas	Absent (2)	—	Yes (1)
Hormocardiol	Sinus of heart	Present (2)	—	—

[a] The numbers in parentheses refer to the sources listed below, and the dashes indicate that no information is available.

Sources: 1, Brugsch *et al.* (1931); 2, Drury (1936); 3, Heinsen (1933); 4, Heinsen and Wolf (1934); 5, Joos (1933); 6, Lindner and Rigler (1931); 7, Melville (1948).

(1934), together with an earlier suggestion (Best *et al.,* 1927) that histamine and choline are extracted from liver in sufficient quantities to account for the vasodilator activity of liver extracts, may explain the activity of preparations in which adenyl compounds could not be found. The recognition of the most likely compounds responsible for dilator activity is doubtless one reason for the disappearance of these crude tissue extracts from commercial production.

It has been mentioned that Eutonon was found to contain choline and tyramine (Heinsen, 1934). The latter substance was found to occur in liver extracts exposed to air for 24–48 hours and to cause an adrenaline-like effect upon the heart and circulation. Many of the commercial preparations used to treat coronary insufficiency were also found to contain tyramine (Grabe *et al.,* 1934). This same substance has recently been found in commercial liver extracts and has been shown to be at least partly responsible for positive inotropic activity observed on isolated papillary muscles by Green and Nahum (1957), who suggested that its presence in extracts is due to bacterial contamination as neither tyrosine nor tyrosine decarboxylase occur normally in mammalian tissues (Hagen and Welch, 1956).

From the foregoing discussion, it will be seen that the early notions of a "cardiac hormone" present in mammalian tissues tended to become centered around substances capable of producing coronary dilatation. Although suggestions had been made that the tissues might contain a digitalis-like substance, the available techniques for testing tissue extracts for digitalis-like activity were far from reliable. The limitations of perfused hearts as indicators of positive inotropic activity are well known, and it is recognized that amplitude of contractions recorded from such preparations are dependent upon other variables such as coronary flow and heart rate. Indeed, substances which increase coronary flow or accelerate the heart rate can often cause an increased amplitude of contraction which is secondary to increase in flow or rate. It was not until 1938 when Cattell and Gold described their isolated papillary muscle preparation that there was available a technique which could detect direct or primary inotropic actions of drugs or extracts on cardiac muscle independently of other variables. Following the description of this technique, others have been developed to demonstrate inotropic actions—for example, isolated auricle or ventricular strip preparations, both of which can be driven electrically in order to keep the rate of contraction constant, and thereby eliminate secondary apparent inotropic effects due solely to alterations in this variable.

We will now consider some experiments which have suggested that mammalian tissues do in fact contain substances with a digitalis-like action. Mention has been made of the early experiments of Asher and Takahashi (1924), in which it was shown that fluid perfused through the liver became positively inotropic when tested on isolated frog and turtle hearts. These observations were confirmed by Roncato (1930) on a Starling heart-lung preparation. When the blood was allowed to perfuse the liver, it acquired a cardiac stimulant action which disappeared after traversing the heart and lungs. From these experiments Roncato concluded that the liver did not detoxify the blood but added either a stimulant or nutrient substance to it which was rapidly absorbed by the heart. The nature of the added substance remained obscure but the effects of hepatic blood were not mimicked by additions of glucose or bile ingredients (Bassani, 1933a,b). Other workers found that inclusion of the liver in a heart-lung circuit produced cardiac responses which resembled those given by small doses of adrenaline, and they suggested that the liver might be contributing small amounts of sympathomimetic amines to the blood perfusing the preparation (Kiese *et al.*, 1936).

These experiments were extended by Rein (1942) who showed that the progressive failure of a heart-lung preparation could be reversed by including the liver in the circuit. Similarly, if the liver was excluded from the circulation of an intact animal, the heart showed signs of progressive deterioration, which could be reversed almost immediately upon reintroduction of the liver. This type of cardiac failure was enhanced by hypoxia, and the diminishing performance was shown to be associated with increased oxygen consumption. The failure was not due to a fall in the blood sugar level and the experimental set-up precluded hemodynamic causes. The liver was thought to play an important part in the oxidative metabolism of the heart, and since small doses of strophanthin exerted similar effects on the failing heart, Rein concluded that it was not beyond the bounds of possibility that the liver was capable of supplying the heart with a material chemically similar to strophanthin.

In the same year, Pinotti (1942), working independently with heart-lung-liver preparations, provided confirmation of Rein's findings. He demonstrated that under the influence of the liver, cardiac energy metabolism proceeded with greater economy and efficiency. Measurement of cardiac work and oxygen consumption showed that the liver factor was labile and had a short duration of action. Although he could not state the chemical nature of the liver substance, Pinotti was of the opinion that it was unlikely to be a sympathomimetic amine or glucose, and agreed with Rein's suggestion that a steroid might be implicated. Further evidence was provided that glucose was not the active substance when it was shown that the diminished cardiac performance following exclusion of the liver from the circulation could be reversed for periods of 6 to 10 minutes by the addition of fresh whole blood (Poli and Rossi, 1949). Poli and Rossi showed that the effect was not mechanical since it was absent after glucose or saline additions, and they concluded that their results supported those of Rein and Pinotti, as it was assumed that fresh whole blood had traversed the liver circulatory pathways.

In the course of further investigations of the influence of the liver upon cardiac function, a new theory concerning the physiological role of the liver emerged. Rein and associates (1949) suggested that although the liver was obviously concerned with pure ingestive functions, it also played an important part in regulating the oxidative balance of the organism, this function becoming more prominent when the organism was suffering from conditions of oxygen insufficiency, and it was shown to be of particular importance in regulating cardiac function during hypoxia. In enabling the organism to overcome the stress of hypoxia, the liver did not appear to exert its beneficial action upon the heart by nervous reflexes, because stimulation of the cut ends of the nerves supplying the liver hilus had no effect. Presuming that this function of the liver was mediated by humoral substances, it was then shown that acetylcholine and histamine administered transhepatically (via the portal vein) had no effect on the failing heart. Similarly, physiological doses of adrenaline administered by this route also failed to overcome the effects of cardiac hypoxia, although when administered via the peripheral circulation the recovery of the heart was dramatic provided that hypotension and cardiac failure were not too far advanced (Bücherl and Rein, 1949). In view of the long latent period between injection and response, 20–40 seconds, the authors gained the impression that the effect of intravenous adrenaline was not a result of direct action on the heart. Because of their experience concerning the sensitivity of the spleen to adrenaline, they considered that adrenaline might stimulate the spleen to release a substance which was not acetylcholine, histamine, or adrenaline, and which in some manner enabled the liver to overcome the hypoxic crisis.

During cardiac hypoxia produced by partial occlusion of the coronary arteries, stimulation of the splenic nerves resulted in the release of a substance transported via the portal vein to the liver, where it caused release of a specific hormonal substance into the blood stream which in turn enabled the heart to overcome the insufficiency brought' about by hypoxia (Bücherl and Rein, 1949). This mechanism was called the "Spleen-Liver reaction," and the substance released from the spleen was termed "Hypoxie-lienen." Blood obtained from the splenic veins of a donor animal during a period of electrical stimulation of the splenic nerves was shown to overcome the effects of hypoxia in a recipient animal when administered transhepatically, in a similar manner to that seen on stimulating the splenic nerves of the recipient. It was shown that cardiac hypoxia was a serious disturbance in splenectomized animals, but splenic blood from a donor animal, administered transhepatically to the splenectomized animal, was able to overcome the untoward effects of the hypoxic condition to a considerable degree (Rein, 1951).

Characteristically, the spleen-liver reaction involves increased blood flow through the hepatic artery and a sustained increase in the aortic blood pressure (Meesmann, and Schmier, 1955). These same authors showed that the coronary blood flow decreased during the spleen-liver reaction but the heart showed no signs of lack of blood (Meesmann and Schmier, 1956a). Measurements of oxygen uptake and carbon dioxide liberation by the heart revealed that these two parameters decreased upon stimulation of the splenic nerves, while anaerobic metabolism remained constant as pyruvate and lactate consumption were not changed (Meesmann and Schmier, 1956b). Because the work of the heart did not decrease during the spleen-liver reaction, these authors concluded that the efficiency of the heart had been improved by means of the spleen-liver reaction. These findings have been confirmed in heart-lung preparations to which spleen and liver from donor animals were added to the perfusion circuit when required (Kako et al., 1960).

Meesmann and Schmier (1955) noted that although intravenous or transhepatic administration of noradrenaline produced rises in systemic blood pressure and hepatic blood flow, the actions were of short duration and could be readily distinguished from those of splenic nerve stimulation. They concluded that neither noradrenaline nor adrenaline were wholly responsible for the mediation of the spleen-liver reaction. It has been suggested that deficiencies of cholinergic and adrenergic substances in the perfusion fluid may be a contributing factor in the decline in mechanical efficiency of the isolated heart-lung preparation (Kako, *et al.,* 1960), but other factors may also be involved. It has been suggested (Danforth *et al.,* 1960) that the beneficial results of inclusion of the spleen and liver in a spontaneously failing heart-lung preparation may be due to restoration of the depleted supply of catecholamines, as it is known that noradrenaline is present in some quantity in these tissues. It has been shown by Danforth *et al.* (1960) that administration of dopa to the perfusion fluid results in an inotropic action which is due to conversion of the dopa to dopamine and noradrenaline. When this effect had worn off and the heart was again in failure, the levels of noradrenaline in the heart remained elevated. Thus the role of noradrenaline in spontaneous failure is not clear and the question whether the spleen and liver supply noradrenaline has not yet been unequivocally solved. Other substances have been studied by transhepatic administration in an endeavor to identify the humoral factor involved in the spleen-liver reaction. These included ferritin, levulose, glucose, lactate, potassium phosphate, kallikrein, adenyl phosphates, 5-hydroxytryptamine, and commercial spleen extract and liver hydrolyzate. All these substances caused coronary vasodilatation instead of the coronary constriction characteristic of the spleen-liver reaction (Meesmann and Schmier, 1956c).

Further study of the effects of liver and splenic venous blood from donor animals added to the venous reservoir of heart-lung preparations were conducted (Alella *et al.,* 1960). These authors showed that splenic and hepatic venous blood produced long-lasting effects similar to those of the spleen-liver reaction observed in whole animals on stimulation of the splenic nerves. These reactions were rarely seen following additions of similar quantities of venous or arterial blood, and the magnitudes and durations of the responses were much less. Areskog (1962a) found it difficult to repeat these experiments, but did show that hepatic venous blood obtained after splenic nerve stimulation contained an elevated K^+ concentration which could possibly obscure an inotropic effect. Splenic blood differed from liver blood in that it caused an increase in coronary blood flow instead of the characteristic decrease found during the spleen-liver reaction or following additions of liver venous blood. This suggests that both liver and splenic venous blood contain cardioactive substances which are possibly different chemically. Schmier (1958) has suggested that hypoxia is not required for the elaboration nor for the action of the active substance in liver venous blood, and certainly, in the spontaneous myocardial insufficiency exhibited by the heart-lung preparation, the additions of liver or splenic venous blood restore the mechanical efficiency of the preparation, in a similar fashion to whole animals in a hypoxic state.

Hatcher and his colleagues (1963) have investigated the cardiovascular adjustments which follow the rapid production of hemorrhagic anemia in dogs after dextran-for-blood exchange. They have shown that recovery involves two phases. Immediate adjustments of the circulatory and respiratory systems to maintain tissue metabolism take place during the first 3 hours, and during this phase there is a more economical utilization of available oxygen. It seems likely that the sympathetic nervous system plays a part in maintaining a high cardiac output during this period (Hatcher *et al.,* 1959), although there is some evidence to the contrary.

During the following 10 days there are long-term cardiovascular compensations which, it has been suggested, involve a humoral mechanism (Hatcher *et al.,* 1954; Justus *et al.,* 1957).

When blood is transfused from such anemic dogs into normal animals arranged for assays of cardiac performance there is no cardiotonic effect if the blood is taken 1 hour after anemia production in the donor dog, but if the blood is taken from 3 hours to 8–9 days after anemia production the blood exhibits cardiotonic activity which is not seen in blood from normal donor dogs. Hatcher considers that these results indicate the presence of a transferable humoral agent capable of inducing cardiovascular changes in a normal dog, which resemble long-term cardiovascular adjustments in anemic dogs. The agent appears to be resistant to destruction since the stimulant effect in the assay dogs persists for several hours. The slow appearance of the cardiotonic agent may reflect the time requirement for its production or may be due to the severe immediate anoxia during the first hour after blood-dextran exchange. The occurrence of cardiotonic activity observed in these experiments was shown not to be caused by the presence of dextran itself or to be produced by it.

The nature of the cardiotonic agent in these experiments is unknown and its role in homeostatic adjustments in anemic anoxia must await its isolation and the development of an appropriate and sensitive assay method.

On the basis of these experiments there is a very strong suggestion that some tissues contain cardioactive substances which differ from the catecholamines and which have a resemblance to the cardiac glycosides in their actions on the heart. Further, if these substances exist, then it is possible that they serve a physiological function in supplementing nervous mechanisms in the regulation of cardiac performance under certain conditions. If cardioactive substances exist in the tissues in a preformed state then it should be possible to extract them from the tissues and subsequently purify the extracts and isolate active chemical substances. The description in the following pages is concerned with recent work designed to explore the questions of evidence and the identity of cardiotonic substances extracted from various tissues. It is thought that some of these substances may have been hitherto unknown chemically or, alternatively, have not been suspected of possible cardioregulatory function. This is a field which is still in its infancy, and consequently there are few well-established reference points; however, the evidence that animal organisms contain substances for humoral regulation of the heart is accumulating and must therefore be considered seriously by all students of cardiac function. It was implied that such substances exist, and that they act in a manner similar to digitalis by Szent-Györgyi (1953) from whom we quote: "As far as I am aware the medical practitioner looks upon digitalis as upon an artificial drug to which he can resort if all other means fail and if the heart has begun to decompensate and has entered upon its last vicious circle. The digitalis glycosides, if I may say so, are no drugs at all. They are substitutes for a missing screw in our machinery, which had a role in one of the most basic physiological regulations."

Some of the substances which have been examined for the role of the "missing screw" include various steroids, polypeptides, and tissue extracts. We shall deal with these in turn. As the toad poisons are cardiotonic steroids which closely resemble the cardiac glycosides chemically and pharmacologically, and the latter have already been considered in Chapter 3, no further mention will be made of these. There is some evidence of new naturally occurring cardiotonic substances being present in invertebrates and other nonmammalian species. Their functions are as yet obscure but it is possible that they act as autopharmacological agents in their own species regulating the performance of the heart. When isolated in purified form these substances could well be tested for activity on mammalian hearts.

II. Steroids

Because of their apparent structural resemblance to the plant glycosides, the steroids which occur in animal organisms have been examined for their cardiotonic properties. However, in general (and with the exception of the toad poisons), the steroids occurring naturally in animals have little cardiotonic action in physiological concentration and this may be related to the steric configuration of the molecule (Bush, 1962; Tamm, 1963). The principal steroids include cholesterol, and those derived from the gonads and the suprarenal cortex. Bile salts do not have marked inotropic actions on perfused frog or rabbit hearts, and only slight increases in force of contraction have been observed (Loynes and Gowdey, 1952).

Cholesterol in purified form has slight positive inotropic effects in concentrations of 10 μg per milliliter on hypodynamic frog and rabbit heart preparations, (Loynes and Gowdey, 1952), but Green (1952) found that cat papillary muscles did not respond with increased force of contraction.

Among the steroids derived from the sexual organs and suprarenal cortex only progesterone showed pronounced diminution or abolition of the staircase phenomenon in the frog heart, although the effect was also seen to a slight degree with cortisone, estrone, and testosterone (Hajdu and Szent-Györgyi, 1952). The results derived from cat papillary muscles (Emele and Bonnycastle, 1956) showed that small concentrations of some adrenal steroids exerted very slight positive inotropic effects, but deoxycorticosterone was without action until concentrations of the order of 0.5% were employed, and then a purely depressant result was observed. Mixtures of naturally occurring adrenal steroids did not cause a spectacular increase in the tension developed by isolated papillary muscles. These experiments were verified (Cobbin, 1959) when it was found that corticosterone caused a very slight increase in force of contraction of papillary muscles in a concentration of 5×10^{-7} gm per milliliter in 2 out of 8 experiments, the remaining 6 showing no effect. Similarly, all concentrations of deoxycorticosterone showed either no effect or a decline in amplitude. All other steroids tested showed no change or slight depressant effects. An opposite finding on dog heart-lung preparations has been reported (Areskog, 1962b,c) where deoxycorticosterone was reported to show an obvious positive inotropic effect, but corticosterone was without effect. On rat heart-lung preparations, agreement with the findings on isolated papillary muscles has been reported for corticosterone, small concentrations increasing the left ventricular work index but larger concentrations caused a decrease in this parameter (Sayers and Solomon, 1960). Although other workers have reported positive inotropic actions for naturally occurring steroids, in the opinion of the authors, these findings do not represent significant changes — such as are seen in response to the catecholamines, cardiac glycosides, or some tissue extracts. We are in agreement with the view expressed by Szent-Györgyi that these substances cannot account for the inotropic activity of plasma. It would seem that many of the effects reported are "pharmacological" effects produced by concentrations of these hormones which are unrelated to the levels found in plasma under physiological conditions.

The situation with respect to aldosterone is worthy of summary. There are few reports of negative inotropic actions of aldosterone, but in some instances there have been statements that this steroid is without effect on cardiac muscle. In the dog heart-lung preparation aldosterone had no action (Areskog, 1962c), and no significant effects were found on electrically stimulated isolated rabbit auricles (Levy and Richards, 1962a), or the tension developed by isolated trabeculae carnae from rat hearts (Ullrick and Hazelwood, 1963), or isolated cat papillary muscles (Cobbin, 1959). Other authors report that aldosterone has a positive inotropic action.

Monkey papillary muscles showed slight positive inotropic responses at concentrations between 10^{-12} and 10^{-11} gm per milliliter whereas 10^{-9} gm per milliliter produced negative inotropic actions (Nayler, 1965). The lowest concentration used in our own experiments with cat papillary muscles was 10^{-9} gm per milliliter, and no effects were observed, either positive or negative. A similar concentration, 10^{-11} gm per milliliter, was found to cause small increases in contractile force of cat papillary muscles (Tanz, 1962). In Nayler's and Tanz's experiments, the time for maximum effect was in excess of one hour. This may explain why Cobbin found no action, for in his experiments the drug was only in the bath for approximately 5 minutes.

Using isolated rat heart-lung preparations, Ballard and co-workers (1960) reported an increase in the left ventricular work index of adrenalectomized rats after doses of aldosterone. If preparations were made from intact rats, and then perfused with blood from adrenalecto-mized rats, plasma extracts of normal rats could restore the left ventricular work index to normal, but extracts of adrenalectomized rats plasma had no such restorative action on the preparation. Whether aldosterone is responsible for the effects of normal extracts remains unsolved. Essentially similar results have been reported (Sayers and Solomon, 1960). The molar concentrations of aldosterone needed to produce these effects are extremely low, and it has been suggested that there is an antagonism between aldosterone and ouabain in similar molar concentrations, for mixtures of the two never showed inotropic responses although either alone would do so (Levy and Richards, 1962b; Lefer and Sayers, 1964).

In open-chest anesthetized dogs, small doses of aldosterone within a very restricted range were shown to produce increased left ventricular contractile force of short duration following intravenous administration (Lichtlen *et al.,* 1964). In summary, it would appear that the effects of aldosterone upon cardiac tissues are very slight and of doubtful significance, and it seems that aldosterone cannot be thought to play an important role in the regulation of cardiac performance.

III. The Actions of Naturally Occurring Polypeptides

Over the last decade, interest has become focused more intensely on the naturally occurring polypeptides found in mammalian organisms. As these substances are being isolated in pure form and their structures determined and confirmed by synthesis, their pharmacological actions are becoming more clearly understood, but as yet their physiological significance is often quite obscure. The apparent primary physiological roles of oxytocin and antidiuretic hormone (vasopressin) are well known, but secondary actions which may be either physiological or pharmacological are gradually being found as more knowledge concerning their actions and interactions with other substances on physiological systems is described. It would appear from reported evidence that neither of these posterior pituitary octapeptides is concerned with regulation of cardiac function despite the fact that antidiuretic hormone has the secondary pharmacological action (as distinct from physiological) of causing quite profound pressor effects in mammals, and in fact is one of the rare substances which produces coronary constriction. This effect is well known to clinicians when vasopressin is released as a result of absorption of nicotine after smoking.

Synthetic oxytocin in rather large doses, 15 mU per milliliter, caused an increase in amplitude of contractions of the isolated cat papillary muscle, and in anesthetized dogs it reduced the incidence of ventricular fibrillation secondary to hypothermia in doses of 1 U per kilogram per minute by infusion (Covino, 1963). Other workers have described contrary results. In experiments on guinea pig atria and dog papillary muscles, concentrations between 0.5 and 40 mU per milliliter of synthetic oxytocin either had no effect or slightly decreased the force of contraction. Doses in excess of 40 mU per milliliter reduced contractility of both preparations in proportion to the administered dosage, and in no instance was an increase in myocardial contractility observed (Nakano and Fisher, 1963). Although synthetic oxytocin was shown to produce initial increase in the cardiac output of anesthetized dogs, it was concluded by Nakano and Fisher that the effect resulted from other observed hemodynamic changes in the circulation, particularly direct vasodilator actions upon the various peripheral vascular circulations. It would appear that cardiac actions of this polypeptide are most probably gross pharmacological effects of doses of the pure substance which are in considerable excess of the normal circulating blood levels.

Another polypeptide, substance P, was described originally by von Euler and Gaddum (1931). Substance P has not yet been isolated in pure form and thus has an unknown amino acid sequence. Substance P is widely distributed in selected areas of central nervous tissue, the alimentary canal, and the retina. Although the physiological significance of Substance P has not been established, many speculations concerning its function have been made (Zetler, 1960). The effects of this compound on the cardiovascular system appear to be primarily vasodilator in nature, and actions upon isolated guinea pig auricles and rabbit papillary muscles are negligible (Haefely and Hürlimann, 1962).

Two naturally occurring polypeptide substances with profound, yet opposing actions upon the cardiovascular system have been isolated and their structures confirmed by synthesis. These are bradykinin and angiotensin. Each has been implicated in pathological disturbances of cardiovascular function. Bradykinin is essentially a potent vasodilator peptide which appears to be released in a variety of near physiological situations and has been proposed as an autopharmacological agent responsible for the regulation of increased blood flow in functional hyperemia associated with activity of salivary and sweat glands (Hilton and Lewis, 1957). Angiotensin is primarily a potent vasoconstrictor peptide formed by the interaction of renin with a precursor substrate in the circulation, and has been linked with the etiology of hypertensive diseases.

The action of bradykinin upon cardiac tissue has been studied but the results are not conclusive. There is general agreement that the polypeptide produces increased cardiac output in anesthetized and conscious animals and also in man, but there is no agreement as to the basic mechanism of this increase. In anesthetized dogs for example, increased cardiac output following administration of bradykinin was accompanied by greatly reduced peripheral resistance and reduced stroke volume (Page and Olmstead, 1961; Rowe *et al.*, 1963), suggesting that the effect resulted from the decreased vascular resistance. In contrast, Montague *et al.* (1963) described increased cardiac output in the rat associated with a small increase in heart rate and accompanied by a large increase in stroke volume. Also in rats, marked cardiac stimulation was observed when the depressor vascular reactions to bradykinin were blocked by prior administration of pentolinium (Rosas *et al.*, 1965). Using dye-dilution measurements of cardiac output of the rat, infusions of bradykinin at the rates of 28 and 63 μg per kilogram per minute caused decreased blood pressure and total peripheral resistance with significant increase in cardiac output and blood flow through the organs (Takacs and Albert, 1965). Similarly, in conscious humans, infusions of bradykinin caused increases in cardiac output which were not accompanied by significant changes in heart rate or arterial blood pressure, and were interpreted as an increase in stroke volume in the presence of lowered peripheral resistance (Kontos *et al.*, 1963). However, all this evidence does not point necessarily to a direct inotropic action of bradykinin on the heart.

Isolated cardiac preparations from guinea pigs have been studied recently, and in the perfused heart very small doses of bradykinin were shown to produce a marked increase in coronary flow associated with a small increase in the amplitude of contraction which paralleled the time course of the coronary effect, and had no significant effect upon the heart rate (see Fig. 7.1; Heeg and Meng, 1965). Isolated auricle preparations responded with increased amplitude of contractions and no change in rate of beating, but no positive inotropic responses were recorded from isolated papillary muscles.

For lack of sufficient evidence, it is not possible to evaluate whether the cardiac stimulant effect of bradykinin in intact animals is due to direct inotropic actions of the polypeptide upon the myocardium or

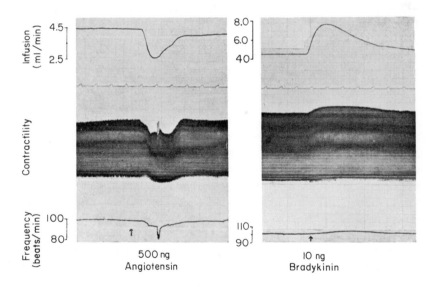

Fig. 7.1. The actions of angiotensin II and bradykinin on the isolated perfused guinea pig heart (Heeg and Meng, 1965).

whether it is secondary to decreased vascular resistance resulting from its potent vasodilator property. The lack of effect upon isolated papillary muscle suggests that the action of the substance is indirect, although the isolated auricle did exhibit enhanced contractions. A third mechanism may be involved in increasing cardiac output and stroke volume in the intact animal for it has been shown that brady-kinin releases adrenaline from the suprarenal medulla (Feldberg and Lewis 1964).

Angiotensin is another naturally occurring polypeptide, but there is much more agreement among various investigators concerning its positive inotropic effects upon ventricular muscle than there is about bradykinin. Even so, reports of apparent cardiac depression have been published from time to time. Unanesthetized dogs responded to angiotensin with a fall in cardiac output, stroke volume, and heart rate when the peripheral resistance increased (Page and Olmstead, 1961). The apparent depression reported here may well be superimposed upon a direct inotropic action of angiotensin, which was obscured by the increased load placed upon the heart secondary to the intensive vaso-constrictor action of the drug. However, it was also found in intact cats that one third of the animals showed myocardial depression accom-panied by diminished coronary blood flow following infusions of angiotensin (Downing and Sonnenblick, 1963). The remainder of the animals exhibited an inconsistent increase in force and velocity of contractions with large doses of angiotensin.

Moderate inotropic actions of angiotensin have been described in isolated perfused hearts of guinea pigs (Bianchi *et al.,* 1960), rabbits (Meier *et al.,* 1958), and in dog heart-lung preparations (Areskog, 1962c). Fowler and Holmes (1964) found that heart-lung preparations of dogs responded to single doses of angiotensin with initial brief de-creases in cardiac output and ventricular contractile force followed by increases in each of these parameters, and the pattern of response was not affected by prior treatment with reserpine. Papillary muscle preparations also responded to angiotensin with increased force of contraction, and thus it was concluded that angiotensin has a direct positive inotropic action upon the heart which is not affected by the state of repletion of the catecholamine stores.

The action of angiotensin in the intact anesthetized rat has been studied recently, and in addition to the arteriolar constriction, a stimulant effect upon the heart was observed. However, the cardiac stimulation was masked by activation of baroreceptor reflexes in intact animals, but when these were abolished by autonomic blockade, the stimulant action was revealed by increases in cardiac output, even though the total peripheral resistance was not altered by the treatment (Gross *et al.,* 1965). Further, the action upon cardiac output could not be explained by changes in heart rate or central venous pressure, and it was suggested that angiotensin had a direct positive inotropic action. The same workers also administered reserpine to a group of rats in doses of 1 mg per kilogram on each of 3 days prior to administration of angiotensin. They reported that slight positive changes in cardiac output occurred, but that they were statistically insignificant in reserpinized animals. The caution one must place upon results derived from animals pretreated with large doses of reserpine has already been emphasized in Chapters 3 and 6 and will not be repeated here. However, it must be pointed out that the dosage of reserpine used may well have had effects over and above depletion of cardiac catecholamines, and the conclusion of the research group that catecholamines account for at least part of the cardiac activity of angiotensin may prove unwarranted.

Evidence that the cardiac actions of angiotensin are independent of the state of repletion of catecholamine stores in the muscle has been presented (Koch-Weser, 1965). It was shown that angiotensin, $10^{-6} M,$ had less inotropic effect than noradrenaline, $10^{-7} M,$ but there were other differences between the two compounds. For instance, each drug caused a rise in the rate of development of maximum tension, but in the case of noradrenaline the time to reach maximum tension and the duration of contraction were reduced, whereas angiotensin had no effect upon these parameters. Koch-Weser concluded that both compounds increased myocardial contractility by increasing the degree of activation of the contractile elements, which amounts to shifting the force-velocity curve to the right. However, the effects of noradrenaline and angiotensin upon the duration of the active state were quite different according to Koch-Weser. No direct measurements of the dimensions of the active state were made and all suppositions about this property were inferred.

Koch-Weser also showed that the inotropic action of angiotensin did not depend upon myocardial noradrenaline stores. Thus pretreatment of animals with reserpine (1 mg per kilogram administered 24 hours previously) had no significant effect upon contractility of papillary muscles in response to angiotensin although the responses to tyramine in concentrations of 10^{-5} M were practically abolished. Further evidence that the inotropic action of angiotensin was independent of stored catecholamine was provided using the β-adrenergic blocking drugs dichloroisoprenaline (DCI) and nethalide (pronethalol). In particular it was shown that nethalide abolished the cardiac stimulant action of given doses of tyramine but had no effect upon those of angiotensin, and Koch-Weser concluded that angiotensin did not depend upon intact catecholamine stores for its inotropic action or act directly upon β-adrenergic receptors. The conclusion finally reached by Koch-Weser was that angiotensin may increase myocardial contractility by augmenting entry of Ca^{++} into the heart muscle fiber, for the effects of angiotensin and of increases in external Ca^{++} concentration upon the mechanical properties of cardiac muscle were similar.

Another recent report on the action of angiotensin upon isolated preparations of cardiac muscle confirmed that the action of the drug upon isolated auricles and papillary muscles of guinea pigs was to cause a weak positive inotropic effect. However, in perfused isolated guinea pig hearts, the drug caused decreased coronary flow and decreased force of contraction (Fig. 7.1; Heeg and Meng, 1965). One might suspect that the effect of angiotensin upon amplitude of contraction in these experiments was secondary to those upon coronary flow or frequency of contraction in view of the evidence cited above. One thing appears to be certain from all these experiments — the various naturally occurring polypeptides have little effect upon cardiac contractility in physiological concentrations and because larger pharmacological doses have no dramatic cardiac actions, it is probable that none of the substances has a cardioregulatory function in the intact animal.

IV. Cardiotonic Substances Extracted from Mammalian Tissues

A. Spleen

The discovery by Rein of the spleen-liver reaction focused attention upon these organs and their possible roles in regulating cardiac performance. Extraction of a cardiac stimulant substance from liver tissue, which stimulated isolated papillary muscles further pointed to the possible importance of this organ (Green, 1952). However, the technique used to extract the stimulant substance involved boiling the tissue with caustic soda for some hours, and it was by no means certain whether the cardiac stimulant substance existed as such in the tissue originally or whether it was an artifact formed by the drastic chemical procedure.

For some years we have been studying cardiac stimulant substances extractable from the tissues, but to increase the probability that no artifacts were introduced by the extraction procedure, we have attempted to use relatively mild conditions. Tissues are obtained fresh from the abattoir and are minced and freeze-dried. The "anhydrous" material actually contains about 2–4% of residual water which can only be removed by prolonged desiccation over P_2O_5 *in vacuo*. As this residual contamination does not appear to matter, secondary drying is not attempted. The dried tissue is pulverized and extracted in a large Soxhlet apparatus using freshly redistilled solvents which are then distilled off under reduced pressure. Preliminary defatting is performed followed by extraction with acetone which removes cardiac stimulant substances. The distribution of cardioactivity is given in Table 7.2 where the approximate concentration of extract required to double the force of contraction of an isolated papillary muscle is expressed as the equivalent quantity of fresh tissue per milliliter of bath solution. Clearly, liver and spleen were the two tissues which contained the highest yields of extractable cardiac stimulants. Because the spleen extracts were less contaminated with impurities, these were subjected to further study (Cobbin and Thorp, 1957). The extracts prepared from suprarenal glands contained large quantities of catecholamines, and when these were destroyed residual activity was negligible.

Ox spleen is known to contain many pharmacologically active substances, including noradrenaline 4 μg per gram, adrenaline, 0.07 μg per gram (von Euler and Purkhold, 1951a), 3-hydroxytyramine, 4 μg per gram (Schümann, 1958), acetylcholine 8 μg per gram, choline 2 mg per gram, histamine, 8 μg per gram, (Dale and Dudley, 1929), and 5-HT 8 μg per gram (Erspamer, 1954). It was shown that these substances did not appear in acetone extracts of freeze-dried spleen in sufficient quantities to account for the stimulant action of the extracts upon isolated papillary muscles (Cobbin and Thorp, 1959), and further evidence to eliminate catecholamines has been provided (Cobbin and Thorp, 1960). It is this latter category of compounds which would be suspected to be the most likely substances which could increase the

Table 7.2

The Relative Cardiotonic Activity of Acetone Extracts
of Mammalian Tissues

Tissue	Mg fresh tissue/ml to double force of papillary muscle
Liver	Approx. 300
Spleen [a]	
1	Less than 100
2	Greater than 2000
3	Less than 100
Suprarenals	Less than 50
Heart	Greater than 400
Skeletal muscle	Approx. 400
Brain	Approx. 1000

[a] Extracted by three different techniques. Number 2 gave incomplete extraction.

isometric force of contraction of cardiac tissue, and to exclude them, many separate types of test have been applied. Incubation at pH 11 for one hour at 37°C in the presence of manganese dioxide destroyed catecholamines (Euler and Purkhold, 1951b) but not the substance present in extracts of spleen. There was no adsorption of catecholamines from the crude extracts onto freshly precipitated aluminum hydroxide using von Euler's modification (1956) of the technique described by Shaw (1938), and the catecholamine-free fraction retained the cardioactivity.

Catecholamines could not be detected in spleen extracts by chromatographic separation (Cobbin and Thorp, 1960). In three different chromatographic solvent systems the R_f values of the cardioactive constituent in spleen extract were determined by cutting the developed paper chromatograms horizontally, eluting the sections, and assaying the eluate. In each system, the R_f value of the spleen activity was different from those of adrenaline, noradrenaline, tyramine, and dopamine (Rockwell and Temple, 1966). Likewise in paper electrophoresis experiments the cardioactive substance in spleen had a mobility differ-

ent from that of the catecholamines (Alexander and Temple, unpublished). The extracts were unchanged in potency by the specific
β-blocking agent DCI in doses sufficient to almost abolish the inotropic
actions of noradrenaline in open-thorax guinea pigs (see Fig. 7.2).

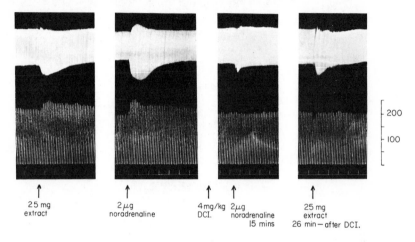

Fig. 7.2. The action of approximately matched doses of a crude extract of spleen and
noradrenaline upon ventricular contractions and heart rate in an anesthetized guinea
pig recorded by a Cushny myocardiograph before and after administration of the β-
adrenergic blocking drug DCI. The effect of spleen extract is not significantly affected
(Cobbin and Thorp, 1960).

Large-scale extraction of ox-spleen, using a 20 liter Soxhlet ex-
tractor, and purification of the resulting extract were undertaken
(Temple *et al.,* 1966) with the aim of identifying the cardiotonic substance. Routine defatting of freeze-dried ox spleen in 2 kg batches
followed by acetone extraction gave, on vacuum evaporation of the
acetone, a brown gum in a yield of approximately 4 mg per gram of
fresh spleen. This crude extract has been purified by a number of
methods as shown in the flow diagram of Fig. 7.3. Liquid-liquid
partitioning and then liquid ion-exchange separation were followed by
a series of chromatographic processes, which included gel filtration,
partition chromatography, and ion-exchange chromatrography. Each
step in the purification process was monitored by bioassay, so that only
the products assaying with positive inotropic activity were used for
further purification stages, the inactive by-products being discarded.

The bioassays routinely used were the isolated cat papillary muscle and the isolated guinea pig auricle preparations (described in Chapter 2).

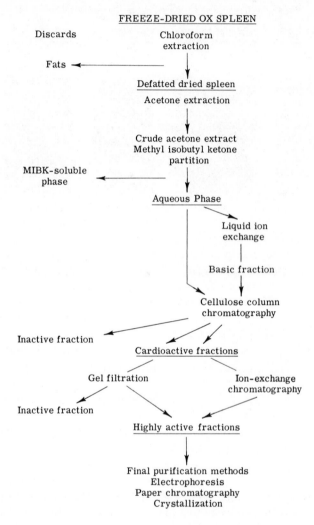

Fig. 7.3. Flow diagram showing the methods used for the extraction and concentration of the cardiotonic factor in spleen. Bioassays indicated the cardioactive fraction at each stage.

The cardiotonic activity can be correlated with an ultraviolet absorption maximum near 260 mμ. The eluate from chromatographic columns has consequently been monitored, where possible, by a continuous flow ultraviolet absorptiometer, using a monochromator setting of 260 mμ. Owing to the chemical diversity of acetone-soluble compounds in spleen, an absorption peak at 260 mμ is not an infallible criterion for cardiotonic activity from spleen extract.

Tests made to determine the partition coefficient of the active material between common immiscible solvents and water indicated that methyl isobutyl ketone (a higher homolog of acetone) gave the most satisfactory purification. On shaking an aqueous solution of crude spleen extract with methyl isobutyl ketone, 40% by weight of the spleen material was extracted by the ketone, leaving all the cardio-active material in the aqueous solution, which was then concentrated *in vacuo*.

Experiments in this laboratory have shown that liquid ion-exchange compounds can be used as a simple means of purifying aqueous solutions of organic or inorganic ionized substances extracted from tissues. When long-chain alkylamines or alkyl phosphoric acids which are themselves insoluble in water are dissolved in a water-immiscible solvent such as chloroform, these solutions will, under suitable conditions of pH and concentration, extract anions and cations, respectively, from aqueous solutions. The technique is similar to that for liquid partitioning, and the ion-exchange reaction is believed to take place at the phase boundary where the hydrophilic basic and acidic groups are concentrated. Temple and Gillespie (1966) have demonstrated that organic basic material extracted into chloroform solutions of di-2-ethylhexyl phosphoric acid (DEHPA) may be recovered from the ion-exchanger solution by shaking it with dilute acid.

When aqueous solutions of crude spleen extract were shaken with 5% chloroform solutions of the anion exchangers LA1 or LA2,* acidic constituents of the spleen sample, comprising 13–45% by weight, were removed, and cardioactivity of the residual spleen constituents increased by a factor of approximately two. Alternatively or subsequently the aqueous spleen solution was extracted with a 5% solution of DEHPA in chloroform, amyl acetate, or dibutyl ether, which re-

---

*Amberlite LA1 and LA2 are high molecular weight secondary amines.

moved almost all the cardioactive material in three partition steps. The active material exchanged quantitatively from DEHPA solution when partitioned with 0.01 N hydrochloric acid, the residue on evaporation of the hydrochloric acid amounting to 10–20% by weight of the original spleen sample and assaying with up to eight times the activity per milligram, depending on the conditions used. The progress of the ion-exchange separation of spleen constituents was followed by measuring the ultraviolet absorbance values at 260 mμ and by bioassay.

Partition chromatography on cellulose using n-butanol saturated with water has been used, in columns packed with up to 5 kg of cellulose. Two distinct bands of activity were often eluted.

Purification of extracts by the molecular sieve principle has also been effective using Sephadex dextran gels and polyacrylamide gels. Sephadex G25, and the more recently introduced Sephadex G15 and G10, have cross-linking such that compounds are separated in the molecular weight ranges below 3500, below 1500, and below 700, respectively. A column of a Sephadex gel may be calibrated by relating molecular weights to elution volumes for known compounds under standard conditions. Then the molecular weight of an unknown compound can be estimated by comparing its elution volume under the same conditions. This was done with Sephadex G25 and G10 for a series of known basic compounds, and a comparison made with the active constituent in spleen extract. The relationship between molecular weight and elution volume from Sephadex columns has been discussed by Whitaker (1963) and Andrews (1964) for proteins and Carnegie (1965) for peptides and amino acids. Figure 7.4 illustrates results from this laboratory (Rockwell and Temple, 1966), which indicate that the molecular weight of the spleen factor lies between 150 and 250.

Ion-exchange chromatography enhanced the cardioactivity of spleen extracts successfully when dextran gels substituted with acidic groups, such as SE Sephadex, or cation exchange resins such as Amberlite CG50, were used. The active spleen constituents were adsorbed onto the acidic ion-exchange groups, the inactive neutral and acidic fractions were separated, and the gradient elution with a decreasing pH eluted the active component in concentrated form (Fig. 7.5.)

A combination of these purification processes, as described by Temple *et al.* (1966), produced the highly concentrated spleen factor as a gum in a yield of approximately 10 mg per kilogram of fresh spleen. Some loss of the original total activity occurred owing to inefficiency

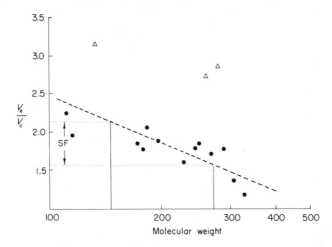

Fig. 7.4. Relationship between molecular weight for a series of nucleosides and corresponding bases and elution volume (V_e) from a column of Sephadex G25, in water. V_0 = void volume. SF = elution of spleen factor from the same column. Δ = aminopurine derivaties (adenine, adenosine, guanosine) for which V_e values are anomalous (see text).

of steps in the purification process. The final concentrated extract gave positive responses on the two bioassay preparations at doses of 5–10 μg, which were approximately equal to the responses from 0.5 μg of adrenaline. Dose-response curves obtained from active spleen samples were, however, not parallel to those for adrenaline on the same assay preparation.

Recent experiments (Jackson and Temple, 1966) have shown that the same cardiotonic factor can be extracted from ox spleen or liver by homogenizing the fresh tissue with water or mixtures of water with ethanol or acetone. The homogenate is centrifuged at a speed (27,000 g) that will precipitate cells and cellular particles not disrupted by the previous treatment. The aqueous supernatant, after precipitation of proteins by addition of alcohol, contains a cardioactive substance which can be extracted by acetone from the dried aqueous residue.

It has been shown to have the same properties as the spleen factor obtained by the process shown in Fig. 7.3.

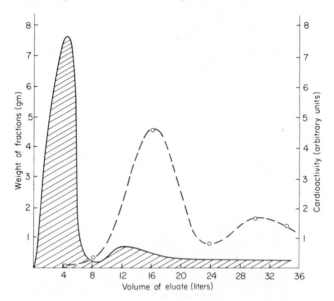

Fig. 7.5. Elution diagram for an extract of spleen from a column of Amberlite CG50 (350 gm) illustrating the separation of cardioactive from inactive material. A gradient elution, H_2O to 0.1 N HCl, was used. Inactive spleen extract was eluted at pH near 7 and the cardiotonic spleen factor at pH 2. Cross hatching indicates weight. Dashed line indicates cardioactivity.

The cardiotonic substance in spleen resembles the cardiac glycosides in some of its properties. The onset of its inotropic action on papillary muscles is gradual, reaching a maximum effect in 5–10 minutes, and is sustained for a long period dependent on the dose administered. In contrast, the catecholamines have a rapid but brief action on papillary muscles. The spleen substance is readily washed out of the bath which suggests that the substance is not very firmly bound to cardiac tissue. The inotropic action is also seen in perfused kitten hearts where it is accompanied by a moderate increase in coronary flow and a slight increase in heart rate (see Fig. 7.6). In open-thorax guinea pigs, intravenous injection of spleen extract will produce an initial inotropic action, as recorded by a Cushny myocardiograph sutured to the ventricle, accompanied by a slight increase in rate, both of which return to their initial values within 5 minutes. However, a secondary inotropic action is then seen which gradually reaches a maximum in a period ranging from 15 to 45 minutes and which is sustained for up to 2 hours following doses of extract equivalent to be-

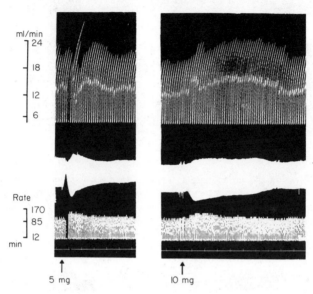

Fig. 7.6. The action of a crude extract of spleen upon coronary flow, amplitude of contractions, and rate of an isolated perfused kitten heart. *Left panel:* The extract was administered close to the aorta in a single injection. *Right Panel:* The dose was given in the reservoir (capacity 30 ml) which was continually supplied with fresh perfusion fluid. This caused progressive dilution of the extract (Cobbin, 1959).

tween 15 and 25 gm of fresh spleen per kilogram (see Fig. 7.7). In kitten heart-lung preparations, with the amplitude of cardiac contraction recorded by a Cushny myocardiograph, the inotropic action is seen almost immediately after additions of the extract are made to the venous reservoir, and it gradually reaches a peak in about 10 minutes and is sustained for a considerable time. There is no significant change in rate but cardiac output is slightly elevated. The time course and nature of all these inotropic properties resembles the action of small doses of cardiac glycosides.

The staircase phenomenon on the frog heart has been used as an assay technique for substances with a digitalis-like action on cardiac muscle (Hajdu, 1957). The staircase phenomenon can be demonstrated in cat papillary muscles and can be abolished and reversed by small doses of cardiac glycosides (see Fig. 7.8) as in the isolated frog heart.

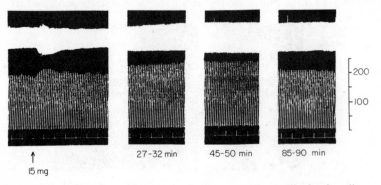

Fig. 7.7. The action of a crude extract of spleen upon the amplitude of cardiac contractions and the heart rate in an anesthetized guinea pig. After an initial effect due to the sudden concentration reaching the heart, there was a progressive increase to a maximum which was found after about 45 minutes and which was well sustained (Cobbin, 1959).

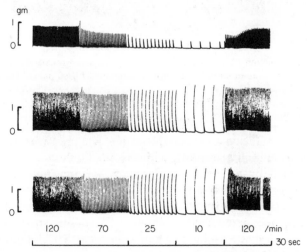

Fig. 7.8. The action of ouabain, 10^{-6} gm per milliliter, upon the staircase phenomenon in an isolated cat papillary muscle. *Upper panel:* a control staircase. The remaining panels show how the drug reversed the pattern 15 and 30 minutes after administration together with a well-developed inotropic effect (Cobbin, 1959).

However, in this test the spleen extract does not resemble the cardiac glycosides, for doses capable of producing a good inotropic response fail to modify the pattern of the staircase (see Fig. 7.9) and indeed their actions resemble the behavior of noradrenaline which also has no

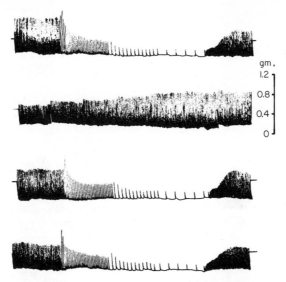

Fig. 7.9. The action of a crude extract of spleen upon the staircase phenomenon in papillary muscle. *Upper panel:* a control staircase, recorded before the muscle became very hypodynamic. *Second panel:* the onset of the inotropic action of the extract for a period of 7 minutes. The remaining panels show the failure to abolish the staircase 15 and 30 minutes afterward, although a well-developed inotropic effect can be seen (Cobbin, 1959).

effect on the cat papillary muscle staircase. This is illustrated in Fig. 7.10 where the inotropic action of noradrenaline is shown in the second panel from the top, and in the third and fourth panels a staircase is elicited 30 and 60 seconds, respectively, after addition of a small dose of noradrenaline. The dotted lines indicate the predicted course of the inotropic response had the frequency of stimulation remained unaltered. This pattern of behavior of spleen extract and noradrenaline leads the authors to believe that the use of a staircase abolition as a means for the detection of inotropic agents is severely limited, for a normal staircase can exist even in the presence of marked inotropic responses.

When adenosine is injected into the left atrium of the guinea pig, one of the most outstanding effects is the production of heart block, the duration of which is a function of the dose. Small doses of cardiac

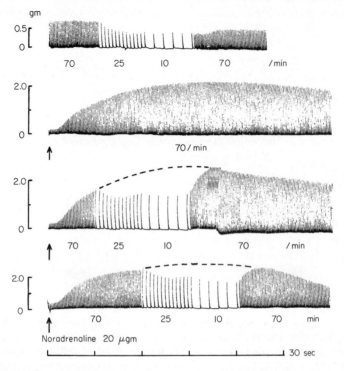

Fig. 7.10. The action of noradrenaline, 10^{-6} gm per milliliter, upon the staircase phenomenon in papillary muscle. *Upper panel:* Control staircase before the muscle became hypodynamic. *Second panel:* The action of noradrenaline at a constant rate of stimulation, 70 per minute. *Third and fourth panels:* The staircase superimposed upon the developing inotropic response to noradrenaline 30 seconds and 1 minute after addition of the drug (Cobbin, 1959).

glycosides, insufficient to produce electrocardiographic changes, are capable of potentiating the period of heart block produced by a constant dose of adenosine (Rand *et al.,* 1955), and the effect is sustained for a considerable period. Small doses of crude spleen extract also produced long-lasting and marked potentiation of the adenosine-induced block. The significance of this result is not clear, for impurities in the crude extract may have produced the potentiation. However, the only other factors known to potentiate adenosine-induced heart block are fall of body temperature (Drury and Szent-Györgyi, 1929), Mg^{++} (Wayne *et al.*, 1949; Green and Stoner, 1950), and certain anti-cholinesterases (Drury *et al.*, 1938). It is possible that the substance in the crude extracts is also responsible for the potentiation of the heart block, but further elucidation must await the isolation of the inotropic substance from spleen.

An investigation was made of a number of known compounds, particularly bases, in which cardiotonic activity had been reported, in order to compare their properties with those of the spleen factor.

Although the spleen substance resembles the cardiac glycosides in some respects, there is little doubt that it is not a steroid. Experiments with ion-exchange resins, liquid ion-exchangers, and electrophoresis have demonstrated that the substance is basic and behaves as a cation Aldosterone, which has been reported to be cardioactive, has been specifically excluded by its different R_f values from spleen factor in two paper chromatographic systems.

A series of neutral amino acids has been shown (Gatgounis and Hester, 1964) to exert some positive effect on arterial blood pressure and cardiac contractile force in dogs; these were L-leucine, DL-serine, glycine, L-alanine, L-cysteine, L-threonine, L-methionine, and L-serine. The basic L-arginine produced a negative inotropic response. The cat papillary muscle assay had earlier been used (Garb, 1955) to demonstrate positive inotropic activity in cysteine, methionine, and glycine. In our hands, cysteine, glycine, and leucine showed no positive inotropic effect on the cat papillary muscle nor on the isolated guinea pig auricle. DL-Histidine at 4 mg per milliliter and DL-serine at 10 mg per milliliter concentration stimulated our papillary muscle preparation slightly, and histidine and proline at 4 mg per milliliter showed a positive effect with the guinea pig auricle although this inotropic action had a toxic component which did not wash out but permanently depressed the action of the auricle. The basic amino acids arginine and lysine were inactive on the papillary muscle at 2 mg per milliliter, and none of the basic amino acids mentioned were electrophoretically comparable to the spleen factor.

Nucleosides and their corresponding purine and pyrimidine bases were investigated by Buckley *et al.* (1961), and positive inotropic activity was demonstrated for inosine, guanosine, thymidine, uridine, and the corresponding free bases, and for caffeine, on failing rabbit heart preparations. In our laboratory, deoxyguanosine and uridine (500 μg doses) and caffeine (100 μg) gave positive responses on the guinea pig auricle (7 ml bath) and cat papillary muscle (1 ml bath) preparations, and no cardiotonic activity was demonstrable with the remaining compounds reported by Buckley *et al.* (1961). Because of the comparable basic nature and molecular weight of the spleen factor, the behavior of these compounds and that of a number of related nucleosides and bases to paper chromatography, paper electrophoresis, Sephadex gel filtration, and dialysis were established. The properties of the spleen factor were compared under the same conditions (Rockwell and Temple, 1966). The results indicated that none of these compounds was responsible for the cardioactivity extracted from spleen. Figure 7.4 shows the elution volumes from a column of Sephadex G25 of nucleoside bases plotted against the logarithm of their molecular weights. The gel filtration rates indicate the anomalously slow elution of aromatic amines, discussed by Carnegie (1965) and others, in the cases of adenine and guanine and their derivatives. Estimation of molecular weights of compounds of unknown structure must therefore be interpreted cautiously. When a number of nucleosides and related bases were dialyzed under standard conditions of concentration and time, a linear relationship was found between percentage dialyzed at time intervals of 1, 2, 3, and 5 hours and log molecular weight. Dialysis results for the spleen factor under the same conditions suggests a molecular weight range of 200–300.

Rosenblum and Stein (1964) showed that guanosine does not act directly upon the heart, but its action is mediated by noradrenaline. Caffeine, however, has been reported by de Gubareff and Sleator (1965) to act by a different mechanism. Our present evidence suggests that the spleen factor most probably acts directly upon the myocardium rather than by release of catecholamines.

The well-known positive inotropic action of Ca^{++} on isolated heart muscle preparation prompted routine checks of the Ca^{++} content of active fractions from spleen purification procedures. Flame photometric measurements of the percentage of Ca^{++} in spleen fractions showed that the Ca^{++} concentration in every case was far below the level at which it could affect the bioassays.

The stability of the inotropic substance to heat has been studied.

Similar concentrations of crude extract in modified Krebs-Henseleit solution were adjusted to various pH values and refluxed for one hour, and then restored to pH 7.5 after cooling under running tap water, and tested on papillary muscles. Figure 7.11 shows the effects of this

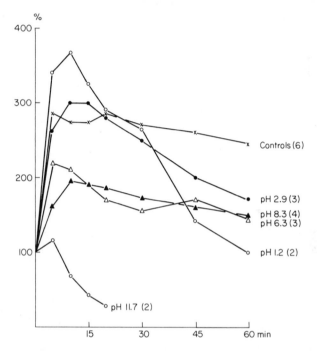

Fig. 7.11. The force of contraction developed by isolated papillary muscles after treatment with solutions of crude spleen extracts which had been refluxed for one hour at the indicated pH values. The number of experiments is shown in parentheses (Cobbin, 1959).

treatment and it will be seen that at acid pH ($\leqslant 3$), the magnitude of the inotropic response is not diminished, but as the pH was made more alkaline the magnitude of the response became less, and in very alkaline solution the activity was completely destroyed. Boiling in strong acid solution (6 N HCl) also caused destruction of the active substance.

Because many polypeptides exhibit a similar pattern of stability to heat according to the pH of solution, it was decided to investigate the effects of proteolytic enzymes upon the spleen substance. Table 7.3 shows results found with chymotrypsin, trypsin, and pronase. The effects of these enzymes upon the spleen substance are negligible, and

Table 7.3

The Effect of Proteolytic Enzymes upon the Cardioactivity of
Crude Spleen Extracts

Enzyme	Time of incubation (hours)	No. of expts.	Degree of inotropic effect	
			Treated	Control
Trypsin				
1 mg/ml	24	8	4.3	4.9
1 mg/ml	48	5	4.5	3.8
Chymotrypsin				
1 mg/ml	24	3	5.4	5.8
1 mg/ml	48	1	4.0	3.9
Pronase[a]				
0.02 mg/ml	22	5	5.5	5.3
10 mg/ml	1.5	3	5.7	4.3

[a] Pronase is a mixture of broad-spectrum proteolytic enzymes from *Streptomyces griseus*.

it is assumed that the active material is most unlikely to be a polypeptide. The resistance to destruction by pronase suggests strongly that the substance in spleen extracts differs from the polypeptide substance with inotropic properties found in normal human plasma (Curtain and Nayler, 1963).

It is difficult to know whether the substance present in splenic extracts is identical with the "Hypoxie-lienen" released from the spleen on stimulation of the splenic nerves and found in splenic venous blood. The use of mild extraction methods and subsequent gentle treatment of crude extracts decrease the likelihood of introduction of artifacts resulting from drastic methods of handling the tissue. The final elucidation as to whether the spleen substance has a physiological role must await its identification and demonstration of its release in physiological situations. This will depend on the discovery of a suitable sensitive analytical method to assay the substance, and it would be preferable that such a method be physical or chemical rather than a biological one depending on inotropic actions for the reasons outlined in Chapter 2.

B. Blood

Since the experiments of Sidney Ringer it has been known that serum has an inotropic action upon the perfused heart, and A. J. Clark (1913) showed that alcoholic extracts of serum contained the activity which he concluded was due to a soap-like substance. There have been other reports of cardiotonic activity in serum since these early experiments, but little of value has emerged yet. No substance has been isolated in pure form and characterized, and no evidence has been presented concerning a possible physiological role for the substances responsible for cardiotonic activity. Indeed it may eventuate that such activity is a pharmacological effect which is the result of the administration of concentrations far in excess of those found physiologically. However, there are cardiotonic substances in serum and it is desirable that these be identified and their full pharmacology studied. Some substances have been described from protein fractions of the serum and others have been shown to reside in the lower molecular weight ranges.

Salter and Taylor (1952) compared serum with the cardiac glycosides and found that the cardioactivity was present in the albumin fraction. In their experiments they found that the serum of healthy young adults had greater activity than serum from older people, and that the maximum activity of 100 ml of serum corresponded approximately to that of 30 μg of ouabain. Only about one third of the total activity present was free. The active substance was fairly stable, losing only 50% of its activity over 4 months at 4°C in solution, whereas freeze-dried albumin remained highly active for longer than a year. Dose-response curves were said to resemble those of ouabain with a similar latent period. A more detailed paper showed that the activity of serum resided in Fractions IV and V (Cohn, 1950) and that the activity was not altered by dialysis or treatment with trypsin, although it was destroyed by heat (Green *et al.*, 1952).

A serum-protein system from human serum has been described (Hajdu and Leonard, 1958), which consists of three proteins termed cardioglobulins A, B, and C. It is claimed that the three components of this cardioglobulin system may be assayed but the procedure is laborious and complex, for assay of each component depends on the presence of each of the other components (Hajdu and Leonard, 1961). Cardioglobulin C is relatively easy to assay and it has been suggested that it is present in increased concentration in human plasma derived from patients with essential hypertension and aortic stenosis, two unrelated syndromes which have in common a high systolic left ventricular isometric tension (Leonard and Hajdu, 1960). Patients with congestive heart failure due to myocardial disease of unknown cause were divisible into two groups, one with normal cardioglobulin C level and the other with extremely low levels of this component (Leonard and Hajdu, 1961). Patients with congestive cardiac failure secondary to valvular disease or muscle disease of known cause also exhibited essentially normal plasma levels of cardioglobulin C. The significance of this system remains obscure.

Human blood plasma was reported to exert a positive inotropic action on the isolated toad heart by Nayler and McCulloch (1960). This action was independent of catecholamines since it was unaffected by reserpinization. Although its action superficially resembled that of the cardiac glycosides, DNP and quinidine sulfate left it unchanged but abolished the response to cardiac glycosides. Curtain and Nayler (1963) extracted from plasma and concentrated chromatographically two cardiotonic substances. One of them, with molecular weight exceeding 50,000, they suggested might be identical to the globulin fraction described by Hajdu and Leonard (1958). The other fraction, with molecular weight 4000–10,000 occurred as 35% of the total plasma activity. It was concentrated by gel filtration on polyacrylamide columns and ion-exchange chromatography on a diethylamino-substituted polyacrylamide, until 1 μg of the material so obtained gave the same response as 0.3 μg of adrenaline on the isolated toad heart. It was shown by its deactivation on exposure to pronase to be a polypeptide, and electrophoresis indicated that at pH 5.8 it was cationic. Its action was not antagonized by the β-blockers DCI nor pronethalol. The lower molecular weight substance was named "Kinekard" (Lowe and Nayler, 1965) and its occurrence was measured in the blood plasma of a number of patients with various circulatory diseases. Kinekard was shown also to occur in the blood plasma of a number of species (Nayler et al., 1965a). Its pharmacology was studied on intact animal preparations (Nayler *et al.,* 1965b), and a pressor effect and an increase in cardiac output were described. Positive inotropic responses were obtained on papillary muscle preparations of the dog, rabbit, and monkey. Its action was shown to differ from those of bradykinin, angiotensin, and vasopressin.

Yet another substance may be extracted from ox blood, which in preliminary experiments appears to be similar to the factor extracted from spleen. When blood was fractionated into erythocytes, leucocytes, and plasma the highest concentration of the substance was in the erythrocyte fraction, and was statistically significantly different from the activity found in plasma. The leucocyte-rich fraction (approximately 2 ml per liter of blood) was devoid of activity. The amount of active substance in red blood cells corresponding to 20 ml of blood almost trebled the force of contraction of isolated papillary muscles, whereas that isolated from the plasma corresponding to 20 ml of whole blood did not quite double the contractile force.

C. β-Palmitoyl Lysolecithin

A further substance has been isolated from mammalian tissues with properties similar to some exhibited by cardiac glycosides (Titus *et al.,* 1956; Hajdu *et al.,* 1957). These authors succeeded in isolating a phospholipid from various tissues, which they were able to characterize as β-palmitoyl lysolecithin, and they confirmed the isolation by synthesis. This substance was distributed unevenly through the tissues (see Table 7.4). The eventual isolation was achieved from beef adrenal medulla which showed the greatest activity of all tissues studied. The assay procedure to follow the purification of crude tissue extracts was based on the staircase phenomenon in the frog heart (Hajdu, 1957). The pure substance was also found to increase the isometric tension developed by strips of squab ventricle. However, a sample of synthetic β-palmitoyl lysolecithin (kindly supplied by Dr. Titus) was found in our laboratory to have no inotropic action on isolated cat papillary muscles in concentrations up to 50 μg per milliliter (Cobbin and Thorp, 1959). Kahn and Schindler (1962) showed that this substance had only negative inotropic actions on isolated perfused guinea pig ventricles, which preceded diastolic arrest.

Experiments with synthetic β-palmitoyl lysolecithin have shown that it bears some resemblance to ouabain, but although it increased the tone, the synthetic lysolecithin never produced contracture of the frog heart even at high doses whereas in the case of ouabain, contracture was readily produced. The effects of the synthetic substance were readily removed by washing the heart with fresh Ringer's solution but those of ouabain were more presistent (Scarinci *et al.*, 1960). At concentrations in excess of 4 μg per milliliter the lysolecithin causes complete hemolysis in rabbit red cells. This fact alone points a corollary to the doubts expressed (Hajdu *et al.*, 1957; Titus, personal communication) as to whether this substance has a physiological role in the mammalian organism.

Table 7.4

The Distribution of β-Palmitoyl Lysolecithin
as Assayed on the Frog Heart

Tissue (beef)	Total μg activity[a]/kg wet tissue
Plasma	180
Red cells	0
Liver	100
Heart	330
Skeletal muscle	10
Adrenal cortex	0
Adrenal medulla	1000

[a] Expressed as microgram equivalents of strophanthidin.
[b] From Hajdu *et al.* (1957).

The effects of α-(β-palmitoyl)-lysolecithin and ouabain have been compared on action potentials recorded from single fibers of guinea pig myocardium (Marro *et al.*, 1961). The most significant effect reported was delay in repolarization of the atrial tissue which was interpreted as a potentiation of the sodium-pump mechanism, an effect opposite to that shown by ouabain. In connection with the studies on lysolecithin, it is of interest to note that Clark (1938) showed that lecithins when impure were capable of stimulating the frog heart, but when they were purified the action was no longer demonstrable. Whether Clark's impure lecithins were contaminated by lysolecithins is not known.

V. Cardiotonic Substances in the Invertebrates and Agnathans

The search for naturally occurring cardiotonic substances has not been confined to mammalian tissues and in recent years numerous reports have appeared in the literature concerning substances of unknown chemical identity which can be extracted from tissues of various arthropods, molluscs, and primitive vertebrates, the Agnathans (sometimes called cyclostomes). These tissue extracts in some instances have been shown to exert their actions on the rate of isolated perfused hearts, but in many cases a positive inotropic action can be demonstrated.

The crabs, *Cancer pagurus* and *Maia squinado,* the lobster, *Homarus vulgaris,* and a stomatopod, *Squilla mantis,* all possess pericardial nervous organs which were thought capable of liberating cardiotonic substances into the pericardial cavities of these species (Alexandrowicz and Carlisle, 1953). These authors prepared simple extracts of the pericardial organs by triturating the tissues with sand in saline and testing the filtered extracts on isolated perfused hearts of these species. In all cases a positive inotropic effect was found together with a positive chronotropic action except in the extracts of *Maia* where a decrease in rate was observed. The effect of one hundredth of the total extract of pericardial organs of *Cancer* was greater in magnitude and similar in time course to the effects of adrenaline and noradrenaline in concentrations of $1:10^6$ (see Fig. 7.12). The active extract also gave a similar fluorescence reaction to catecholamines. Blood taken from the pericardial cavity was shown to possess stimulant activity and to fluoresce whereas blood from the leg arteries was negative in both tests.

Similar experiments were reported (Carlisle, 1956) and the active substance shown to be destroyed by amine oxidase and *o*-diphenol oxidase. The active substance gave color reactions compatible with those of indole alkylamines, which led to the suggestion that the activity was due to 5,6-dihydroxytryptamine (Carlisle and Knowles, 1959), although this substance is reported to be chemically unstable (Schlossberger and Kuch, 1960).

The pericardial organs of four species of crabs were removed and extracts assayed on the isolated perfused heart of the lobster and matched with doses of 5-hydroxytryptamine (see Fig. 7.13, Maynard and Welsh, 1959). The extracts showed a steeper dose-response curve than 5-hydroxytryptamine, and the effects on the heart were not always parallel. That the active substance was not 5-hydroxytrypta-

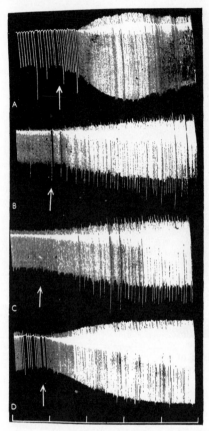

Fig. 7.12. The actions on the same heart of *Cancer* of: A and D: Pericardial organ extract of *Cancer;* B: adrenaline, 10^{-6} gm per milliliter; C: noradrenaline, 10^{-6} gm per milliliter (Alexandrowicz and Carlisle, 1953). (Reproduced by permission of the Council of the Marine Biological Association of the United Kingdom.)

mine was subsequently confirmed (Cooke, 1962) using LSD which completely antagonized the cardiac stimulation produced by 5-hydroxytryptamine but left the responses to pericardial organ extracts unchanged. Maynard and Welsh showed that for maximum activity of extracts, 95% ethanol was the solvent of choice. The active substance was dialyzable and was not destroyed by heating to 96–100°C for 15–20 minutes in sea water at pH 7–8. Chromatography and fluores-

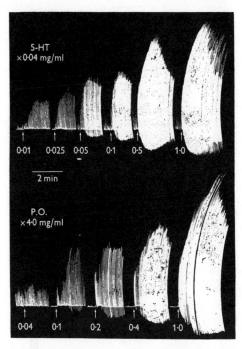

Fig. 7.13. Comparison of the actions of crab pericardial organ (P.O.) extracts and 5-hydroxytryptamine (5-HT) upon the isolated perfused heart of the lobster (Maynard and Welsh, 1959).

cence spectra showed that 5-hydroxytryptamine was present in concentrations too low to account for the cardioactivity and that another substance was present. Because treatment of active extracts with trypsin destroyed the cardiac action these authors were led to suggest that a polypeptide substance was present and responsible for the cardiac stimulation.

A further study on the pericardial organs of crabs has been made, and the crude extracts were part purified by paper chromatography and paper electrophoresis (Belamarich, 1963). There were two active regions on the paper strips both of which were destroyed by treatment with trypsin or chymotrypsin and which had isoelectric points about pH 3. Preliminary amino acid analysis suggests that both of these acid peptides are closely related. Because only small quantities of active substance were available—estimated to be about 12 μg per crab—it was not possible to perform a test for the presence of tryptophan in the active peptides. If tryptophan were in fact present, then this could account for the similarity in action to 5-hydroxytryptamine as reported in earlier studies.

The significance of these cardiac stimulant substances remains speculative. The pericardial organs are neurosecretory structures located in the pericardial cavities of decapod and stomatopod crustaceans, and an electron microscopic study of the organs from *Squilla mantis* has revealed the presence of two types of neurosecretory vesicles (Knowles, 1960). Electrical stimulation of the pericardial organs liberates cardiac stimulant material, (Cooke, unpublished data, cited by Belamarich, 1963). Thus it is possible that these substances may be neurotransmitter substances differing from acetylcholine and noradrenaline, or they may form part of a hormone system for control of the crustacean heart, whose release is controlled by nervous means similarly to posterior pituitary hormones in mammals.

Another arthropod, *Periplaneta americana,* the cockroach, has a heart which remains functional for several hours when isolated and perfused. Extracts of the corpora cardia of this insect produced an increase in the rate and amplitude of the heart beat, and in suitable dilutions the effect on cardiac rate was abolished while the inotropic response remained (Cameron, 1953). The effects of the extract were readily washed out and denervation of the glands did not result in loss of the active substance. Solutions of the extract gave a positive test for *o*-diphenols but the active substance was not adrenaline, although it is suggested that it may serve the functions of adrenaline in the insect.

Extracts of tissues from *Helix aspersa,* the common English snail, also produce stimulation of rate and amplitude of the mollusc heart. The cardioaccelerator property can be demonstrated in acetone-water extracts prepared from the brain, mouth, foot, and heart of the snail, and although the pharmacological actions of these extracts resembled those of 5-hydroxytryptamine, there is pharmacological, chemical, and chromatrographic evidence that the active substance is different (Kerkut and Laverack, 1960). Chemical tests suggested that the cardiac stimulant is an aromatic amine possessing one or more hydroxyl groups, one of which is possibly in the 5-position, although the substance does not appear to be an indole.

Studies on Primitive Vertebrates

Among the vertebrates, the primitive agnathans are particularly interesting. The Californian hagfish, *Polistotrema stoutii,* was shown to possess no regulatory nerves to control the heart (Greene, 1902) and in this respect, it resembles the embryonic hearts of higher animals which are capable of beating prior to the entry of nerves (Patten, 1949). Confirmation of the aneural nature of the hagfish has been reported (Augustinsson *et al.,* 1956; Jensen, 1961) although a related cyclostome, the lamprey (*Petromyzon fluviatilis*), was shown to possess nervous elements in the cardiac tissue (Augustinsson *et al.,* 1956).

The hagfish heart contains an abundance of catecholamines (Bloom *et al.,* 1961), 86% of the total being adrenaline (Östlund, 1954). Acetylcholine, histamine, and 5-hydroxytryptamine are also present but in very low quantities (Augustinsson *et al.,* 1956; Bloom *et al.,* 1961). Despite the relatively high amounts of adrenaline no chromaffin cells could be demonstrated in the hagfish *Myxine glutinosa* (Augustinsson *et al.,* 1956), although both light and electron microscopy revealed the presence of a large number of specific granular cells similar to those of the adrenal medulla (Bloom *et al.,* 1961). The heart of the hagfish is insensitive to catecholamines (Östlund, 1954), although after reserpine depletion the heart responds to these hormones. Similarly, the heart of the hagfish is insensitive to acetylcholine (Östlund, 1954; Augustinsson *et al.,* 1956; Jensen, 1958); β-palmitoyl lysolecithin and 5-hydroxytryptamine were also without effect (Jensen, 1958).

When extracts of the heart of the Californian hagfish were prepared, it was found that these increased the rate of the failing perfused hagfish or regularized the pattern of contractions (Jensen, 1958). The hagfish extract would also restart stopped perfused mussel hearts (Jensen, 1958) and increased the rate of the isolated frog heart, without any marked inotropic effect (Jensen, 1961). These effects of the crude extract could not be explained in terms of catecholamines.

Recently the active cardiac stimulant in the branchial heart of the hagfish has been isolated in crystalline form (Jensen, 1963), and named eptatretin. This substance is neither catecholamine, indole, nor polypeptide and appears to be a highly unstable aromatic amine or amide. In the steps leading to isolation of the active substance, frog auricles were used to monitor the activity of the hagfish extracts. This preparation showed both positive inotropic and chronotropic responses to eptatretin. In open-chest dogs and heart-lung preparations it has been shown that the failed ischemic heart responded to eptatretin with markedly improved effective work capacity, and a greatly increased aortic blood flow, with a diminution in venous pressure. These findings suggest that eptatretin, like the cardiac glycosides and catecholamines, exerts a direct action on mammalian cardiac tissue. Further studies on eptatretin are awaited with interest.

References

Alella, A., Braasch, W., Meesmann, W., and Schmier, J. (1960). *Arch. Ges. Physiol.* **271**, 1.

Alexandrowicz, J. S., and Carlisle, D. B. (1953). *J. Marine Biol. Assoc. U.K.* **32**, 175.

Andrews, P. (1964). *Biochem. J.* **96**, 595.

Areskog, N. (1962a). *Acta. Soc. Med. Upsaliensis* **67**, 153.

Areskog, N. (1962b). Acta Universitas Upsaliensis. Abstracts of Upsala Dissertations in Medicine No. 10.

Areskog, N. (1962c). *Acta. Soc. Med. Upsaliensis* **67**, 164.

Asher, L. (1925). *Arch. Ges. Physiol.* **209**, 605.

Asher, L. (1926). *Klin. Wochschr.* **5**, 1236.

Asher, L., and Beyeler, K. (1926). *Biochem. Z.* **178**, 351.

Asher, L., and Richardet, W. (1925). *Biochem. Z.* **166**, 317.

Asher, L., and Takahashi, K. (1924). *Biochem. Z.* **149**, 468.

Augustinsson, K.-B., Fänge, R., Johnels, A., and Östlund, E. (1956). *J. Physiol. (London)* **131**, 257.

Ballard, K., Lefer, A., and Sayers, G. (1960). *Am. J. Physiol.* **199**, 221.

Bassani, B. (1933a). *Arch. Ital. Biol.* **90**, 26.

Bassani, B. (1933b). *Arch. Fisiol.* **32**, 223.

Belamarich, F. A. (1963). *Biol. Bull.* **124**, 9.

Best, C. H., Dale, H. H., Dudley, H. W., and Thorpe, W. V. (1927). *J. Physiol. (London)* **62**, 397.

Bianchi, A., de Schaepdryver, A. F., de Vleeschhouwer, G. R., and Preziosi, P. (1960). *Arch. Intern. Pharmacodynamie* **124**, 21.

Bloom, G., Östlund, E., von Euler, U. S., Lishajko, F., Ritzen, M., and Adams-Ray, J. (1961). *Acta Physiol. Scand.* **153**, Suppl. No. 185.

Brugsch, T., Horsters, A., and Rothman, H. (1931). *Med. Klin. (Munich)* **27,** 1378.
Bücherl, E., and Rein, H. (1949). *Naturwissenschaften* **36,** 260.
Buckley, N. M., Tsuboi, K. K., and Zeig, N. J. (1961). *Circulation Res.* **9,** 242.
Bush, I. E. (1962). *Pharmacol. Rev.* **14,** 317.
Cameron, M. L. (1953). *Nature* **172,** 349.
Carlisle, D. B. (1956). *Biochem. J.* **63,** 32P.
Carlisle, D. B., and Knowles, F. (1959). "Endocrine Control in Crustaceans." Cambridge Univ. Press, London and New York.
Carnegie, P. R. (1965). *Proc. Biochem. Soc.* **95,** 9P.
Cattell, McK., and Gold, H. (1938). *J. Pharmacol. Exptl. Therap.* **62,** 116.
Clark, A. J. (1913). *J. Physiol. (London)* **47,** 66.
Clark, A. J. (1938). "Metabolism of the Frog's Heart." Oliver & Boyd, Edinburgh.
Cobbin, L. B. (1959). Ph.D. Thesis, University of Sydney.
Cobbin, L. B., and Thorp, R. H. (1957). *Nature* **180,** 242.
Cobbin, L. B., and Thorp, R. H. (1959). *Brit. J. Pharmacol.* **14,** 392.
Cobbin, L. B., and Thorp, R. H. (1960). *Nature* **186,** 473.
Cohn, E. J. (1950). *J. Am. Chem. Soc.* **72,** 465.
Cooke, I. (1962). *Gen. Comp. Endocrinol.* **2,** 29.
Covino, B. G. (1963). *Am. Heart. J.* **66,** 627.
Curtain, C. C., and Nayler, W. G. (1963). *Biochem. J.* **89,** 69.
Dale, H. H., and Dudley, H. W. (1929). *J. Physiol. (London)* **68,** 97.
Danforth, W. H., Ballard, F. B., Kako, K., Choudhury, J. D., and Bing, R. J. (1960). *Circulation* **21,** 112.
de Gubareff, T., and Sleator, W. (1965). *J. Pharmacol. Exptl. Therap.* **148,** 202.
Demoor, J. (1922). *Arch. Intern. Physiol.* **20,** 29.
Downing, S. E., and Sonnenblick, E. H. (1963). *J. Appl. Physiol.* **18,** 585.
Drury, A. N. (1936). *Physiol. Rev.* **16,** 292.
Drury, A. N., and Szent-Györgyi, A. (1929). *J. Physiol. (London)* **68,** 213.
Drury, A. N., Lutwak-Mann, C., and Solandt, O. M. (1938). *Quart. J. Exptl. Physiol.* **27,** 215.
Emele, J. B., and Bonnycastle, D. D. (1956). *Am. J. Physiol.* **185,** 103.
Erspamer, V. (1954). *Pharmacol. Rev.* **6,** 425.
Faust, E. S. (1921). *Verhandl. Schweiz. Naturforsch Ges.* (1920 Session), Sect. 10, p. 229.
Feldberg, W., and Lewis, G. P. (1964). *J. Physiol. (London)* **171,** 98.
Fowler, H. O., and Holmes, J. C. (1964). *Circulation Res.* **14,** 191.
Garb, S. (1955). *J. Pharmacol. Exptl. Therap.* **115,** 300.
Gatgounis, J., and Hester, W. (1964). *Proc. Soc. Exptl. Biol. Med.* **116,** 430.
Grabe, F., Krayer, O., and Seelkopf, K. (1934). *Klin. Wochschr.* **13,** 1381.
Green, H. H., and Stoner, H. B. (1950). "Biological Actions of the Adenine Nucleotides." H. K. Lewis, London.
Green, J. P. (1952). *Am. J. Physiol.* **170,** 330.
Green, J. P., and Nahum, L. H. (1957). *Circulation Res.* **5,** 634.
Green, J. P., Giarmin, N. J., and Salter, W. T. (1952). *J. Pharmacol. Exptl. Therap.* **106,** 346.
Greene, C. W. (1902). *Am. J. Physiol.* **6,** 318.

270   7. *Naturally Occurring Cardiotonic Substances*

Gross, M., Montague, D., Rosas, R., and Bohr, D. F. (1965). *Circulation Res.* **16,** 155.
Haberlandt, L. (1925). *Klin. Wochschr.* **4,** 1778.
Haberlandt, L. (1929). *Med. Welt* **3,** 307.
Haefely, W., and Hürliman, A. (1962). *Experientia* **18,** 297.
Hagen, P., and Welch, A. D. (1956). *Recent Progr. Hormone Res.* **12,** 27.
Hajdu, S. (1957). *J. Pharmacol. Exptl. Therap.* **120,** 90.
Hajdu, S., and Leonard, E. (1958). *Circulation Res.* **6,** 740.
Hajdu, S., and Leonard, E. (1961). *Circulation Res.* **9,** 881.
Hajdu, S., and Szent-Györgyi, A. (1952). *Am. J. Physiol.* **168,** 159.
Hajdu, S., Weiss, H., and Titus, E. (1957). *J. Pharmacol. Exptl. Therap.* **120,** 99.
Hatcher, J. D., Sunahara, F. A., Edholm, O. G., and Woolner, J. M. (1954). *Circulation Res.* **2,** 499.
Hatcher, J. D., Sadik, N., and Baumber, J. (1959). *Proc. Can. Federation Biol. Soc.* **2,** 28.
Hatcher, J. D., Jennings, D. B., Parker, J. O., and Garvock, W. B. (1963). *Can. J. Biochem. Physiol.* **41,** 1887.
Heeg, E., and Meng, K. (1965). *Arch. Exptl. Pathol. Pharmakol.* **250,** 35.
Heinsen, H. A. (1933). *Klin. Wochschr.* **12,** 1722.
Heinsen, H. A. (1934). *Klin. Wochschr.* **13,** 1597.
Heinsen, H. A., and Wolf, H. J. (1934). *Klin. Wochschr.* **13,** 523.
Hilton, S. M., and Lewis, G. P. (1957). *Brit. Med. Bull.* **13,** 189.
Hochrein, M., and Keller, C. J. (1931). *Arch. Exptl. Pathol. Pharmakol.* **159,** 438.
Jackson, D. M., and Temple, D. M. (1966). Australian Biochem. Conf. Abstr. *Australian J. Sci.,* In press.
Jensen, D. (1958). *J. Gen. Physiol.* **42,** 289.
Jensen, D. (1961). *Comp. Biochem. Physiol.* **2,** 181.
Jensen, D. (1963). *Comp. Biochem. Physiol.* **10,** 129.
Joos, G. (1932). *Klin. Wochschr.* **11,** 1906.
Joos, G. (1933). *Klin. Wochschr.* **12,** 777.
Justus, D. W., Cornett, R. W., and Hatcher, J. D. (1957). *Circulation Res.* **5,** 207.
Kahn, J. B., and Schindler, R. (1962). *Experientia* **18,** 79.
Kako, K., Choudhury, J. D., and Bing, R. J. (1960). *J. Pharmacol. Exptl. Therap.* **130,** 46.
Kerkut, G. A., and Laverack, M. S. (1960). *Comp. Biochem. Physiol.* **1,** 62.
Kiese, M., Gummel, H., and Garan, R. S. (1936). *Arch. Exptl. Pathol. Pharmakol.* **184,** 197.
Knowles, F. G. W. (1960). *Nature* **185,** 709.
Koch-Weser, J. (1965). *Circulation Res.* **16,** 230.
Kontos, H. A., Magee, J. H., Shapiro, W., and Patterson, J. L. (1963). *Federation Proc.* **22,** 425.
Krayer, O. (1933). *Deut. Med. Wochschr.* **59,** 576.
Lefer, A., and Sayers, G. (1964). *Federation Proc.* **23,** 122.
Leonard, E., and Hajdu, S. (1960). *Clin. Res.* **8,** 187.
Leonard, E., and Hajdu, S. (1961). *Circulation Res.* **9,** 891.
Levy, J. V., and Richards, V. (1962a). *Proc. Soc. Exptl. Biol. Med.* **111,** 602.

Levy, J. V., and Richards, V. (1962b). *Federation Proc.* **21,** 126.

Lichtlen, P. R., Solomon, N., Bernstein, L., Friesinger, G. C., and Ross, R. S. (1964). *Federation Proc.* **23,** 358.

Lindner. F., and Rigler, R. (1931). *Arch. Ges. Physiol.* **226,** 697.

Lowe, T. E., and Nayler, W. G. (1965). *Lancet* **ii,** 218.

Loynes, J. S., and Gowdey, C. W. (1952). *Can. J. Med. Sci.* **30,** 325.

Lu, F. C. (1950). *Rev. Can. Biol.* **9,** 219.

Marro, F., Valzelli, G., and Capraro, V. (1961). *Boll. Soc. Ital. Biol. Sper.* **37,** 1516.

Maynard, D. M., and Welsh, J. H. (1959). *J. Physiol. (London)* **149,** 215.

Meesmann, W., and Schmier, J. (1955). *Arch. Exptl. Pathol. Pharmakol.* **227,** 265.

Meesmann, W., and Schmier, J. (1956a). *Arch. Ges. Physiol.* **263,** 293.

Meesmann, W., and Schmier, J. (1956b). *Arch. Ges. Physiol.* **263,** 304.

Meesmann, W., and Schmier, J. (1956c). *Z. Kreislauforsch* **45.** 335.

Meier, R., Tripod, J., and Studer, A. (1958). *Arch. Intern. Pharmacodynamie* **117,** 185.

Melville, K. I. (1948). *Rev. Can. Biol.* **7,** 491.

Montague, D., Rosas, R., and Bohr, D. F. (1963). *Science* **141,** 907.

Nakano, J., and Fisher, R. D. (1963). *J. Pharmacol. Exptl. Therap.* **142,** 206.

Nayler, W. G. (1965). *J. Pharmacol. Exptl. Therap.* **148,** 215.

Nayler, W. G., and McCulloch, M. (1960). *Australian J. Exptl. Biol. Med. Sci.* **38,** 127.

Nayler, W. G., Price, J. M., and Lowe, T. E. (1965a). *Comp. Biochem. Physiol.* **15,** 503.

Nayler, W. G., Robertson, P. G. C., Price, J. M., and Lowe, T. E. (1965b). *Circulation Res.* **16,** 553.

Oppenheimer, E. T. (1929). *Am. J. Physiol.* **90,** 656.

Östlund, E. (1954). *Acta Physiol. Scand.* **31,** Suppl. 112.

Page, I. H., and Olmstead, F. (1961). *Am. J. Physiol.* **201,** 92.

Patten, B. M. (1949). *Physiol. Rev.* **29,** 31.

Pinotti, O. (1942). *Arch. Fisiol.* **42,** 170.

Poli, G., and Rossi, C. R. (1949). *Arch. Fisiol.* **48,** 143.

Rand, M. J., Stafford, A., and Thorp, R. H. (1955). *J. Pharmacol. Exptl. Therap.* **114,** 119.

Rein, H. (1942). *Klin. Wochschr.* **21,** 873.

Rein, H. (1951). *Arch. Ges. Physiol.* **253,** 435.

Rein, H., Mertens, O., and Bücherl, E. (1949). *Naturwissenschaften* **36,** 233.

Ringer, S. (1885). *J. Physiol. (London)* **6,** 361.

Rockwell, G., and Temple, D. M. (1966). Australian Biochem. Conf. Abstr. *Australian J. Sci.,* In press.

Roncato, A. (1930). *Arch. Fisiol.* **84,** 23.

Rosas, R., Montague, D., Gross, M., and Bohr, D. F. (1965). *Circulation Res.* **16,** 150.

Rosenblum, I., and Stein, A. A. (1964). *J. Pharmacol. Exptl. Therap.* **145,** 78.

Rowe, G. G., Alfonso, S., Castillo, C. A., Lioy, F., Lugo, J. A., and Crumpton, C. W. (1963). *Am. Heart. J.* **65,** 656.

Salomon, H., and Zuelzer, G. (1929). *Z. Ges. Exptl. Med.* **66,** 291.

Salter, W. T., and Taylor, R. M. (1952). *Federation Proc.* **11,** 388.

Sayers, G., and Solomon, N. (1960). *Endocrinology* **66,** 719.

Scarinci, V., Parenti, M. A., Cantone, A., and Ravazzoni, C. (1960). *Arch. Intern. Pharmacodynamie* **123**, 472.

Schlossberger, H. G., and Kuch, H. (1960). *Chem. Ber.* **93**, 1318.

Schmier, J. (1958). *In* "Liver Function" (R. W. Brauer, ed.), Am. Inst. Biol. Sci. Publ. 4, p. 390. Washington, D.C.

Schümann, H. J. (1958). *Arch. Exptl. Pathol. Pharmakol.* **234**, 17.

Shaw, F. H. (1938). *Biochem. J.* **32**, 19.

Szent-Györgyi, A. (1953). "Chemical Physiology of Contraction in Body and Heart Muscle." Academic Press, New York.

Takacs, L., and Albert, K. (1965). *Arch. Intern. Pharmacodynamie* **155**, 117.

Tamm, C. (1963). *Proc. 1st Intern. Pharmacol. Meeting, Stockholm, 1961* pp. 11–26. Pergamon Press, Oxford.

Tanz, R. D. (1962). *J. Pharmacol. Exptl. Therap.* **135**, 71.

Temple, D. M., and Gillespie, R. (1966). *Nature* **209**, 714.

Temple, D. M., Thorp, R. H., and Gillespie, R. (1966). *Comp. Biochem. Physiol.* **17**, 1089.

Titus, E., Weiss, H., and Hajdu, S. (1956). *Science* **124**, 1205.

Ullrick, W. C., and Hazelwood, R. L. (1963). *Am. J. Physiol.* **204**, 1001.

von Euler, U. S. (1956). "Noradrenaline," p. 63. Thomas, Springfield, Illinois.

von Euler, U. S., and Gaddum, J. H. (1931). *J. Physiol. (London)* **72**, 74.

von Euler, U. S., and Purkhold, A. (1951a). *Acta Physiol. Scand.* **24**, 212.

von Euler, U. S., and Purkhold, A. (1951b). *Acta Physiol. Scand.* **24**, 218.

Wayne, E. J., Goodwin, J. F., and Stoner, H. B. (1949). *Brit. Heart J.* **11**, 55.

Whitaker, J. R. (1963). *Anal. Chem.* **35**, 1950.

Zetler, G. (1960). *In* "Polypeptides Which Affect Smooth Muscles and Blood Vessels" (M. Schacnter, ed.), p. 79. Pergamon Press, Oxford.

Zuelzer, G. (1930). *Med. Klin (Munich)* **26**, 695.

Zuelzer, G. (1942). *Med. Record* **155**, 441.

AUTHOR INDEX

Numbers in italics show the pages on which the complete references are listed.

273

SUBJECT INDEX

284